Your comprehensive guide to dog friendly

www.dogfriendly.co.uk

Dog Frie

First published in Great Britain in 2008
by Dog Friendly

Copyright © 2008 Dog Friendly

Dog Friendly have asserted their moral rights
to be identified as the author

The information in this book is true and complete to the best of our
knowledge. All recommendations are made without any guarantee on the part
of the publisher, who also disclaims any liability incurred in connection with the
use of this data or specific details.

The Dog Friendly team telephone every venue at least once a year to ensure
that our data base is accurate as it can be – but things do change.
So please always check before you visit.

A CIP Catalogue of this book is available from
the British Library

ISBN 978-0-9560459-5-9

Printed and bound in
Great Britain by
Print Direction
www.printdirection.co.uk

In Memory of Blossom, our retired greyhound
who changed our lives for the better and
inspired us to start Dog Friendly

Blossom
1993 to 2006

Pubs

Your comprehensive guide to dog friendly Pubs

www.dogfriendly.co.uk

England

and the Isles around Britain

Bedfordshire

The Stone Jug
Address: Back St, Clophill, Bedfordshire. MK45 4BY
Phone Number: 01525 860526
Details: allowed everywhere

The Royal George
Address: 57 High Street, Stagsden, Bedfordshire. MK43 8SG
Phone Number: 01234 822801
Details: allowed everywhere

Sow & Pigs
Address: 19 Church Square, Toddington, Bedfordshire. LU5 6AA
Phone Number: 01525 873089
Details: allowed everywhere but not in eating areas

The Griffin Hotel
Address: Station Road, Toddington, Bedfordshire. LU5 6BN
Phone Number: 01525 872030
Details: allowed everywhere

Avon

The Old Crown
Address: Bath, Kelston, Avon. BA1 9AQ
Phone Number: 01225 423032
Details: allowed everywhere but not in the restaurant

The Bell

Address: The Street, Waltham St Lawrence, Berkshire, Berkshire. RG10 0JJ

Phone Number: 0118 9341788

Details: allowed everywhere

Stag and Hounds

Address: Forest Road, Binfield, Berkshire. RG42 4HA

Phone Number: 01344 483553

Details: allowed everywhere but not in the restaurant

Miller of Mansfield

Address: Goring On Thames, Goring On Thames, Berkshire. RG8 9AW

Phone Number: 01491 872829

Details: allowed everywhere but not in eating areas

The White Hart

Address: Church Street, Hampstead Norreys, Berkshire. RG18 0TB

Phone Number: 01635 202248

Details: allowed everywhere but not in the restaurant

The Belgian Arms

Address: Holyport Street, Holyport, Berkshire. SL6 2JR

Phone Number: 01628 634468

Details: allowed everywhere but not in the restaurant

The Red Lion Inn

Address: Red Lion Church Road, Mortimer West End, Berkshire. RG7 2HU

Phone Number: 01189 700169

Details: allowed everywhere but not in the restaurant an Christmas presents are given to the dogs

Bell & Bottle

Address: 37 School Green, Shinfield, Berkshire. RG2 9EE

Phone Number: 01189 883563

Details: allowed in public bar but not in the restaurant

The Stag

Address: Hawthorne Lane, Farnham Common, Slough, Berkshire. Sl2 3ta

Phone Number: 01753 642226

Details: allowed everywhere as long as they are kept on a lead

The White Horse

Address: Village Lane, Hedgerley, Slough, Berkshire. SL2 3UY

Phone Number: 01753 643225

Details: allowed in the public bar and garden if kept on a lead

The Bull

Address: High Street, Sonning, Berkshire. RG4 6UP

Phone Number: 01189 693901

Details: allowed everywhere but not in the restaurant area

The Old Boot Inn

Address: Stanford Dingley, Stanford Dingley, Berkshire. RG7 6LT

Phone Number: 01189 744292

Details: allowed everywhere but not in the restaurant area

The Bull

Address: Reading Road, Streatley, Berkshire. RG8 9JJ

Phone Number: 01491 872392

Details: allowed everywhere but not in the restaurant area and not alone in the bedrooms

Hit or Miss Inn

Address: Penn St Village, Penn St, AMERSHAM, Buckinghamshire. HP7 0PX
Phone Number: 01494 713109
Details: allowed everywhere

The Royal Standard of England

Address: Brindle Lane, Forty Green, Beaconsfield, Buckinghamshire. HP9 1XT
Phone Number: 01494 673382
Details: allowed everywhere

The Bounty

Address: Riverside, Bourne End, Buckinghamshire. SO8 5RG
Phone Number: 01628 520056
Details: allowed everywhere, inside on a lead and dog show in september

The Royal Oak

Address: Carlton, Bedfordshire. MK43 7LP
Phone Number: 01234 720441
Details: allowed everywhere preferably on a lead

Unicorn

Address: Village High Street, Cublington, Buckinghamshire. LU7 0LQ
Phone Number: 01296 681261
Details: allowed everywhere but not in the restaurant

Prince Albert

Address: Moor End Frieth, Frieth, Buckinghamshire. RG9 6PY
Phone Number: 01494 881683
Details: allowed everywhere as long as they are kept on a lead

Stag and Huntsman

Address: Hambledon, Buckinghamshire.
Phone Number: 01491 571227
Details: allowed everywhere

The Old Queens Head

Address: Hammersley Lane, Penn, High Wycombe, Buckinghamshire. HP10 8EY
Phone Number: 01494 813371
Details: allowed everywhere but not in the restaurant

The Royal Oak

Address: Frieth Rd, Marlow, Buckinghamshire. SL7 2JF
Phone Number: 01628 488611
Details: allowed everywhere and selected parts of the dining area

Black Boy

Address: Oving, Buckinghamshire. HP22 4HN
Phone Number: 01296 641258
Details: allowed everywhere

www.dogfriendly.co.uk

The Red Lion

Address: Chenies, Rickmansworth, Buckinghamshire. WD3 6ED
Phone Number: 01923 282722
Details: allowed everywhere but not in the restaurant area

The Frog

Address: Skirmett, Buckinghamshire. RG9 6TG
Phone Number: 01491 638996
Details: allowed everywhere but not in the restaurant area

George and Dragon

Address: High Street, West Wycombe, Buckinghamshire. HP14 3AB
Phone Number: 01494 464414
Details: allowed everywhere

The Brickmakers Arms

Address: Whitchurch, Buckinghamshire. HP22 4JS
Phone Number: 01296 641377
Details: allowed everywhere preferably kept on a lead

The Green Dragon

Address: Water Street, Cambridge, Chesterton, Cambridgeshire. CB4 1NZ
Phone Number: 01223 505035
Details: allowed everywhere

The Ship Inn

Address: Brandon Creek, Downham Market, Cambridgeshire. PE38 0PP
Phone Number: 01353 676 288
Details: allowed everywhere preferably on a lead

The Fish and Duck

Address: Main Street, Witchford, Ely, Cambridgeshire. CB6 2HQ
Phone Number: 01353 649580
Details: allowed everywhere

The Axe & Compass

Address: High St, Huntingdon, Hemingford Abbots, Cambridgeshire. PE28 9AH
Phone Number: 01480 463605
Details: allowed everywhere

The Fish & Duck

Address: Holt Fen, Little Thetford, Cambridgeshire. CB6 3HR
Phone Number: 01353 649 580
Details: allowed everywhere

The Wagon & Horses

Address: 39 High St, Milton, Cambridgeshire. CB4 6DF
Phone Number: 01223 860313
Details: allowed everywhere

The Ferryboat Inn

Address: Hollywell, St Ives, Cambridgeshire. PE27 4TG
Phone Number: 01480 463227
Details: allowed everywhere

www.dogfriendly.co.uk

Cheshire

The Windmill

Address: Holehouse Lane, Whiteley Green, Adlington, Cheshire. Sk10 5sj
Phone Number: 01625 574222
Details: allowed in the bar and the garden

The Grosvenor Arms

Address: Aldford, Cheshire.
Phone Number: 01244 620228
Details: allowed in one bar

Harrington Arms

Address: Church Lane, Gawsworth, Cheshire. SK11 9RJ
Phone Number: 01260 223325
Details: allowed everywhere preferably on a lead

The Railway

Address: 42 Mill Lane, Heatley, Lymm, Cheshire. WA13 9SQ
Phone Number: 01925 752742
Details: allowed everywhere

The Boot and Shoe

Address: 82 Hospital Street, Nantwich, Cheshire. CW5 5RB
Phone Number: 01270 625193
Details: allowed everywhere preferably on a lead

Royal Oak

Address: Buxton Road, High Lane, Stockport, Cheshire. SK6 8AY
Phone Number: 01663 762380
Details: allowed everywhere

The Dysart Arms

Address: Bowes Gate Road, Bunbury, Tarporley, Cheshire. CW6 9PH
Phone Number: 01829 260183
Details: allowed everywhere

www.dogfriendly.co.uk

Crooklets Inn

Address: Crooklets, Bude, Cornwall. EX23 8NF
Phone Number: 01288 352335
Details: allowed everywhere preferably on a lead at meal times

Preston Gate

Address: Preston Gate, Poughill, Bude, Cornwall. EX23 9ET
Phone Number: 01288 354017
Details: allowed everywhere

The North Inn

Address: The Square, Cornwall. TR19 7DN
Phone Number: 01736 788417
Details: allowed everywhere

Tom Sawyers Tavern

Address: Hannafore, West Looe, Cornwall.
Phone Number: 01503 262 782
Details: allowed everywhere preferably to be kept on a lead

The Old Albion Inn

Address: Langurroc Road, Crantock, Cornwall. TR8 5RB
Phone Number: 01637 830243
Details: allowed everywhere

The Borough Arms

Address: Dunmere, Cornwall. PL31 2RD
Phone Number: 01208 73118
Details: allowed everywhere but not in the restaurant

The Bucket of Blood Inn

Address: Phillack Road, Hayle, Cornwall. TR27 5AE
Phone Number: 01736 752378
Details: allowed everywhere

The Crown Inn

Address: Lanlivery, Cornwall. Pl30 5BT
Phone Number: 01208 872707
Details: allowed everywhere but not in the restaurant

The Ship Inn

Address: Lerryn, Cornwall. PL22 0PI
Phone Number: 01208 872374
Details: allowed everywhere but not in the restaurant preferably to be kept on a lead at all times

Crows Nest

Address: Liskeard, Cornwall. PL14 5JQ
Phone Number: 01579 345930
Details: allowed everywhere

The Earl of Chatham

Address: Grenville Rd, Lostwithiel, Cornwall. PL22 0EP
Phone Number: 01208 872269
Details: allowed everywhere and in the bedrooms

www.dogfriendly.co.uk

The Royal Oak

Address: Duke Street, Lostwithiel, Cornwall. PL22 0AG
Phone Number: 01208 872552
Details: allowed everywhere preferably on a lead

The Exmoor Sandpiper

Address: Lynmouth, Cornwall. EX35 6NE
Phone Number: 01598 741263
Details: allowed everywhere

The Fountain Inn

Address: St. George Square, Mevagissey, Cornwall. PL26 6QH
Phone Number: 01726 842320
Details: allowed everywhere but not in the restaurant area but must be kept on a lead

The Pandora Inn

Address: Mylor Bridge, Cornwall.
Phone Number: 01326 372678
Details: allowed everywhere but preferably on a lead

Shipwrights

Address: North Quay, Padstow, Cornwall. PL28 8AF
Phone Number: 01841 532451
Details: allowed everywhere

The Old Ship Hotel

Address: Mill Square, Padstow, Cornwall. PL28 8AE
Phone Number: 01841 532357
Details: allowed all over the hotel as long as they are on a lead

The Punchbowl & Ladle

Address: Feock, Truro, Penelewey, Cornwall. TR3 6QY
Phone Number: 01872 862237
Details: allowed in the bar area preferably on a lead

The Plume of Feathers

Address: Truro, Penhallow, Cornwall. TR4 9LT
Phone Number: 01872 571389
Details: allowed everywhere preferably on a lead

The Dolphin

Address: Quay Street, Penzance, Cornwall. TR18 4BD
Phone Number: 01736 364106
Details: allowed everywhere preferably on a lead

The Watering Hole

Address: Perranporth, Cornwall. TR6 OBH
Phone Number: 01872 572 888
Details: allowed everywhere preferably on a lead

The Old Millhouse Inn

Address: Mill Hill, Looe, Polperro, Cornwall. PL13 2RP
Phone Number: 01503 272362
Details: allowed everywhere preferably on a lead

The Three Pilchards

Address: The Quay, Looe, Polperro, Cornwall. PL13 2QZ

Phone Number: 01503 272233
Details: allowed everywhere

Whortleberry Tea Rooms

Address: High Street, Porlock, Cornwall. TA24 8PY
Phone Number: 01643 862337
Details: allowed in the garden water is provided

The Mermaid Inn

Address: Porth, Cornwall. TR7 3NB
Phone Number: 01637 872954
Details: allowed everywhere preferably on a lead

The Ship Inn

Address: Truro, Portloe, Cornwall. TR2 5RA
Phone Number: 01872 501356
Details: allowed everywhere

The Feathers

Address: The Quay, Portscatho, Cornwall. TR2 5HF
Phone Number: 01872 580321
Details: allowed everywhere preferably on a lead

The Brunel

Address: 83 Fore St, Saltash, Cornwall.
Phone Number: 01752 842261
Details: allowed everywhere preferably on a lead

Driftwood Spars Hotel

Address: Trevaunance Cove, St Agnes, Cornwall. TR5 0RT
Phone Number: 01872 552428

Details: allowed everywhere preferably on a lead

St Agnes Hotel

Address: Churchtown, St Agnes, Cornwall. TR5 0QP
Phone Number: 01872 552307
Details: allowed everywhere preferably on a lead

The Castle Inn

Address: 16 Fore Street, St Ives, Cornwall. TR26 1AB
Phone Number: 01736 796833
Details: allowed everywhere preferably on a lead

The Union

Address: Fore Street, St Ives, Cornwall. TR5
Phone Number: 01736 796486
Details: allowed everywhere

The King's Arms

Address: 5 Market Square, St Just, Cornwall.
Phone Number: 01736 788545
Details: allowed everywhere preferably to be kept on a lead

The White Hart

Address: The Square, Helston, St Keverne, Cornwall. TR12 6ND
Phone Number: 01326 280325
Details: only allowed in the bar but not bedrooms

The Fountain Bar

Address: Marine Parade, St Mawes, Cornwall. TR2 5DJ
Phone Number: 01326 270266
Details: allowed everywhere

The Rising Sun

Address: The Square, St Mawes, Cornwall. TR2 5DJ
Phone Number: 01326 270233
Details: allowed in the public bar and bedrooms but the restaurant

The Victory Inn

Address: St Mawes, Cornwall.
Phone Number: 01326 270324
Details: allowed everywhere but not the restaurant

Falcon Inn

Address: St Mawgan, Cornwall.
Phone Number: 01637 860225
Details: allowed everywhere but not the restaurant

Sloop Inn

Address: The Wharf, St. Ives, Cornwall.
Phone Number: 01736 796584
Details: allowed everywhere preferably on a lead

Port William

Address: Trebarwith Strand, Cornwall. PL34 0HP
Phone Number: 01840 770230
Details: allowed in the bar but not in the restaurant area

Springer Spaniel

Address: A388 Callington, Lauceston, Treburley, Cornwall. PL15 9NS
Phone Number: 01579 370424
Details: allowed everywhere but not in the restaurant

Gurnards Head Hotel

Address: Zennor, Treen, Cornwall. TR26 3DE
Phone Number: 01736 796928
Details: allowed in the bedrooms and bar not in the dining room

The Red Lion Inn

Address: Blackwater, Truro, Cornwall. TR4 8EU
Phone Number: 01872 560289
Details: allowed everywhere

The Cumberland Hotel

Address: Townfoot, Alston, Cumbria. CA9 3HX
Phone Number: 01434 381875
Details: allowed everywhere

Golden Rule

Address: Smithy Brow, Ambleside, Cumbria.
Phone Number: 015394 33363
Details: allowed everywhere preferably on a lead

Wainwrights Inn

Address: Chapel Stile, Great Langdale, Ambleside, Cumbria. LA22 9JD
Phone Number: 015394 38088
Details: allowed everywhere

The Punchbowl Inn & Restaurant

Address: Penrith, Askham, Cumbria. CA10 2PF
Phone Number: 019317 12443
Details: allowed in the bars but not in the restaurant

Coledale Inn

Address: Braithewaite, Cumbria. CA12 5TN
Phone Number: 01768 778272
Details: allowed in the bars but not the restaurant

The Samson Inn

Address: Gilsland, Brampton, Cumbria. CA8 7DR
Phone Number: 016977 47220
Details: allowed everywhere as long as they are kept under control

The Tithebarn

Address: 41 Station St, Cockermouth, Cumbria. CA13 9QW
Phone Number: 01900 822179
Details: allowed in the pub preferably to be kept on a lead

The Black Bull

Address: Coppermines Road, Coniston, Cumbria. LA21 8HL
Phone Number: 015394 41335
Details: allowed in the bar and lounge but not the restaurant

The Stag Inn

Address: Dufton, Cumbria. CA16 6BD
Phone Number: 01768 351608
Details: allowed in the main area but not in the dining room

Britannia Inn

Address: Elterwater, Cumbria.
Phone Number: 01539 437210
Details: allowed in the bar but not in the restaurant area

www.dogfriendly.co.uk

Stickle Barn Tavern

Address: Great Langdale, Elterwater, Cumbria. LA22 9JU
Phone Number: 01539 437356
Details: allowed everywhere preferably on a lead www.langdaleweb.co.uk

The Boot Inn

Address: Eskdale, Cumbria. CA19 1TG
Phone Number: 01946 723224
Details: allowed everywhere but not in the restaurant area

The Three Greyhounds

Address: Great Asby, Cumbria. CA16 6EX
Phone Number: 01768 351428
Details: allowed in but must be kept on a lead and under control

Sticklebarn Tavern

Address: Great Langdale, Cumbria. LA22 9JU
Phone Number: 01539 437356
Details: allowed everywhere not in the bunk house accommodation

The Old Dungeon Ghyll Hotel

Address: Great Langdale, Cumbria. L22 9JY
Phone Number: 01539 437272
Details: allowed everywhere but not in the dining area preferably kept on a lead

The Kings Arms Hotel

Address: The Square, Hawkshead, Cumbria. LA22 0NZ
Phone Number: 015394 36372
Details: allowed everywhere but not in the dining room

The Watermill Inn

Address: Kendal, Ings, Cumbria. LA8 9PY
Phone Number: 01539 821309
Details: allowed everywhere preferably be kept on a lead

The Dog and Gun

Address: 2 Lake Road, Keswick, Cumbria. GA12 5BT
Phone Number: 01768 773463
Details: allowed everywhere

The Keswick Lodge

Address: Main Street, Keswick, Cumbria. CA12 5HZ
Phone Number: 01768 774584
Details: allowed everywhere

The Screes Inn

Address: Nether Wasdale, Cumbria. CA20 1ET
Phone Number: 01946 726262
Details: allowed everywhere

Newby Bridge Hotel

Address: Newby Bridge, Cumbria. LA12 8NA
Phone Number: 01539 531222
Details: allowed everywhere but not in the dining room four poster bed made especially for the dogs

The Tower Bank Arms

Address: Near Sawrey, Nr. Hawkshead, Cumbria. LA22 0LF
Phone Number: 01539 436 334
Details: allowed everywhere preferably to be kept on a lead

The Outgate

Address: Nr Hawkeshead, Outgate, Cumbria. LA22 0NQ
Phone Number: 01539 436413
Details: allowed everywhere but not in the dining areas

Punchbowl Inn

Address: Ashkham, Penrith, Cumbria. CA10 2PF
Phone Number: 019317 12443
Details: allowed everywhere but not in the rooms

The Sun Inn

Address: Pooley Bridge, Penrith, Cumbria. CA10 2NN
Phone Number: 01768 486205
Details: allowed everywhere but not in the dining room and top bar

Church House Inn

Address: Torver, Cumbria. LA21 8A2
Phone Number: 01539 441282
Details: allowed everywhere

The Britannia

Address: Penny Bridge, Ulverston, Cumbria. LA12 7RJ
Phone Number: 01229 861480
Details: allowed everywhere preferably to be kept on a lead

Lathkill Hotel

Address: Overhaddon, Bakewell, Derbyshire. DE45 1JE
Phone Number: 01629 812501
Details: allowed everywhere but not in the restaurant at night

Holly Bush Inn

Address: Holly Bush Lane, Makeney, Belper, Derbyshire. DE56 0RX
Phone Number: 01332 841729
Details: allowed everywhere but not in the dining room preferably on a lead

The Bear Inn

Address: Alderwasley, Belper, Derbyshire. DE56 2RD
Phone Number: 01629 822585
Details: allowed in the bar but preferably kept on a lead

The Red Lion Inn

Address: Main Street, Birchover, Derbyshire. DE4 2BN
Phone Number: 01629 650363
Details: allowed everywhere preferably on a lead

The Windmill

Address: Mansfield Road, Breadsall Hilltop, Derbyshire. DE21 4FY
Phone Number: 01332 835991
Details: allowed in the bar but not in the restaurant area

Dog & Partridge Inn

Address: Bridgemont, Derbyshire. SK23 7PB
Phone Number: 01663 732 284
Details: allowed everywhere preferably on a lead

Pack Horse Inn

Address: Crowdecote, Buxton, Derbyshire. SK17 0DB
Phone Number: 01298 83618
Details: allowed everywhere

The Anglers Rest

Address: Millers Dale, Buxton, Derbyshire. SK17 8SN
Phone Number: 01298 871 323
Details: allowed everywhere - also allowed in self catering flats

The Red Lion

Address: Litton, Buxton, Derbyshire. SK17 8QU
Phone Number: 01298 871458
Details: allowed everywhere

The George

Address: Castleton Street, Castleton, Derbyshire. S33 8WG
Phone Number: 01433 620 238
Details: allowed everywhere not allowed in the restaurant preferably on a lead

The Ramblers Rest

Address: Mill Bridge, Castleton, Derbyshire. S33 8 WR
Phone Number: 01433 620125
Details: allowed everywhere not in the restaurant area

The Crown

Address: Shardlow, Cavendish Bridge, Derbyshire. DE72 2HL
Phone Number: 01332 792392
Details: allowed everywhere preferably on a lead

The Church Inn

Address: Church Inn Cottage, Chelmorton, Derbyshire. SK17 9SL
Phone Number: 01298 85319
Details: allowed in the pub areas but not in the bedrooms

The Boat Inn

Address: Scarthin, Cromford, Derbyshire. DE4 3QF
Phone Number: 01629 823282
Details: allowed everywhere but not allowed in the restaurant

The Abbey

Address: Darely Street, Darley Abbey, Derbyshire. DE22 1DX
Phone Number: 01332 558297
Details: allowed everywhere except in the restaurant

The Rambler Inn

Address: Hope Valley, Edale, Derbyshire. S33 7ZA
Phone Number: 01433 670268
Details: allowed in the bar and dining area but not in the hotel bedrooms

The Queen Anne

Address: Great Hucklow, Derbyshire. SE17 8RF
Phone Number: 01298 871246
Details: allowed everywhere

Pear Tree Inn

Address: Hadfield Road, Hadfield, Derbyshire. SK13 1PY
Phone Number: 01457 854 385
Details: allowed everywhere in the pub

Charles Cotton Hotel

Address: Hartington, Derbyshire. SK17 0AL
Phone Number: 01298 84229
Details: allowed everywhere

The Waltzing Weasel

Address: New Mills Road, Birch Vale, High Peak, Derbyshire. SK22 1BT
Phone Number: 01663 743402
Details: allowed everywhere but not the restaurant

The Packhorse Inn

Address: Bakewell, Little Longstone, Derbyshire. DE45 1NN
Phone Number: 01629 640471
Details: allowed everywhere preferably kept on a lead and under control

Three Horseshoes

Address: Brick Kiln Lane, Morley Smithy, Morley, Derbyshire. DE7 6DF

Phone Number: 01332 834395

Details: allowed everywhere

The Bear Inn

Address: 17 West St, Swadlincote, Derbyshire. DE6 2HS

Phone Number: 01335 343183

Details: allowed in the pub preferably if kept on a lead

The George Hotel

Address: Commercial Rd, Tideswell, Derbyshire. SK17 8NU

Phone Number: 01298 871382

Details: allowed everywhere

The Three Stags Heads

Address: Buxton, Wardlow Mires, Derbyshire. SK17 8RW

Phone Number: 01298 872268

Details: allowed everywhere preferably on a lead

Hunters Lodge Inn

Address: Charmouth Road, Axminster, Devon. EX13 5SZ
Phone Number: 01297 33286
Details: allowed everywhere preferably on a lead

Barrel o Beer

Address: Fore Street, Beer, Devon. EX12 3EQ
Phone Number: 01297 20099
Details: allowed everywhere but not in the restaurant area and have to be kept on a lead

The Old Chapel Inn

Address: St Anne's Chapel, Bigbury-On-Sea, Devon. TQ7 4HQ
Phone Number: 01548 810241
Details: allowed everywhere

The Blue Anchor

Address: Fore Street, Brixham, Devon. TQ5 8AH
Phone Number: 01803 859373
Details: allowed everywhere

The Smugglers Haunt

Address: Church Hill East, Brixham, Devon. TQ5 8HH
Phone Number: 01803 853050
Details: allowed everywhere

The Abbey Inn

Address: 30 Buckfast Road, Buckfast, Devon. TQ11 0EA
Phone Number: 01364 642343
Details: allowed everywhere but not in the restaurant

Gidleigh Park

Address: Chagford, Devon. TQ13 8HH
Phone Number: 01647 432367
Details: dogs allowed in 2 of the rooms which are just outside the hotel but not inside the main hotel

The George Inn

Address: Chard Street, Chardstock, Devon. EX13 7BX
Phone Number: 01460 220241
Details: allowed everywhere preferably on a lead

The Cott Inn

Address: Cott Lane, Dartington, COTT, Devon. TQ9 6HE
Phone Number: 01803 863777
Details: allowed everywhere except the main restaurant

The Forest Inn

Address: Hexworthy, Dartmoor, Devon. PL20 6SD
Phone Number: 01364 631211
Details: allowed everywhere preferably on a lead

www.dogfriendly.co.uk

The Dartmouth Arms

Address: 26 Lower Street, Dartmouth, Devon. TQ6 9AN
Phone Number: 01803 832903
Details: allowed everywhere

The Royal Castle

Address: 11 The Quay, Dartmouth, Devon. TQ6 9PS
Phone Number: 01803 833033
Details: allowed everywhere

The Peter Tavy Inn

Address: Devon.
Phone Number: 01822 810 348
Details: allowed everywhere preferably if they are on a lead

Double Locks

Address: Canal Banks, Exeter, Devon. EX2 6LT
Phone Number: 01392 256 947
Details: allowed everywhere

Fingle Bridge Inn

Address: Drewsteignton, Exeter, Devon. EX6 6PW
Phone Number: 01647 281 287
Details: allowed in the bar preferably on leads

The Thatched House

Address: Exwick Road, Exeter, Devon. EX4 2BQ
Phone Number: 01392 272920
Details: allowed everywhere but not in the restaurant

The Turf Hotel

Address: Turf Locks, Exminster, Devon. EX6 8EE
Phone Number: 01392 833128
Details: allowed everywhere but not in the restaurant area and preferably on leads

The Rydon Inn

Address: Holsworthy, Devon. EX22 7HU
Phone Number: 01409 259444
Details: allowed inside and in the garden but not allowed in the restaurant and perferably on leads

Sidmouth Arms

Address: Upottery, Honiton, Devon. EX14 9PN
Phone Number: 01404 861252
Details: allowed everywhere preferably kept on a lead

The Port Light Hotel

Address: Bolberry Down, Marlborough, Kingsbridge, Devon. TQ7 3DY
Phone Number: 01548 561384
Details: allowed everywhere

The Dog & Donkey

Address: 24 Knowle Village, Budleigh Salterton, Knowle, Devon. EX9 6AL
Phone Number: 01395 442021
Details: allowed everywhere

The Manor Inn

Address: Lower Ashton, Devon. EX6 7QL
Phone Number: 01647 252 305
Details: allowed in the bar but preferably kept on a lead

www.dogfriendly.co.uk

The Rising Sun

Address: Lynmouth, Devon. X35 6EQ
Phone Number: 01598 753 223
Details: allowed in the bar and there are 2 rooms in the hotel allocated for dogs preferably dogs to be kept on a lead

The California Country Inn

Address: California Cross, Ivybridge, Modbury, Devon. PL21 0SG
Phone Number: 01548 821 449
Details: allowed in the bar

Clay Cutters

Address: Chudleigh Knighton, New Abbot, Devon. TQ13 OEY
Phone Number: 01626 853 345
Details: allowed everywhere but not in the restaurant preferably be kept on leads

The Duke of York

Address: Iddesleigh, Okehampton, Devon. EX19 8BG
Phone Number: 01837 810253
Details: allowed everywhere preferably to be kept on leads in the dining room

The Post Inn

Address: Exeter Road, Whiddon Down, Okehampton, Devon. EX20 2QT
Phone Number: 01647 231 242
Details: allowed only in the bar area preferably to be kept on leads at all times

The Tors

Address: Belstone, OKEHAMPTON, Devon. EX20 1QZ
Phone Number: 01837 840689

Details: allowed everywhere but not in the restaurant area

The King's Arms

Address: Fore Street, Otterton, Devon. EX9 7HB
Phone Number: 01395 568416
Details: allowed everywhere

The Hunters Inn

Address: Heddon Valley, Parracombe, Devon. EX31 4PY
Phone Number: 01598 763230
Details: allowed in the bar and through the hotel and into bedrooms but not the restaurant

Six Bells

Address: Payhembury, Devon. EX14 3HR
Phone Number: 01404 841261
Details: allowed in the bar but not in the restaurant area

The Journey's End

Address: Ringmore, Devon. TQ7 4HL
Phone Number: 01548 810205
Details: allowed everywhere preferably kept on a lead

Feathers Hotel

Address: 35 High Street, Budleigh, Salterton, Devon. EX9 6LE
Phone Number: 01395 442 042
Details: allowed everywhere doggy biscuits & water is supplied

The London Inn

Address: The Green, Teignmouth, Shaldon, Devon. TQ14 0DN

Phone Number: 01626 872453

Details: allowed everywhere preferably kept on a lead and under control

Hare & Hounds

Address: Putts Corner, Sidbury, Devon. EX10 0QQ

Phone Number: 01404 41760

Details: allowed everywhere but not in the restaurant preferably on a lead

The Queens Arms

Address: Kingsbridge, Slapton, Devon. TQ7 2PN

Phone Number: 01548 580800

Details: allowed everywhere preferably to be kept on leads

The Tower Inn

Address: Kingsbridge, Slapton, Devon. TQ7 2PN

Phone Number: 01548 580216

Details: allowed everywhere preferably to be kept on leads

The Sea Trout

Address: Staverton, Devon. TQ9 6PA

Phone Number: 01803 762274

Details: allowed everywhere but not in the restaurant area and must be kept on a lead at all times

The Green Dragon

Address: Church Road, Stoke Flemming, Devon. TQ6 0PX

Phone Number: 01803 770238

Details: allowed in the bar area but not in the restaurant

The Passage House

Address: Ferry Road, Exeter, Topsham, Devon. EX3 0JN

Phone Number: 01392 873653

Details: allowed in the bar area only

Devon Arms

Address: 8-10 Park Lane, Torquay, Devon. TQ1 2AU

Phone Number: 01803 292360

Details: allowed everywhere preferably kept on a lead

Steam Packet Inn

Address: St Peters Key, Totnes, Devon. TQ9 5EN

Phone Number: 01803 863 880

Details: only allowed in the bar and terrace ideally they should be kept on a lead when they are inside

The Boathouse

Address: The Planes, The Waterside, Totness, Devon. TQ9 5YS

Phone Number: 01803 864069

Details: dogs allowed outside on the terrace but not inside the bar & restaurant

The Maltsters Arms

Address: Tuckenhay, Devon. TQ9 7EH

Phone Number: 01803 732350

Details: allowed everywhere

The Ring O'Bells

Address: West Alvington, Devon. TQ7 3PG

Phone Number: 01548 852437

Details: allowed everywhere water is provided

Whitchurch Inn

Address: Whitchurch, Devon.
Phone Number: 01822 612181
Details: allowed everywhere doggy biscuits & water is supplied

The Kings Arms

Address: Fore Street, Winkleigh, Devon. BS19 8HQ
Phone Number: 01837 83384
Details: allowed in the bar but not in the restaurant area

Ilchester Arms

Address: Abbotsbury, Dorset. DT3 4JR
Phone Number: 01305 871243
Details: allowed in the pub but not in the bedrooms upstairs

The Fox Inn

Address: Dorchester, Ansty, Dorset. DT2 7PN
Phone Number: 01258 880328
Details: allowed in the bar & bedrooms but not in the restaurant

The Three Tuns

Address: Ringwood Road, Bransgore, Dorset. BH23 8JH
Phone Number: 01425 672232
Details: allowed in the bar but not in the restaurant area

The George

Address: The Street, Charmouth, Dorset. DT6 6QE
Phone Number: 01297 560280
Details: allowed everywhere but not in the dining area preferably kept on a lead

The Saxon

Address: Child Okeford, Dorset. DT11 8HD
Phone Number: 01258 860310
Details: allowed in the bar and the gardens but not in the restaurant area

The Avon Causeway

Address: Avon Causeway Road, Christchurch, Dorset. BH23 6AS
Phone Number: 01202 482714
Details: allowed in the bar area but not in the restaurant

The George

Address: 2A Castle Street, Christchurch, Dorset. BH23 1DT
Phone Number: 01202 479383
Details: allowed everywhere apart from dining area preferably kept on a lead

The Nelson

Address: 75 Muddeford, Christchurch, Dorset. BH23 3NJ
Phone Number: 01202 485105
Details: allowed in the bar but preferably kept on a lead

The Sandpiper

Address: 97 Bure Lane, Mudeford, Christchurch, Dorset.
Phone Number: 01425 275163
Details: allowed everywhere

Ye Old George Inn

Address: 2a Castle Street, Christchurch, Dorset. BH23 1DT
Phone Number: 01202 479383
Details: allowed everywhere water is provided

www.dogfriendly.co.uk

The Black Dog Inn

Address: 50 Main Street, Dorchester, Dorset. DT2 8ES

Phone Number: 01305 852360

Details: allowed in the bar not the restaurant and preferably on a lead

The Moonfleet Manor Hotel

Address: Fleet Road, Dorset. DT3 4ED

Phone Number: 01305 786948

Details: allowed everywhere but not in the restaurant area and must be kept on a lead

The Drovers Inn

Address: Gussage All Saints, Dorset. BH21 5ET

Phone Number: 01258 840084

Details: allowed everywhere but preferably on a lead

The Scott Arms

Address: 742 West Street, Corfe Castle, Kingston, Dorset. BH20 5LH

Phone Number: 01929 480270

Details: allowed in the bar but not in the restaurant area they also provide water bowls

The Loders Arms

Address: Loders, Dorset. DT6 3SA

Phone Number: 01308 422431

Details: allowed in the bar but not in the restaurant preferably on a lead

The Castle

Address: Lulworth Cove, Dorset. BH20 5RN

Phone Number: 01929 400311

Details: allowed everywhere but not in the restaurant

Pilot Boat

Address: Bridge Street, Lyme Regis, Dorset. DT7 3QA

Phone Number: 01297 443157

Details: allowed everywhere preferably to be on a lead

St Peter's Finger

Address: Dorcester Road, Lytchett Minster, Dorset.

Phone Number: 01202 622275

Details: allowed in the bar and garden preferably on leads

Piddle Inn

Address: High St, Piddletrenthide, Dorset. DT2 7QF

Phone Number: 01300 348468

Details: allowed in the bar preferably on leads

The Poachers Inn

Address: Piddletrenthide, Dorset. DT2 7QX

Phone Number: 01300 348358

Details: allowed everywhere but not in the restaurant and must be kept on a lead

The Kings Arms

Address: 2 Front Street, Weymouth, Portesham, Dorset. DT3 4ET

Phone Number: 01305 871342

Details: allowed everywhere except for the restaurant preferably on a lead

Three Horseshoes

Address: Bridport, Powerstock, Dorset. DT6 3TF

Phone Number: 01308 485328

Details: allowed everywhere in the bedrooms and bar area

Crown Inn

Address: Church Street, Puncknowle, Dorset.

Phone Number: 01305 224291

Details: allowed everywhere preferably to be on a lead

The Queens Head

Address: The Cross, Burley, Ringwood, Dorset. BH24 4AB

Phone Number: 01425 403423

Details: allowed everywhere but not in the restaurant preferably to be kept on a lead at all times

Grange Hotel

Address: Southborne, Dorset. DH6 3NL

Phone Number: 01202 433 093

Details: allowed everywhere except the dining area

Saxon Arms

Address: The Square, Stratton, Dorset. DT2 9WG

Phone Number: 01305 260020

Details: allowed everywhere but not in the restaurant area

The Springhead Restaurant

Address: Sutton Road, Weymouth, Sutton Poynz, Dorset. DT3 6LW

Phone Number: 01305 832117

Details: allowed everywhere but not in the restaurant preferably to be kept on a lead at all times

The Red Lion

Address: 63 High St, Swanage, Dorset. BH19 2LY

Phone Number: 01929 423533

Details: allowed everywhere as long as they are kept on a lead

The White Swan

Address: The Square, High Street, Swanage, Dorset. BH19 2LJ

Phone Number: 01929 423 804

Details: dogs are not allowed in the B&B but are allowed in the pub

Kings Arms

Address: 41 North Street, Wareham, Dorset. BH20 4AD

Phone Number: 01929 552503

Details: allowed everywhere preferably on a lead

The Fox Inn

Address: 8 West St, Corfe Castle, Wareham, Dorset. BH20 5HD

Phone Number: 01929 480449

Details: allowed everywhere preferably on a lead

Old Rooms Inn

Address: Cove Row, Weymouth, Dorset. DT4 8TT

Phone Number: 01305 771130

www.dogfriendly.co.uk

Details: allowed in the pub but not in the restaurant and have to kept on a lead

The Bridge Inn

Address: Bridge Inn Lane, Preston, Weymouth, Dorset. DT3 4ET

Phone Number: 01305 871342

Details: allowed everywhere but have to be kept on a lead

The Nothe Tavern

Address: Barrack Road, Weymouth, Dorset. DT4 8TZ

Phone Number: 01305 839255

Details: allowed in parts of the pub but must be kept on a lead

The Lamb Inn

Address: Burley Road, Winkton, Dorset. BH23 7AN

Phone Number: 01424 672427

Details: allowed everywhere prferably to be on a lead and must be kept under control

Maltravers, Square & Compass

Address: Worth Maltravers, Swanage, Worth, Dorset. BH19 3LF

Phone Number: 01929 439229

Details: allowed everywhere but must be kept under control

The Lord Crewe Arms

Address: Blanchland, Durham. DH8 9SP
Phone Number: 01434 675251
Details: allowed everywhere but not in the restaurant

The Manor House Inn

Address: Carterway Heads, Shotley Bridge, Consett, Durham. DH8 9LX
Phone Number: 01207 255268
Details: allowed in the bar & lounge but not the restaurant

The Moorcock Inn

Address: Hill Top, Eggleston, Durham. DL12 0AU
Phone Number: 01833 650395
Details: allowed everywhere but not in the restaurant

The Beamish Mary Inn

Address: No Place, Durham. DH9 0QH
Phone Number: 0191 3700237
Details: allowed everywhere

The Court Inn

Address: , Durham. DH1 3AW
Phone Number: 0191 384 7350
Details: allowed everywhere

The Causeway

Address: Elwick Broad, Cleveland, Hartlepool, Durham. TS24 7QT
Phone Number: 01429 273954

Details: allowed everywhere preferably on a lead

Dun Cow

Address: The Village, Seaton, Seaham, Durham. SR7 0NA
Phone Number: 0191 5131133
Details: allowed everywhere but preferably on a lead

Seven Stars

Address: High Street North, Shincliffe Village, Shincliffe, Durham. DH1 2NU
Phone Number: 0191 384 8454
Details: only in the bar and must be kept on a lead

The Rose Tree

Address: Low Road West, Shincliffe, Durham.
Phone Number: 0191 3868512
Details: only in the bar

www.dogfriendly.co.uk

Essex

White Harte

Address: The Quay, Burnham On Crouch, Essex. CMO 8AS
Phone Number: 01621 782106
Details: only in bar not the restaurant area

Bell

Address: Castle Hedington, Essex.
Phone Number: 01787 460350
Details: allowed everywhere preferably to be on a lead

Swan

Address: The Street, Chappel, Essex. CO6 2DD
Phone Number: 01787 222353
Details: allowed every but not in the restaurant and have to be kept on a lead

Forest Gate Inn

Address: 111 Bell Common, Epping, Essex. CM16 4DZ
Phone Number: 01992 572312
Details: allowed everywhere preferably to be kept on a lead

Square and Compass

Address: Fuller Street, Essex.
Phone Number: 01787 461196
Details: allowed in the bar preferably on leads

Green Man

Address: Gosford, Essex.
Phone Number: 01787 472746
Details: not allowed in the restaurant but everywhere else

Rainbow and Dove

Address: Hastingwood Road, Harlow, Hastingwood, Essex. CM17 9JX
Phone Number: 01279 415419
Details: during the day not the evening preferably to kept on leads

Jolly Sailor

Address: Basin Road, Maldon, Heybridge, Essex. CM9 4RS
Phone Number: 01621 854210
Details: allowed everywhere but must be kept on leads

Shepherd and Dog

Address: Mor Road, Langham, Essex.
Phone Number: 01206 272711
Details: allowed everywhere preferably be kept on a lead

Ye Olde Smack Inn

Address: 7 High St, Leigh On Sea, Essex. SS9 2EN
Phone Number: 01702 476765
Details: allowed everywhere preferably on a lead

www.dogfriendly.co.uk

The Generals Arms

Address: The Ridge, Little Baddow, Essex. CM3 4SE

Phone Number: 01245 222069

Details: allowed everywhere but not in the restaurant preferably kept on a lead

Green Man

Address: Kelvedon Road, Little Braxted, Essex.

Phone Number: 01621 891659

Details: allowed in the pub preferably to be on a lead

Crown

Address: The Crown High Street, Saffron Walden, Little Walden, Essex. CB10 1XA

Phone Number: 01799 522475

Details: allowed everywhere preferably to be kept on a lead

The Victoria Tavern

Address: 165 Smarts Lane, Loughton, Essex. RG10 4BP

Phone Number: 020 8508 1779

Details: allowed in the bar but not the restaurant and have to be kept on a lead

The White Hart

Address: The Tye, Ingatestone, Margaretting, Essex. CM4 9JX

Phone Number: 01277 840478

Details: allowed everywhere

Viper

Address: The Common, Mill Green Road, Mill Green, Essex. CM4 0PT

Phone Number: 01277 352010

Details: allowed In the pub but have to be kept on a lead

Ferry Boat

Address: Ferry Lane, North Fambridge, Essex. CM3 6LR

Phone Number: 01621 740208

Details: allowed in the bar and preferably to be on a lead

Cricketers Arms

Address: The Inn on the Green, Rickling Green, Essex. CB11 3YG

Phone Number: 01799 543210

Details: allowed in the bar and preferably to be on a lead

Ye Olde Albion Inn

Address: High Street, Rowhedge, Essex. CO5 7ES

Phone Number: 01206 728972

Details: allowed everywhere and preferably be kept on a lead

The Queen's Head

Address: 3 Lower Street, Stanstead Mountfitchet, Essex. CM24 8LN

Phone Number: 01279 812458

Details: allowed everywhere prferably on a lead

The Hoop

Address: Stock, Essex. CM4 9BD

Phone Number: 01277 841137

Details: allowed in one part of the bar and they must be kept on a lead

www.dogfriendly.co.uk

The Crown

Address: Park St, Colchester, STOKE BY Nayland, Essex. CO6 4SE
Phone Number: 01206 262001
Details: allowed everywhere preferably kept on a lead

Prince of Wales

Address: Woodham Road, STOW Maries, Essex. CM3 6SA
Phone Number: 01621 828971
Details: allowed in the bar but must be kept under control and on a lead

Bell

Address: Wensdon Ambo, Essex.
Phone Number: 01799 540382
Details: allowed in the bar but not in the dining room and must also be on leads

The Black Horse Inn

Address: Littleworth, Stroud, Amberley, Gloucestershire. GL5 5AL

Phone Number: 01453 872556

Details: allowed everywhere as long as they are kept under control

The Kings Arms

Address: The Street, Badminton, Gloucestershire.

Phone Number: 01454 238245

Details: allowed in the bar but not in the restaurant area and must be kept on a lead

The Bibury Court Hotel

Address: Cirenchester, Bibury, Gloucestershire. GL7 5NT

Phone Number: 01285 740337

Details: allowed in the bedrooms and bar not in the dining room preferably kept on a lead

The Duke of Wellington

Address: Sherborne Street, Bourton On The Water, Gloucestershire. GL54 2BY

Phone Number: 01451 820 539

Details: allowed everywhere preferably on a lead and under control & allowed in the bedrooms

The Crown

Address: Cerney Wick, Gloucestershire.

Phone Number: 01793 750369

Details: dogs only allowed in the bar and must be kept on a lead

The Seven Tuns

Address: Queen Street, Chedworth, Gloucestershire. GL54 4AE

Phone Number: 01285 720242

Details: allowed everywhere preferably on a lead

The Eight Bells

Address: Church Street, Chipping Campden, Gloucestershire. GL55 6JD

Phone Number: 01386 840371

Details: but only allowed in the bar and must be kept on a lead

Somewhere Else

Address: 65 Castle Street, Cirencester, Gloucestershire. GL7 1QD

Phone Number: 01285 643199

Details: allowed everywhere but must be kept on a lead

The Tunnel House Inn

Address: Coates, Gloucestershire. GL7 6PW

Phone Number: 01285 770280

Details: allowed everywhere

The New Inn

Address: Main Street, Coln-St-Aldwyns, Gloucestershire. GL7 5AN

www.dogfriendly.co.uk

Phone Number: 01285 750651

Details: allowed everywhere preferably to be kept on a lead

The Wild Duck Inn

Address: Drakes Island, Cirenchester, Ewen, Gloucestershire. GL7 6BY

Phone Number: 01285 770310

Details: allowed in the bar area and allowed in the bedrooms

The Jolly Tar

Address: Queens Rd, Swindon, Hannington, Gloucestershire. SN6 7RP

Phone Number: 01793 762245

Details: allowed in the bar area preferably on a lead

The Riverside

Address: Lechlade, Gloucestershire. GL7 3AQ

Phone Number: 01367 252229

Details: allowed in the bar preferably on leads

The Fountain Inn

Address: Parkend, Lydney, Gloucestershire. GL15 4JD

Phone Number: 01594 562189

Details: not allowed in the restaurant but everywhere else and must be kept under control

The Britannia Inn

Address: Newmarket Road, Nailsworth, Gloucestershire. GL6 0DG

Phone Number: 01453 832501

Details: allowed everywhere but not in the restaurant preferably kept on a lead

Woolpack

Address: Slad, Gloucestershire. GL6 7QA

Phone Number: 01452 813429

Details: allowed everywhere preferably be kept on a lead

The Eagle and Child

Address: Digbeth Street, Stow On The Wold, Gloucestershire. GR54 1AB

Phone Number: 01451 830563

Details: allowed everywhere preferably be kept on a lead

The Bush Inn

Address: Ovington, Alresford, Hampshire. SO24 0RE

Phone Number: 01962 732764

Details: allowed in the bar but must be kept under control and on a lead

The Ship Inn

Address: Bishop's Sutton, Alresford, Hampshire. SO24 0AQ

Phone Number: 01962 732 863

Details: allowed everywhere but not in the dining area preferably kept on a lead

The Oak Inn

Address: Pinkney Lane, Lyndhurst, Bank, Hampshire. SO43 7FE

Phone Number: 023 8028 2350

Details: allowed everywhere preferably to be kept on a lead doggie biscuit & water provided

Sun

Address: Alton, Bentworth, Hampshire. GU34 5JT

Phone Number: 01420 562338

Details: allowed everywhere but must be kept under control

The Hampshire Bowman

Address: Dundridge Lane, Bishops Waltham, Hampshire. SO32 1GD

Phone Number: 01489 892940

Details: allowed everywhere, www.hampshirebowman.com

The Filly Inn

Address: Lymington Road, Setley, Brockenhurst, Hampshire. SO42 7UF

Phone Number: 01590 623449

Details: allowed in the bar and must be kept on a lead

The Turf Cutters Arms

Address: Main Road, East Boldre, Hampshire. SO42 7WL

Phone Number: 01590 612331

Details: allowed everywhere and the bedrooms preferably on a lead

County Hampshire
The Chestnut Horse

Address: Easton, Hampshire. SO21 1EG

Phone Number: 01962 779257

Details: allowed in the bar area

County Hampshire
The Bluebell

Address: 29 South Street, Emsworth, Hampshire. PO10 7EG

Phone Number: 01243 373394

Details: allowed everywhere preferably on a lead

The Wheelwrights Arms

Address: 27 Emsworth Road, Emsworth, Hampshire. PO9 2SN

www.dogfriendly.co.uk

Phone Number: 02392 483365

Details: allowed everywhere preferably on a lead and kept under control

The Compasses Inn

Address: Damerham, Hants, Fordingbridge, Hampshire. SP6 3HQ

Phone Number: 01725 518231

Details: allowed everywhere but not in the restaurant area but must be kept on a lead

The Royal Oak

Address: Lyndhurst, Fritham, Hampshire. SO43 7HJ

Phone Number: 02380 812606

Details: allowed everywhere preferably kept on a lead

The Foresters Arms

Address: Abbotswell Road, Frogham, Hampshire. SP6 2JA

Phone Number: 01425 652294

Details: allowed everywhere apart from the restaurant area

The Jolly Roger

Address: 156 Priory Rd, Gosport, Hampshire. PO12 4LQ

Phone Number: 0239 258 2584

Details: allowed everywhere but must be kept on a lead

The King & Queen

Address: High St, Hamble, Hampshire. SO31 4HA

Phone Number: 02380 454247

Details: allowed everywhere

Steep

Address: Harrow, Hampshire.

Phone Number: 01730 262685

Details: allowed everywhere but they must be on a lead

The Royal Oak

Address: 19 Langstone High St, Langstone, Havant, Hampshire. PO9 1RY

Phone Number: 02392 483125

Details: allowed everywhere apart from the restaurant and must be kept on a lead

The Trout Inn

Address: Main Rd, Itchen Abbas, Hampshire. SO21 1BQ

Phone Number: 01962 779537

Details: allowed everywhere but must be on a lead and kept under control

High Corner Inn

Address: Linwood, Hampshire. BH24 3QY

Phone Number: 01425 473973

Details: allowed everywhere preferably to be on a lead

The Red Shoot Inn

Address: Linwood, Hampshire. BH24 3QT

Phone Number: 01425 473789

Details: allowed everywhere but must be kept under control and on a lead

The Kings Head

Address: Quay Hill, Lymington, Hampshire. SO41 3AR

Phone Number: 01590 672709

Details: allowed everywhere preferably on a lead

The New Forest Inn

Address: Emery Down, Lyndhurst, Hampshire. SO43 7DY

Phone Number: 023 8028 2329

Details: allowed everywhere preferably on a lead

The Oak Inn

Address: Pinkney Lane, Lyndhurst, Hampshire. SO43 7FE

Phone Number: 023 8028 2350

Details: allowed everywhere water and dog biscuits are provided

The Half Moon & Spreadeagle

Address: Winchester Road, Micheldever, Hampshire. SO21 3DG

Phone Number: 01962 774339

Details: dogs are allowed everywhere but must be kept under control and also on a lead

The Trusty Servant

Address: Minstead, Hampshire. SO43 7FY

Phone Number: 023 8081 2137

Details: allowed in the bar not allowed in the bedrooms and preferably on a lead and under control

Royal Oak

Address: Ringwood Road, North Gorley, Hampshire. SP6 2PB

Phone Number: 01425 652244

Details: allowed in the bar but must be on a lead

The Vine Inn

Address: High Street, Old Burlesdon, Hampshire. SO13 8DJ

Phone Number: 023 8040 3836

Details: allowed in the bar and have to be kept on a lead

Queens Head

Address: The Cross, Burley, Ringwood, Hampshire. BH24 4AB

Phone Number: 01425 403423

Details: allowed everywhere and must be on leads

The Alice Lisle

Address: Rockford, Ringwood, Rockford Green, Hampshire. BH24 3NA

Phone Number: 01425 474700

Details: allowed in the bar and are not allowed in the garden

Seaview Hotel

Address: High Street, Seaview, Hampshire.

Phone Number: 01983 612711

Details: allowed everywhere apart from the restaurant and must be kept on a lead

The Wheatsheaf

Address: Botley Road, Shedfield, Hampshire. FA32 2JG

Phone Number: 01329 833024

Details: allowed in the bar preferably on leads

www.dogfriendly.co.uk

The Fisherman's Haunt

Address: Salisbury Road, Winkton, Sopley, Hampshire.
Phone Number: 01202 477283
Details: allowed everywhere preferably kept on a lead

The Woolpack

Address: Sopley, Hampshire. BH23 7AX
Phone Number: 01425 672252
Details: allowed in one bar and must be on a lead

The Jolly Sailor

Address: Lands End Road, Old Bursledon, Southampton, Hampshire. SO31 8DN
Phone Number: 023 8040 5557
Details: allowed everywhere preferably on a lead

The London Hotel

Address: 2 Terminus Terrace, Southampton, Hampshire. SO14 3DT
Phone Number: 023 8071 0652
Details: allowed in the bar during the day not evening and have to be kept on a lead

Hare and Hounds Pub

Address: Durnstown, Sway, Hampshire. SO41 6AL
Phone Number: 01590 682404
Details: allowed everywhere apart from the restaurant and must be kept on a lead

The Fisherman's Rest

Address: Sareham, Titchfield, Hampshire. PO15 5RA
Phone Number: 01329 845065
Details: designated area for dogs and preferably kept on a lead

Red Lion

Address: Commercial Road, Totton, Hampshire. SO40 3AF
Phone Number: 0238 0863273
Details: allowed everywhere preferably kept on a lead

The Chequers Inn

Address: Well, Hampshire. RG29 1PL
Phone Number: 01256 862605
Details: allowed in the bar preferably on a lead and under control

The Exchange

Address: 9 Southgate Street, Winchester, Hampshire. SO23 9DZ
Phone Number: 01962 854718
Details: allowed everywhere preferably on a lead

The King Alfred

Address: 11 Saxon Road, Hyde, Winchester, Hampshire. SO23 7DJ
Phone Number: 01962 854370
Details: allowed in the bar and garden but must be on a lead

The Plough

Address: Sparsholt, Winchester, Hampshire. SO21 2NW
Phone Number: 01962 776353
Details: allowed everywhere preferably on a lead

The Wykeham Arms

Address: 75 Kings Gate Street, Winchester, Hampshire. SO23 9PE
Phone Number: 01962 853834
Details: allowed in the bar but not the restaurant

The Compass Inn

Address: Winsor Road, Windsor, Hampshire. SO4 02HE
Phone Number: 02380 812237
Details: allowed every preferably kept on a lead

The Cricketers

Address: Cricket Hill Lane, Yateley, Hampshire. GU46 6BA
Phone Number: 01252 872105
Details: allowed into the main bar

The Swan Hotel

Address: Church Street, Kington, Herefordshire. HR5 3AZ
Phone Number: 01544 230510
Details: allowed in but have to be kept on a lead

The Horsehoe Inn

Address: The Homend, Ledbury, Herefordshire. HR8 1BP
Phone Number: 01531 632 770
Details: allowed in the bar preferably on a lead

The Valiant Trooper

Address: Aldbury, Hertfordshire.
Phone Number: 01789 450414
Details: allowed everywhere but not in the restaurant

Bridgewater Arms

Address: Little Gaddesden, Berkhamstead, Hertfordshire. HP4 1PF
Phone Number: 01442 842408
Details: allowed in the bar and preferably on a lead

The Black Horse

Address: Dog Kennel Lane, Chorleywood, Hertfordshire. WD3 5EG
Phone Number: 01923 282252
Details: allowed everywhere but not in the main restaurant and have to be on a lead

The Cart and Horses

Address: Quickmoor Lane, Commonwood, Hertfordshire. WD4 9BA
Phone Number: 01923 263763
Details: allowed in the garden not inside the pub

The Inn On The Green

Address: Wadderton Road, Datchworth, Hertfordshire. SG3 6TB
Phone Number: 01438 812496
Details: allowed in the bar & the garden and must be kept under control

The Wagon & Horses

Address: Watling Street, Elstree, Hertfordshire. WD6 3AA
Phone Number: 0208 953 1406
Details: allowed in the bar area and must be on a lead

The Plough & Harrow

Address: 88 Southdown Road, Harpenden, Hertfordshire. AL5 1TR
Phone Number: 01582 715844
Details: allowed everywhere must be on a lead

Alford Arms

Address: Frithsden, Hemel Hempstead, Hertfordshire. HPI 3DD
Phone Number: 01442 864480
Details: allowed in the bar but not in the restaurant

www.dogfriendly.co.uk

King William IV

Address: Cockernhoe, Mangrove Green, Hertfordshire.

Phone Number: 01582 728086

Details: allowed in the bar but not the restaurant and have to be kept on a lead

Hadley Hotel

Address: Hadley Road, New Barnet, Hertfordshire. EN5 5QN

Phone Number: 0208 4490161

Details: allowed everywhere and must be on a lead

The Swan

Address: Bedmond Road, Pimlico, Hertfordshire.

Phone Number: 01923 263093

Details: allowed in the bar & garden must be on leads

The Queen Adelaide

Address: High St, Croydon Village, Royston, Hertfordshire. SG8 0DN

Phone Number: 01223 208278

Details: only guide dogs are accepted

The Cock Inn

Address: Church Lane, Church End, Sarrat, Hertfordshire.

Phone Number: 01923 282 908

Details: allowed everywhere but must be kept on a lead and under control

Waggon & Horses

Address: 19 Church Street, Steeple Morden, Hertfordshire. SG8 0NJ

Phone Number: 01763 852829

Details: allowed everywhere but not the restaurant

The Chequers

Address: 16 London Road, Woolmer Green, Hertfordshire. SG3 6JP

Phone Number: 01438 813216

Details: allowed in the bar and not the restaurant and must be kept under control and on a lead

The White Lion

Address: Main Road, Arreton, Isle Of Wight. PO30 3AA

Phone Number: 01983 528479

Details: allowed in the garden and the bar

The Wight Mouse Inn

Address: Newport Road, Chale, Isle Of Wight. PO38 2HA

Phone Number: 01983 730431

Details: allowed in the bar and are allowed in some of the hotel rooms also dogs must be kept on a lead

The Pointer Inn

Address: High Street, Newchurch, Isle Of Wight. PO36 ONN

Phone Number: 01983 865202

Details: allowed in the bar and preferably to be on a lead

The Blacksmiths Arms

Address: Calbourne Road, Newport, Isle Of Wight. PO30 5SS

Phone Number: 01983 529263

Details: allowed everywhere but must be on a lead

The New Inn

Address: Main Road, Shafleet, Newport, Isle Of Wight. PO30 4NS

Phone Number: 01983 531314

Details: allowed everywhere but must be kept under control

King Lud

Address: 2 The Esplanade, Ryde, Isle Of Wight.

Phone Number: 01983 562 942

Details: allowed everywhere preferably on a lead

The Spyglass

Address: Esplanade, Ventnor, Isle Of Wight. PO38 1JX

Phone Number: 01983 855338

Details: allowed everywhere preferably kept on a lead

www.dogfriendly.co.uk

Kent

Three Chimneys

Address: Hareplain Road, Ashford, Biddenden, Kent. TN27 8LW

Phone Number: 01580 291472

Details: allowed everywhere preferably kept on a lead

The Wheatsheaf

Address: Hever Road, Bough Beech, Kent. TN8 7NU

Phone Number: 01732 700254

Details: allowed everywhere

Huntsman and Horn

Address: Broomfield, Kent. CT6 7AF

Phone Number: 01227 365995

Details: allowed in the bar preferably to be kept on a lead

Gate Inn

Address: Marshside, Chislet, Canterbury, Kent. CTE 4EB

Phone Number: 01227 860498

Details: allowed everywhere

The Saxon Inn

Address: Child Okeford, Kent.

Phone Number: 01258 860310

Details: allowed in the bar but not the restaurant and have to be kept on a lead

The Bulls Head

Address: Royal Parade, Chislehurst, Kent. BR7 6NR

Phone Number: 020 8467 1727

Details: allowed in the bar and must be kept on a lead

The Ocean Inn

Address: 2 High Street, Dymchurch, Kent. TN29 0NG

Phone Number: 01303 872152

Details: allowed everywhere apart from the restaurant and preferably kept on a lead

Rose and Crown

Address: Selling, Faversham, Kent. ME13 9RY

Phone Number: 01227 752214

Details: allowed everywhere apart from the dining area and must be kept on a lead

The Ship Inn

Address: Red Street, Southfleet, Gravesend, Kent. DA13 9NS

Phone Number: 01474 833238

Details: allowed everywhere apart from the restaurant and preferably kept on a lead

Kings Arms

Address: 1 High St, Ashford, Headcorn, Kent. TN27 9NH

Phone Number: 01622 890 216

Details: allowed everywhere preferably be kept on a lead

Bandstand Café-Bar

Address: Central Parade, Herne Bay, Kent. CT6 5JJ

Phone Number: 01227 372555

Details: allowed everywhere preferably to be kept on a lead

The Ship Inn

Address: 17 Central Parade, Herne Bay, Kent. CT6 5HT

Phone Number: 01227 364638

Details: allowed everywhere but not in the restaurant

The Peacock

Address: Iden Green, Goudhurst Road, Kent. TN17 2PB

Phone Number: 01580 211233

Details: allowed everywhere as long as they are kept on a lead

The Greyhound

Address: Commonside, Keston, Kent. BR2 6BP

Phone Number: 01689 856338

Details: allowed everywhere preferably to be kept on a lead

The Fayreness Hotel

Address: Marine Drive, Kingsgate, Kent. CT10 3LG

Phone Number: 01843 868641

Details: allowed everywhere preferably to be on a lead

The Cock Inn

Address: Henley Street, Luddesdown, Kent. DA13 OXB

Phone Number: 01474 814 208

Details: allowed everywhere

The Cricketers

Address: Meopham Green, Wrotham Rd, Meopham, Kent. DA13 0QA

Phone Number: 01474 812163

Details: allowed everywhere prferably kept on a lead

The Crown

Address: 10 the High Street, Orford, Kent. TN14 5PQ

Phone Number: 01959 522847

Details: allowed everywhere and have a big garden and preferably be kept on a lead

The Bridges

Address: Horton Road, South Darenth, Kent. DA4 9AX

Phone Number: 01322 860588

Details: allowed everywhere and preferably be kept on a lead

The George Inn

Address: Taylors Lane, Trottiscliffe, Kent. MA19 5DR

Phone Number: 01732 822 462

Details: allow small dogs

The Plough

Address: Trottiscliffe, Kent. ME19 5DR

Phone Number: 01732 822 233

Details: allowed in the bar and must be kept under control

The George & Dragon

Address: Speldhurst Hill, Speldhurst, Tunbridge Wells, Kent. TN3 0NN
Phone Number: 01892 863125
Details: allowed in the bars

The Hare

Address: Langton Road, Langton Green, Tunbridge Wells, Kent. TN3 0JA
Phone Number: 01892 862419
Details: allowed in the bar but not the food area preferably be kept on a lead

The Spread Eagle

Address: 119 Forest Road, Tunbridge Wells, Kent. TN2 5B2
Phone Number: 01892 525 414
Details: allowed everywhere apart from the restaurant and must be kept under control

The Swan on the Green

Address: The Village Green, West Peckham, Kent. ME18 5JW
Phone Number: 01622 812271
Details: allowed everywhere preferably kept on a lead

The Grasshopper on the Green

Address: The Green, Westerham, Kent. TN16 1AS
Phone Number: 01959 562926
Details: allowed in the bar and must be kept under control

The Swan Inn

Address: 1 Swan Street, Wittersham, Kent. TN30 7PH
Phone Number: 01797 270913
Details: allowed in the bar and preferably to be on a lead

The Kings Arms

Address: Meopham Green, Wrotham Rd, MEOPHAM, Kent. DA13 0QB
Phone Number: 01474 813323
Details: allowed everywhere apart from the restaurant and preferably kept on a lead

The Pendle Inn

Address: Barley, Lancashire. BB12 9JX
Phone Number: 01282 614 808
Details: allowed in the bar and must be kept under control

The George Washington Pub

Address: Main Street, Warton, Carnforth, Lancashire.
Phone Number: 01524 732865
Details: allowed everywhere preferably to be kept on a lead

Assheton Arms

Address: Downham, Lancashire. BB7 4BJ
Phone Number: 01200 441227
Details: allowed in the bar and must be kept under control

Inn at Whitewell

Address: Forest Of Bowland, Lancashire. BB7 3AT
Phone Number: 01200 448222
Details: allowed everywhere apart from in the restaurant

The Lomax Arms

Address: Blackburn Road, GREAT Harwood, Lancashire. BB6 7DZ
Phone Number: 01254 882397
Details: allowed everywhere and must be kept on a lead

The Shovels Inn

Address: Green Meadow Lane, Hambleton, Lancashire. F16 9AL
Phone Number: 01253 700209
Details: allowed everywhere apart from the restaurant and must be kept on a lead

The Horse & Jockey

Address: 9 Chorlton Green, Manchester, Lancashire. M21 9HS
Phone Number: 0161 881 6494
Details: allowed everywhere but have to be on leads

Eagle and Child

Address: Malt Kiln Lane, Ormskirk, Parbold, Lancashire. L40 3FG
Phone Number: 01257 462297
Details: allowed everywhere

The White Bull

Address: The Square, Great Eccleston, Preston, Lancashire. PR3 0ZB
Phone Number: 01995 670203
Details: allowed everywhere but must be kept on a lead

The Wheatsheaf

Address: 34 Woodplumpton Road, Woodplumpton, Lancashire. PR4 0NE
Phone Number: 01772 690301
Details: allowed in the bar area and preferably on a lead

www.dogfriendly.co.uk

Leicestershire

The White Hart

Address: 82 Market St, Ashby-De-La-Zouch, Leicestershire. LE65 1AP
Phone Number: 01530 414531
Details: allowed in the bar area

The Queens Head

Address: 2 Long Street, Belton, Leicestershire. LE12 9TP
Phone Number: 01530 222 359
Details: allowed in the bar but not in the restaurant

Old Plough

Address: 18 Front Street, Birstall, Leicestershire. LE4 4DP
Phone Number: 01162 674836
Details: allowed everywhere but must be kept on a lead

Old Plough

Address: 2 Church Street, Braunston, Leicestershire. LE15 8QT
Phone Number: 01572 722714
Details: allowed everywhere as long as they are kept under control

Old Plough Inn

Address: Hight Street, Braunston, Leicestershire.
Phone Number: 01788 890000
Details: allowed in the bar

Bell Inn

Address: Main Street, East Langton, Leicestershire. LE16 7TW
Phone Number: 01858 545278
Details: must be kept on a lead

The New Plough Inn

Address: 24 Leicester Road, Hinckley, Leicestershire. LE10 1LS
Phone Number: 01455 615037
Details: allowed everywhere preferably kept on a lead

Swan in the Rushes

Address: 21 The Rushes, Loughborough, Leicestershire. LE11 5BE
Phone Number: 01509 217014
Details: allowed everywhere preferably kept on a lead

The Three Crowns

Address: 45 Far Street, Loughborough, Leicestershire. LE12 6TZ
Phone Number: 01509 880153
Details: only allowed in the bar and must be kept on a lead

The Cherry Tree

Address: Kettering Road, Market Harborough, Leicestershire. LE16 8AE
Phone Number: 01858 463525
Details: allowed in the bar but must be kept on a lead

www.dogfriendly.co.uk

The Cow & Plough

Address: Gartree Road, OADBY, Leicestershire. LE2 2FB

Phone Number: 0116 272 0852

Magda Cock

Address: Main Street, Peatling, Leicestershire. LE8 5UQ

Phone Number: 01162 478308

Details: only small dogs and must be on leads

Queens Head

Address: Main Street, Saddington, Leicestershire. LE8 OQH

Phone Number: 01162 402536

Details: allowed in the bar but not the restaurant and have to be kept on a lead

www.dogfriendly.co.uk

Lincolnshire

Gipsy Queen

Address: Station Road, Bardney, Lincolnshire. LN3 5UF

Phone Number: 01526 397188

Details: allowed everywhere prferably kept on a league

The Adam and Eve

Address: The Adam And Eve, Lincoln, Lincolnshire. LN2 1NT

Phone Number: 01522 537108

Details: allowed everywhere preferably on a lead

The Victoria

Address: 6 Union Road, Lincoln, Lincolnshire.

Phone Number: 01522 536048

Details: allowed everywhere but not when food is being served and they must be kept on a lead

The White Hart Hotel

Address: Bailgate, Lincoln, Lincolnshire. LN1 3AR

Phone Number: 0870 4008117

Details: allowed everywhere

The Daniel Lambert

Address: Stamford, Lincolnshire. PE9 2HN

Phone Number: 01780 755 991

Details: allowed everywhere but not in the restaurant

Chequers Inn

Address: Main Street, Woolsthorpe By Belvoir, Lincolnshire.

Phone Number: 01476 870701

Details: allowed everywhere except for where food is being served and must be kept under control

www.dogfriendly.co.uk

The Sun and Dove

Address: 61 Coldharbour Lane, Camberwell, London. SE5 9NS
Phone Number: 020 7733 1525
Details: allowed everywhere preferably on a lead

The Bell and Crown

Address: 11-13 Thames Road, Chiswick, London. W4 3PL
Phone Number: 020 8994 4164
Details: allowed everywhere preferably on a lead

The Crown & Greyhound

Address: 73 Dulwich Village, Dulwich, London. SE21 7BJ
Phone Number: 020 8299 4976
Details: allowed in the front part of the bar and must be on a lead

Castle Inn

Address: 36 St. Marys Rd, Ealing, London. W5 5EU
Phone Number: 020 8567 3285
Details: preferably on a lead

The Bishop

Address: 27 Lordship Lane, East Dulwich, London. SE22 8EW
Phone Number: 020 8693 3994
Details: must be kept on a lead

The Clock House

Address: 196a Peckham Rye, East Dulwich, London. SE22
Phone Number: 020 8693 2901
Details: only allowed on the hard wood area and prferably kept on a lead

The Union on Royal Hill

Address: 56 Royal Hill, Greenwich, London. SE10 8RT
Phone Number: 020 8692 6258
Details: allowed everywhere and must be kept under control

The Black Lion

Address: 2 South Black Lion Lane, Hammersmith, London. W6 9TJ
Phone Number: 0208 748 2639
Details: allowed in the bar and must be kept on a lead

The Dove Inn

Address: 19 Upper Mall, Hammersmith, London. W6 9TA
Phone Number: 020 8748 5405
Details: allowed everywhere and must be kept on a lead

The Thatched House

Address: 115 Dalling Road, Hammersmith, London. W6 0ET
Phone Number: 020 8748 6174
Details: phone back and speak to manager

www.dogfriendly.co.uk

The Wells Tavern

Address: 30 Well Walk, Hampstead Heath, London. NW3 1BX

Phone Number: 020 7794 3785

Details: allowed in the bar but must be kept under control

The William IV (KW4)

Address: 77 Hampstead High St, Hampstead, London. NW3 1RE

Phone Number: 0207 4355747

Details: allowed everywhere but must be kept under control

The Grey Hound

Address: Church End, Hendon, London. NW4 4JT

Phone Number: 0208 457 9730

Details: allowed everywhere preferably be kept on a lead

The Commercial

Address: 210-212 Railton Rd, Herne Hill, London. SE24 0JT

Phone Number: 020 7501 9051

Details: allowed everywhere but must be kept on a lead

The Northgate

Address: 113 Southgate Road, Islington, London. N1 3JS

Phone Number: 020 7359 7392

Details: allowed everywhere but not in the restaurant area

Coach & Horses

Address: 27 Barnes High Street, London. SW13 9LW

Phone Number: 0208 876 2695

Details: allowed everywhere preferably to be on a lead

Ealing Park Tavern

Address: 222 South Ealing Road, London. W5 4RO

Phone Number: 0208 758 1879

Details: dogs are allowed in the bar but not in the restaurant

Lord Palmerston

Address: Dartmouth Park Hill, London. NW5 1HU

Phone Number: 020 7485 1578

Details: allowed everywhere

Paradise By Way of Kensal Green

Address: 29 Kilburn Lane, London. W10

Phone Number: 0871 3322016

Details: allowed everywhere but not in the restaurant

Orange Brewery

Address: 37-39 Pimlico Road, Belgravia, London.

Phone Number: 020 7730 5984

Details: only small dogs

The Cats Back

Address: 86 Point Pleasant, Putney, London. SW18 1NN

Phone Number: 020 8877 0818

Details: allowed in the bar and preferably to be on a lead

The Coach & Horses

Address: Clapham Park Road, London. SW4

Phone Number: 020 7622 3815

Details: allowed everywhere but they must be on a lead

The Crown

Address: 223 Grove Road, Victoria Park, London. E3 5SN

Phone Number: 020 8981 9998

Details: allowed in the bar but not the restaurant and have to be kept on a lead

The Grapes

Address: Narrow Street, Limehouse, London. E14 8BP

Phone Number: 020 7987 4396

Details: allowed in the bar preferably on leads

The Herne Tavern

Address: 2 Forest Hill Road, London. SE22 0RR

Phone Number: 020 8299 9521

Details: allowed in the bar and garden preferably on leads

The Junction Tavern

Address: 101 Fortess Road, Kentish Town, London. NW5 1AG

Phone Number: 020 7485 9400

Details: allowed in the bar and garden not in the restaurant and have to be on a lead

The Mason's Arms

Address: 169 Battersea Park Road, London. SW8 4BT

Phone Number: 020 7622 2007

Details: allowed in the bar and preferably to be on a lead

The Mucky Pup

Address: 39 Queens Head Street, London. N1 8QN

Phone Number: 020 7226 2572

Details: allowed everywhere and must be kept under control

The Spaniard's Inn

Address: Spaniard's Lane, London. NW3 7JJ

Phone Number: 020 8731 6571

Details: allowed everywhere except for upstairs

The Sun Inn

Address: 7 Church Road, Barnes, London. SW13 9HE

Phone Number: 020 8876 5256

Details: allowed everywhere

The Vine

Address: 86 Highgate Road, London. NW5 1PB

Phone Number: 020 7209 0038

Details: allowed everywhere but not in the restaurant

The White Bear

Address: Ickenham Road, Ruslip, London. HA4 7DF

Phone Number: 01895 632078

Details: allowed everywhere free doggy biscuit & water

The Anglesea Arms

Address: 15 Sellwood Terrace, South Kensington, London. SW7 3QG

Phone Number: 020 7373 7960

Details: allowed everywhere but not in the dining area

The Clifton

Address: 96 Cliffton Hill, St John's Wood, London. NW8 OJT

Phone Number: 0207 373 3427

Details: allowed in the bar but not where food is being served and must be kept under control

Mint

Address: 5 Streatham High Road, Streatham, London. SW16 1EF

Phone Number: 020 8677 0007

Details: allowed everywhere and preferably be kept on a lead and water bowls are provided

Tide End Cottage

Address: 8 Ferry Road, Teddington, London. TW11 9NN

Phone Number: 020 8977 7762

Details: allowed everywhere preferably on a lead

The Trafalgar Arms

Address: 148 Tooting High Street, Tooting, London. SW17

Phone Number: 020 8767 6059

Details: allowed everywhere and dogs do not have to be on a lead

White Swan

Address: Riverside, Twickenham, London. TW1 3DN

Phone Number: 0208 892 2166

Details: allowed in the bar but must be kept under control and on a lead

The Earl Spencer

Address: 262 Merton Rd, Wandsworth, London. SW18 5JL

Phone Number: 020 8870 9244

Details: allowed everywhere preferably be kept on a lead and water bowls are provided

The Crooked Billet

Address: 15 Crooked Billet, Wimbledon Common, London. SW19 4RQ

Phone Number: 0208 946 4942

Details: allowed everywhere preferably kept on a lead

www.dogfriendly.co.uk

The Cross Keys Inn

Address: Running Hill Lane, Uppermill, Manchester, Greater Manchester.

Phone Number: 01457 874626

Details: allowed in the bar area must be kept under control and on a lead

Church Inn

Address: Church Lane, Uppermill, Saddleworth, Greater Manchester.

Phone Number: 01457 820902

Details: allowed everywhere preferably be kept on a lead

Norfolk

The Ship Inn

Address: Coast Road, Bacton, Norfolk. NR12 0EW

Phone Number: 01692 650420

Details: allowed in the bar area but must be on a lead and kept under control

The Briseley Bell

Address: The Green, Briseley, Norfolk. NR20 5DW

Phone Number: 01362 668686

Details: allowed in the bar when food is not being served and are allowed outside on the common

Hoste Arms

Address: The Green, Burnham Market, Norfolk. PE31 8HD

Phone Number: 01328 738777

Details: allowed in the bar & lounge but not the restaurant

The Reedcutter

Address: Station Rd, Cantley, Norfolk. NR13 3SH

Phone Number: 01493 701099

Details: allowed everywhere but not in the restaurant and must be kept under control

County Norfolk

The George Hotel

Address: High Street, Cley, Norfolk. NR25 7RN

Phone Number: 01263 740652

Details: allowed everywhere except in the restaurant and must be kept under control

The Three Swallows

Address: Newgate Green, Cley, Norfolk. NR25 7TT

Phone Number: 01263 740526

Details: allowed everywhere and kept under control

Three Horseshoes

Address: Warham, Fakenham, Norfolk. NR23 1NL

Phone Number: 01328 710547

Details: allowed everywhere and kept under control

The Decoy Tavern

Address: Beccles Rd, Fritton, Great Yarmouth, Norfolk. NR31 9AB

Phone Number: 01493 488277

Details: allowed in the bar preferably kept on a lead

Walpole Arms

Address: The Common, Itteringham, Norfolk. NR11 7AR

Phone Number: 01263 587258

Details: allowed in the bar and must be kept on a lead

www.dogfriendly.co.uk

House on the Green

Address: Ling Common Road, North Wootton, Kings Lynn, Norfolk. PE30 3RE

Phone Number: 01553 631323

Details: only allowed in the bar and they must be kept under control

King's Arms

Address: High Street, Ludham, Norfolk. NR29 5QQ

Phone Number: 01692 678386

Details: allowed in the main bar and must be kept under control and are allowed in the garden

Anchor Inn

Address: The Street, Morston, Norfolk. NR25 7AA

Phone Number: 01263 741 392

Details: allowed in the bar (not open for another 2 months)

Lodge Hotel Bar

Address: Old Hunstanton, Norfolk. PE36 6HX

Phone Number: 01485 532896

Details: allowed in the bar and not the restaurant and must be kept under control

The Ancient Mariner Inn

Address: Golf Course Road, Old Hunstanton, Norfolk. PE36 6JJ

Phone Number: 01485 534411

Details: allowed in the bar, garden and some of the bedrooms and kept under control

Rose & Crown

Address: Old Church Road, Snettisham, Norfolk. PE31 7LX

Phone Number: 01485 541382

Details: allowed in the bar and preferably on a lead

Lifeboat

Address: Ship Lane, Thornham, Norfolk. PE36 6LT

Phone Number: 01485 512236

Details: allowed in the bar and must be kept under control

The Globe Inn

Address: Wells-Next-The-Sea, Norfolk. NR23 1EU

Phone Number: 01328 710206

Details: allowed in the bar but not in the bedrooms and preferably on a lead

The Fisherman's Return

Address: The Lane, Winterton-On-Sea, Norfolk. NR29 4BN

Phone Number: 01493 393305

Details: allowed everywhere

Northamptonshire

The Windmill

Address: Main street, Badby, Northampton. NN11 3AN

Phone Number: 01327 702 363

Details: allowed in the bar & bedrooms but not in the restaurant and must be kept under control

The Walnut Tree Inn

Address: 21 Station Rd, Blisworth, Northampton. NN7 3DS

Phone Number: 01604 859551

Details: allowed in the main bar and must be kept under control

The Bakers Arms

Address: 34 High St, Bugbrooke, Northampton. NN7 3PG

Phone Number: 01604 830 865

Details: allowed everywhere as long as they are kept under control

The Coach & Horses

Address: Great Brington, Warwick Street, Daventry, Northampton. NN11 4AJ

Phone Number: 01327 876 692

Details: allowed everywhere preferably kept on a lead

Althorp Coaching Inn

Address: Main St, Great Brington, Northampton. NN7 4JA

Phone Number: 01604 770651

Details: allowed in the bar and preferably on a lead

King William IV

Address: 2 Green End, Kingsthorpe, Northampton. NN2 6RD

Phone Number: 01604 711326

Details: allowed everywhere preferably on a lead

Queen Adelaide

Address: 15 Manor Road, Kingsthorpe, Northampton. NN2 60J

Phone Number: 01604 714524

Details: allowed everywhere and must be kept under control

The Wharf Inn

Address: Welford Road, Welford, Northampton. NN6 6JQ

Phone Number: 01858 575075

Details: allowed everywhere but not in the restaurant and must be kept on a lead

www.dogfriendly.co.uk

The Hope and Anchor

Address: 44 Northumberland Street, Almouth, Northumberland. NE66 2RA

Phone Number: 01665 830363

Details: allowed everywhere apart from the restaurant and preferably on a lead

The Saddle

Address: 24/25 Northumberland Street, Almouth, Northumberland. NE66 2RA

Phone Number: 01665 830476

Details: allowed everywhere and must be kept under control

The Schooner

Address: Northumberland Street, Alnmouth, Northumberland. ME66 2RS

Phone Number: 01665 830216

Details: allowed everywhere but must be kept on a lead

The Sun Inn

Address: Northumberland Street, Alnmouth, Northumberland.

Phone Number: 01665 830983

Details: allowed everywhere and must be kept under control

The Mizen Head Hotel

Address: Bamburgh, Northumberland. NE69 7BS

Phone Number: 01668 214254

Details: allowed everywhere an must be kept under control (not open till june)

The Burton House

Address: Busty Bank, Burnopfield, Northumberland. NE16 6NF

Phone Number: 01207 271850

Details: allowed everywhere and kept under control

Manor House Inn

Address: Shorttey Bridge, Carterway Heads, Northumberland. DH8 9LX

Phone Number: 01207 255268

Details: allowed in the bar & lounge but not the restaurant and must be kept under control

The Robin Hood Inn

Address: Military Road, East Wallhouses, Northumberland. NE18 0LL

Phone Number: 01434 672273

Details: allowed everywhere but not in the restaurant and must be kept on a lead

Moorcock Inn

Address: Hill Top, Eggleston, Northumberland. DL12 9AU

Phone Number: 01833 650395

Details: allowed in the bars but not in the lounge and must be kept on a lead

www.dogfriendly.co.uk

The Blackcock Inn

Address: Falstone, Northumberland. NE48 1AA

Phone Number: 01434 240200

Details: allowed everywhere but must be kept under control

The Priory

Address: The Square, Scorton, Northumberland. PR3 1AU

Phone Number: 01524 791255

Details: allowed in the pub preferably on leads and kept under control

The Star Inn

Address: 22 Middle Street, Beeston, Nottinghamshire. NG9 1FX

Phone Number: 0115 922 22234

Details: allowed in the bar area but not the restaurant and must be on a lead

The Victoria Hotel

Address: Beeston, Nottinghamshire. NG9 1JG

Phone Number: 0115 9254049

Details: allowed in the bar but must be kept on leads

Stratford Haven

Address: 2 Stratford Road, West Bridgeford, Nottinghamshire. NG2 6BA

Phone Number: 01159 825981

Details: allowed everywhere as long as they are kept on a lead

www.dogfriendly.co.uk

Oxfordshire

The Black Horse

Address: Gozzards Ford, Abingdon, Oxfordshire. OX13 6JH

Phone Number: 01865 390 530

Details: allowed in the bar and must be on a lead

The King's Head Inn

Address: The Green, Bledington, Oxfordshire. OX7 6XQ

Phone Number: 01608 658 365

Details: allowed everywhere as long as they are kept under control

The Trout at Tadpole Bridge

Address: Buckland Marsh, Oxfordshire. SN7 8RF

Phone Number: 01367 870382

Details: allowed in the bars and bedrooms as long as they are kept control

The crown Inn

Address: 54 School Rd, Finstock, Oxfordshire. OX7 3DJ

Phone Number: 01993 868431

Details: allowed everywhere but the dining room and must be on a lead

John Barleycorn Inn

Address: GORING ON THAMES, Oxfordshire.

Phone Number: 01491 872509

Details: allowed in the bar but not the dining room and must be kept on a lead

The Golden Ball

Address: Lower Assendon, Henley-On-Thames, Oxfordshire. RG9 6AH

Phone Number: 01491 574157

Details: allowed everywhere as long as they are on a lead

The Little Angel

Address: Remenham Lane, Henley-On-Thames, Oxfordshire. RG9 2LS

Phone Number: 01491 411008

Details: allowed everywhere preferably kept on a lead

The Plough

Address: 24 High Street, Long Wittenham, Oxfordshire. OX1 44QH

Phone Number: 01865 407738

Details: allowed everywhere but the restaurant and they must be kept on a lead and under control

The New Inn

Address: 45 Main Road, Cheney, Middleton, Oxfordshire. OX17 2ND

Phone Number: 01295 710 399

Details: allowed everywhere except from the restaurant and preferably have to be on a lead

www.dogfriendly.co.uk

Bell

Address: Shenington, Oxfordshire. OX15 6NQ

Phone Number: 01295 670274

Details: allowed everywhere prferably on a lead

The Swan Hotel Pub

Address: 9 Upper High Street, Thame, Oxfordshire. OX9 3ER

Phone Number: 01844 261211

Details: allowed in the pub but not the hotel

Bull and Butcher

Address: Turville Bull, Oxfordshire. RG9 6QU

Phone Number: 01491 638283

Details: allowed in the bar area and must be on a lead

The Greyhound

Address: High Street, Whitchurch On Thames, Oxfordshire. RG8 7EL

Phone Number: 01189 842160

Details: allowed in providing they are on a lead

Somerset

Cox's Mill

Address: Cheddar Gorge, Somerset. BS27 3QE

Phone Number: 01934 742346

Details: allowed in the pub and restaurant and preferably on a lead

The York Inn

Address: Honiton Road, Churchinford, Somerset. TA3 7RF

Phone Number: 01823 601333

Details: allowed everywhere as long as they are kept on a lead

The Salthouse

Address: Salthouse Rd, Clevedon, Somerset. BS21 7TY

Phone Number: 01275 343303

Details: allowed in the bar as long as they are under control

Crown Inn

Address: Exford, Somerset.

Phone Number: 01643 831 554

Details: allowed everywhere but not in the restaurant and preferably kept on a lead

White Horse

Address: Exford, Somerset. TA24 7PY

Phone Number: 01643 831229

Details: allowed in the bedrooms & the bar and preferably must be on a lead

The Dolphin

Address: 22 Silver Street, Ilminster, Somerset. TA19 0DR

Phone Number: 01460 579041

Details: allowed in the bar preferably on a lead

The Royal Oak of Luxborough

Address: Luxborough, Somerset.

Phone Number: 01984 640319

Details: allowed in the bar and bedrooms A £5 charge per night and preferably kept on leads

The Notley Arms

Address: Monksilver, Somerset. TA4 4JT

Phone Number: 01984 656217

Details: allowed everywhere preferably on a lead

The Royal Oak

Address: Royal Oak Inn, Over Stratton, Somerset. TA13 5LQ

Phone Number: 01460 240906

Details: allowed in the bar and preferably kept on a lead

Halfway House

Address: Pitney Hill, Langport, Pitney, Somerset. TA10 9AB

Phone Number: 01458 251593

Details: allowed everywhere as long as they are kept under control

www.dogfriendly.co.uk

Royal Oak

Address: High Street, Porlock, Somerset. TA24 8PS

Phone Number: 01643 862798

Details: allowed everywhere preferably kept on a lead and under control

The Rock Inn

Address: Somerset. TA4 2AX

Phone Number: 01984 623293

Details: allowed everywhere but not the dining room and kept under control

The Ship Inn

Address: Somerset.

Phone Number: 01643 862753

Details: allowed everywhere except for the restaurant preferably on a lead and are allowed in the bedrooms

Sparkford Inn

Address: High Street, Sparkford, Somerset. BA22 7JH

Phone Number: 01963 440218

Details: allowed in the bar and preferably must be kept on a lead

Fleur de Lys

Address: West Street, Stoke-Sub-Hamdon, Somerset. TA14 6TU

Phone Number: 01935 822510

Details: allowed in the bar and must be kept under control and preferably on a lead

The Prince of Wales

Address: Ham Hill, Stoke-Sub-Hamdon, Somerset. TA14 6RW

Phone Number: 01935 822848

Details: allowed in the bar and out in the garden

Carew Arms

Address: Crowcombe, Taunton, Somerset. TA4 4AD

Phone Number: 01984 618631

Details: allowed in the bar and preferably on a lead

The White Horse Inn

Address: High St, Stogumber, Taunton, Somerset. TA4 3TA

Phone Number: 01984 656277

Details: allowed everywhere preferably on a lead

Anchor Inn

Address: Anchor Street, Watchet, Somerset. TA23 0AZ

Phone Number: 01984 631387

Details: preferably on a lead

The Bell Inn

Address: Watchet, Somerset. TA23 0AN

Phone Number: 01984 631279

Details: allowed everywhere as long as they are on a lead

Cabots Bars

Address: Knightstone Road, Weston-Super-Mare, Somerset. BS23 2AH

Phone Number: 01934 621467

Details: allowed everywhere as long as they are on a lead

www.dogfriendly.co.uk

The Royal Oak

Address: Exmoor National Park, Withypool, Somerset. TA24 7QP

Phone Number: 016438 51455

Details: allowed everywhere but not in the restaurant and must be on a lead

The Pall Tavern

Address: Silver Street, YEOVIL, Somerset. BA20 1HW

Phone Number: 01935 476521

Details: allowed everywhere preferably on a lead

The Stags Head Inn

Address: Pound Lane, Yarlington, Somerset. BA9 8DG

Phone Number: 01963 440393

Details: allowed in the bar as long as they are under control and on a lead

The Boat

Address: Cannock Road, Brewood, Staffordshire. ST19 5DT
Phone Number: 01785 714 178
Details: allowed everywhere and must be kept under control

The Boat Inn

Address: Basford Bridge Lane, Cheddleton, Staffordshire. ST13 7EQ
Phone Number: 01538 360683
Details: allowed in the bar area preferably on a lead

The Hollybush

Address: Canal Side, Denford, Leek, Staffordshire. ST13 7JT
Phone Number: 01538 371819
Details: allowed in the bar & lounge prferably on a lead

The Boat Inn

Address: Cannock Road, Penkridge, Staffordshire. ST19 5DT
Phone Number: 01785 714178
Details: allowed everywhere and must be on a lead

The Spittal Brook

Address: 106 Litchfield Rd, Stafford, Staffordshire. ST17 4LP
Phone Number: 01785 245268
Details: allowed everywhere but must be kept under control

Broughton Arms

Address: Sandbach Road, Rode Heath, Stoke-On-Trent, Staffordshire. ST7 3RU
Phone Number: 01270 878661
Details: allowed in a small area and have to be on a lead

The Greyhound

Address: Manor Court Street, Penkhull, Stoke-On-Trent, Staffordshire. ST4 5DW
Phone Number: 01782 848 978
Details: allowed everywhere but not where food is being served and must be kept on a lead

www.dogfriendly.co.uk

The Queens Head

Address: The Street, Brandeston, Suffolk. IP13 7AD
Phone Number: 01728 685307
Details: allowed only in the bar and must be on a lead

The Dog & Duck

Address: Station Road, Campsea Ashe, Suffolk. IP13 0PT
Phone Number: 01728 748439
Details: allowed everywhere but they must be on a lead

The Bull Inn

Address: High St, Cavendish, Suffolk. CO10 8AX
Phone Number: 01787 280245
Details: allowed in the bar area and must be kept under control

The White Horse

Address: The Street, Easton, Suffolk. IP13 0ED
Phone Number: 01728 746456
Details: allowed in the bar area and preferably on a lead

The Black Lion

Address: Lion Road, Glemsford, Suffolk. CO10 7RF
Phone Number: 01787 280684
Details: allowed in the bar and must be kept on a lead

Vulcan Arms

Address: Sizewell, Leisten, Suffolk. IP16 4UD
Phone Number: 01728 830 748
Details: allowed in the bar and must be kept on a lead

The Swan Inn

Address: 9 High St, Needham Market, Suffolk. IP6 8AL
Phone Number: 01449 720280
Details: allowed in the bar but must be kept under control and on a lead

The Kings Head

Address: High Street, Southwold, Suffolk. IP18 6AD
Phone Number: 01502 724517
Details: allowed the bar but not the accomodation

The Anchor

Address: Main Street, Walberswick, Suffolk. IP18 6UA
Phone Number: 01502 722112
Details: allowed in the bar and the family room and must be kept under control

The Bell Inn

Address: Ferry Road, Walberswick, Suffolk. IP18 6TN
Phone Number: 01502 723109
Details: allowed everywhere apart from the dining room on the weekend an they must be kept on a lead

www.dogfriendly.co.uk

The Abinger Hatch

Address: Abinger Lane, Abinger Common, Surrey. RH5 6HZ
Phone Number: 01306 730737
Details: allowed everywhere and must be kept under control

The Plough

Address: South Road, Cheapside, Surrey. GU21 4JL
Phone Number: 01483 714105
Details: allowed everywhere as long as they are on a lead

The Ramblers Rest

Address: Outwood Lane, Chipstead, Surrey. TR5 3NP
Phone Number: 01737 552661
Details: allowed in the bar and must be kept under control

The Cricketers

Address: Downside Common, Cobham, Surrey. KT11 3NX
Phone Number: 01932 862105
Details: allowed in the pub not the restaurant and must be on a lead

The Plough

Address: Coldharbour, Surrey.
Phone Number: 01306 711793
Details: allowed in the bar but not the restaurant and must be on a lead

Well House Inn

Address: Chipstead Lane, Mugswell, Coulsdon, Surrey. CR5 3SQ
Phone Number: 01737 830 640
Details: allowed in two of the bars and preferably on a lead, doggie biscuits and water provided

Fox & Hounds

Address: Bishopsgate Road, Englefield Green, Surrey. TW20 OXU
Phone Number: 01784 433098
Details: allowed in the bar not the restaurant and preferably on a lead

Barley Mow

Address: Littleworth Road, Sale, Farnham, Surrey. GU10 1NE
Phone Number: 01252 782200
Details: allowed in the bar but not in the restaurant and must be kept under control

The Sun Inn

Address: The Common, Dunsfold, Godalming, Surrey. GU8 4LE
Phone Number: 01483 200242
Details: allowed everywhere but not in the restaurant and must be kept under control, doggie biscuits available

The Kings Arms

Address: Liongate, Hampton Court Road, Hampton, Surrey. KT8 9DD

Phone Number: 020 8977 1729

Details: allowed in the bar but not the restaurant and not allowed in the hotel and must be kept under control

Devils Punchbowl

Address: Hindhead, Surrey. GU26 6AG

Phone Number: 01428 606565

Details: allowed everywhere apart from the restaurant area and have to be on a lead

The Old House at Home

Address: 63-65 West St, Dormansland, Lingfield, Surrey. RH7 6QP

Phone Number: 01342 832117

Details: allowed everywhere as long as they are kept on a lead

The Running Horses

Address: Mickleham, Surrey. RH5 6DU

Phone Number: 01372 372279

Details: allowed everywhere as long as they are kept under control and on a lead

The Spotsman

Address: Mogador Road, Mogador, Surrey. KT20 7ES

Phone Number: 01737 246655

Details: allowed in the bar area not the restaurant

Woodies

Address: Thetford Road, New Malden, Surrey. KT3 5DX

Phone Number: 020 8949 5824

Details: allowed everywhere as long as they are kept under control

The Royal Oak

Address: Chart Lane, South Dorking, North Holmwood, Surrey. RH5 4DJ

Phone Number: 01306 885420

Details: allowed in the bar and must be kept under control

The Queen's Head

Address: 13 High Street, Nutfield, Surrey. RH1 4HH

Phone Number: 01737 823619

Details: allowed in the bar and must be kept under control

The Old School House

Address: Ockley, Surrey. RH5 5TH

Phone Number: 01306 627430

Details: allowed in the bar area as long as they are on a lead

The Red Cross Inn

Address: 96 High Street, Reigate, Surrey. RH2 9AP

Phone Number: 01737 225352

Details: allowed in the bar area as long as they are on a lead

The Skimmington Castle

Address: Bonny's Road, Reigate, Surrey. RH2 8RL

Phone Number: 01737 243100

Details: allowed in the front side of the pub and they have to be on a lead

County Surrey
The New Inn

Address: 345 Petersham Road, Ham Common, Richmond, Surrey. TW10 5LA

Phone Number: 020 8940 9444

Details: allowed everywhere as long as they are kept under control

www.dogfriendly.co.uk

The Greyhound

Address: 82 Kew Green, Richmond Upon Thames, Surrey. TW9 3AP

Phone Number: 0208 940 0071

Details: allowed everywhere except for the restaurant and kept under control

The Prince of Wales

Address: Shere Lane, Shere, Surrey. GU5 9HS

Phone Number: 01483 202313

Details: dogs are allowed as long as kept under control and on a lead

The Royal Oak

Address: Caterfield Lane, Staffhurst Wood, Surrey. RH8 0RR

Phone Number: 01883 722207

Details: allowed everywhere but not in the restaurant prferably on a lead

The Bricklayers Arms

Address: The Shamley Green, Surrey. GU5 OUA

Phone Number: 01483 898377

Details: allowed everywhere but not the restaurant and must be kept on a lead

The Parrot Inn

Address: Forest Green, Surrey. RH5 5RZ

Phone Number: 01306 621 339

Details: allowed everywhere but not in the restaurant and must be kept under conrol

The Chequers

Address: Chequers Lane, Walton On The Hill, Surrey. KT20 7SF

Phone Number: 01737 812364

Details: allowed in the main garden bar and must be on a lead

The Fox and Hounds

Address: Walton Street, Walton On The Hill, Surrey. KT20 7RU

Phone Number: 01737 817 744

Details: allowed in the main bar but must be on a lead

The Swan

Address: 50 Manor Road, Walton-On-Thames, Surrey. KT12 2PF

Phone Number: 01932 225964

Details: allowed everywhere as long as they are kept under control

The Weir

Address: Towpath, Waterside Drive, Walton-On-Thames, Surrey. KT12 2JB

Phone Number: 01932 784530

Details: allowed everywhere

Half Moon

Address: Church Road, Windlesham, Surrey. GU20 6BN

Phone Number: 01276 473 329

Details: allowed in the bar and garden and preferably kept on a lead

County Surrey

The Surrey Cricketers

Address: Chertsey Road, Windlesham, Surrey. GU20 6HE

Phone Number: 01276 472192

Details: allowed in when food is not being served and they must be on a lead

Rose Cottage Inn

Address: Alciston, Sussex. BN26 6UW
Phone Number: 01323 870377
Details: allowed in the bar but not in the restaurant and must be on a lead

The Gardeners Arms

Address: Selsfield Road, Ardingly, Sussex. RH17 6TJ
Phone Number: 01444 892 328
Details: allowed everywhere and must be kept under control

Greys

Address: 105 Southover Street, Brighton, Sussex. BN2 9UA
Phone Number: 01273 680 734
Details: allowed everywhere and must be on a lead

The Fox Inn

Address: Bucks Green, Sussex. RH12 3JP
Phone Number: 01403 822386
Details: allowed everywhere and must be kept on a lead

The Fox & Hounds

Address: Singleton, Chichester, Sussex.
Phone Number: 01243 811251
Details: allowed everywhere and must be kept on a lead

The Six Bells Inn

Address: Chiddingly, Sussex. BN8 6HE
Phone Number: 01825 872227
Details: allowed everywhere and must be kept on a lead

The Old Vine

Address: Cousley Wood, Sussex. TN5 6ER
Phone Number: 01892 782271
Details: allowed in the bar and must be kept on a lead

Coach and Horses

Address: Haywards Heath, Danehill, Sussex. RH17 7JF
Phone Number: 01825 740369
Details: allowed in the bar and preferably kept on a lead

The Tiger Inn

Address: The Green, East Dean, Sussex. BN20 0DA
Phone Number: 01323 423209
Details: dogs are welcome, preferably on a lead water is provided

CJ's Coffee Bar

Address: 55-57 High Street, East Grinstead, Sussex. RH19 3DD
Phone Number: 01342 301910
Details: preferably on a lead

The Ship Inn

Address: Ship Street, East Grinstead, Sussex. RH19 4EG
Phone Number: 01342 312089

www.dogfriendly.co.uk

Details: allowed everywhere but must be under control

Details: allowed everywhere and be kept under control

The Lamb Inn

Address: 36 High St, Old Town, Eastbourne, Sussex. BN21 1HH
Phone Number: 01323 720545
Details: allowed everywhere and must be on a lead

Bull Inn

Address: Goring Street, Goring-By-Sea, Sussex. BN12 5AR
Phone Number: 01903 248133
Details: allowed in the bar area but not in the restaurant and must be on a lead

The Foresters

Address: Fairwap, Sussex. TN22 3BP
Phone Number: 01825 712808
Details: allowed in the bar area must be kept under control and on a lead

The Royal Oak Inn

Address: Horsham Road, Handcross, Sussex. RH17 6DJ
Phone Number: 01444 401406
Details: dogs are allowed in some of the bedrooms as long as they are kept under control

The Ram

Address: Firle, Sussex. BN8 6NS
Phone Number: 01273 858222
Details: allowed everywhere but must be kept under control

The Anchor

Address: Church St, Hartfield, Sussex. TN7 4AG
Phone Number: 01892 770424
Details: allowed in the bar but not the restaurant and must be kept on a lead

The Griffin

Address: Fletching, Sussex. TN22 3SS
Phone Number: 01825 722890
Details: allowed everywhere apart from the restaurant and must be on leads

The Fountain Inn

Address: 81 Rusper Road, Horsham, Sussex. RH12 4BJ
Phone Number: 01403 255428
Details: allowed everywhere

The Hatch Inn

Address: Colemans Hatch, Forest Row, Sussex. TN7 4EJ
Phone Number: 01342 822363
Details: allowed in the bar providing they are kept under control

The Queen's Head

Address: Chapel Road, Barns Green, Horsham, Sussex. RH13 OPS
Phone Number: 01403 730436
Details: allowed in the bar but not the dining room and must be kept on a lead, doggie biscuits are provided

The Trevor Arms

Address: Lewes, Glynde, Sussex. BN8 6SS
Phone Number: 01273 858208

The Green Man

Address: Horsted Keynes, Sussex. RH17 7AS
Phone Number: 01825 790656
Details: allowed in the bar area preferably on a lead

The Connaught

Address: 48 Hove Street, Hove, Sussex. BN3 2DH
Phone Number: 01273 206578
Details: allowed everywhere must be kept under control and on a lead

The Neptune Inn

Address: 10 Victoria Terrace, Kingsway, Hove, Sussex. BN3 2WB
Phone Number: 01273 736390
Details: allowed in the bar and must be kept on a lead

Eight Bells

Address: Jevington, Sussex. BM26 5QB
Phone Number: 01323 484442
Details: allowed everywhere but must be kept on a lead

The Royal Oak

Address: 1 Church Rd, Newick, Lewes, Sussex. BN8 4JU
Phone Number: 01825 722506
Details: allowed everywhere and have to be kept under control

John Harvey Tavern

Address: Bear Yard, Cliffe High Street, Lewes, Sussex. BN7 2AN
Phone Number: 01273 474808
Details: allowed everywhere preferably on a lead

The Black Horse

Address: 55 Western Road, Lewes, Sussex. BN7 1RS
Phone Number: 01273 473653
Details: allowed in the bars and have to be kept on a lead

The Lewes Arms

Address: Mount Place, Lewes, Sussex. BN7 1XL
Phone Number: 01273 473152
Details: allowed everywhere as long as they are kept under control

The Snowdrop Inn

Address: South Street, Lewes, Sussex. BN7 2BU
Phone Number: 01273 471018
Details: allowed everywhere as long as they are on a lead, doggie biscuits & water provided

The White Horse

Address: Easedourne Street, Midhurst, Sussex. GU29 0AL
Phone Number: 01730 813521
Details: allowed in the bar and must be kept on a lead

Star Inn

Address: Church Street, Old Heathfield, Sussex. TN21 9AH
Phone Number: 01435 863570
Details: allowed in the bar preferably on a lead

The Halfway Bridge Inn

Address: Halfway Bridge, Petworth, Sussex. GU28 9BP
Phone Number: 01892 770278

www.dogfriendly.co.uk

Details: allowed in the bar and must be on a lead

The Stag Inn

Address: Balls Cross, Petworth, Sussex. GU28 9JP

Phone Number: 01403 820241

Details: allowed everywhere but always on a lead

The Piltdown Man

Address: Piltdown, Sussex. TN22 3XL

Phone Number: 01825 723563

Details: allowed everywhere but not allowed on the animal farm and dogs must be on leads

Half Moon

Address: Ditching Road, Plumpton, Sussex. BN7 3AF

Phone Number: 01273 890 253

Details: allowed everywhere but must be on a lead

The Sussex Ox

Address: Milton Street, Polegate, Sussex. BN26 5RL

Phone Number: 01323 870840

Details: allowed in the bar & gardens and they must be on leads

Frankland Arms

Address: London Road, Washington, Pulborough, Sussex. RH20 4AL

Phone Number: 01903 892220

Details: allowed in the bar & garden but they must be on leads

The Old Ship

Address: Uckfield Rd, Ringmer, Sussex. BN8 5RP

Phone Number: 01273 814223

Details: allowed everywhere in the pub as long as they are kept under control

Turners Bar & Restaurant

Address: Selsfield Road, Turners Hill, Sussex. RH10 4PP

Phone Number: 01342 715 347

Details: allowed everywhere and dogs must be kept under control

The Horse Guards

Address: Tillington, Sussex. GU28 9AF

Phone Number: 01798 342332

Details: allowed everywhere and kept under control

War-Bill-in-Tun

Address: Warbleton, Sussex. TN21 9BD

Phone Number: 01435 830636

Details: allowed everywhere preferably kept on a lead

The Selsey Arms

Address: West Dean, Sussex. PO18 0AX

Phone Number: 01243 811465

Details: allowed in the bar

Dorset Arms

Address: Withyham, Sussex.

Phone Number: 01892 770195

Details: allowed in the bar preferably kept on a lead

The Frog and Bullrush

Address: High Street, Bidford on Avon, Alcester, Warwickshire. B50
Phone Number: 01789 772369
Details: allowed everywhere preferably on a lead

The Cherington Arms

Address: Shipston-on-Stour, Cherington, Warwickshire. CV36 5HS
Phone Number: 01608 686233
Details: allowed in the bar area on a lead

Castle

Address: Edge Hill, Warwickshire.
Phone Number: 01295 670255
Details: allowed in the bar area but not the rooms

The New Inn

Address: Leam Terrace, Leamington Spa, Warwickshire. CV31 1DW
Phone Number: 01926 422861
Details: allowed everywhere owners discretion

Fleur-de-Lys

Address: Lapworth Street, Lowsonford, Warwickshire. B95 5HJ
Phone Number: 01564 782431
Details: allowed everywhere and they have to be kept on a lead

The Merchants Inn

Address: 5 Little Church Street, Rugby, Warwickshire. CV21 3AN
Phone Number: 01788 571119
Details: allowed in the bar and must be kept under control

Griffin

Address: Coleshill Road, Church End, Shustoke, Warwickshire. B46 2LB
Phone Number: 01675 481205
Details: allowed in the bar and preferably on a lead

The Rose & Crown

Address: 30 Market Place, Warwick, Warwickshire. CV34 4SH
Phone Number: 01926 411117
Details: allowed in the bar but not the food area and have to be kept under control

The Fish Inn

Address: Wixford, Warwickshire. B49 6DA
Phone Number: 01789 778593
Details: allowed in the bar and preferably should be on leads

www.dogfriendly.co.uk

West Midlands

The Griffin Inn

Address: Church Road, Shustoke, Birmingham, Midlands, West. B46 2LB

Phone Number: 01675 481205

Details: allowed in the pub and have to be on a lead

The Cat Inn

Address: Bridgenorth Road, Enville, Midlands, West. DY7

Phone Number: 01384 872209

Details: dogs are allowed in the pub and must be kept under control

The Navigation

Address: Old Warwick Road, Lapworth, Midlands, West. B94 6NA

Phone Number: 01564 783337

Details: allowed in the bar area and must be kept under control

www.dogfriendly.co.uk

The Red Lion

Address: Baydon, Wiltshire.
Phone Number: 01672 540348
Details: allowed in the bar area

The Old Bear Inn

Address: Cricklade, Wiltshire.
Phone Number: 01793 750005
Details: allowed everywhere

The Landsdowne Arms

Address: Derry Hill, Wiltshire. SN11 9NS
Phone Number: 01249 812422
Details: allowed everywhere

The Artichoke Inn

Address: The Nursery, Bath Road, Devizies, Wiltshire. SN10 2AA
Phone Number: 01380 723400
Details: allowed in the bar but must be kept under control and on a lead

The Cuckoo Inn

Address: Hamptworth Road, Hamptworth, Wiltshire. SP5 2DU
Phone Number: 01794 390302
Details: allowed in the bar but must be kept on a lead

The Lamb

Address: Hindon, Wiltshire. SP3 6DP
Phone Number: 01747 820573
Details: allowed everywhere

The Plough Inn

Address: High St, Wanborough, Swindon, Wiltshire. SN4 0AE
Phone Number: 01793 790523
Details: allowed everywhere preferably on a lead

www.dogfriendly.co.uk

Worcestershire

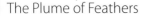

The Plume of Feathers

Address: Gloucester Road, Castlemorton, Worcestershire. WR13 6JB
Phone Number: 01684 833554
Details: allowed everywhere

The Malvern Hills Hotel

Address: Wynds Point, Jubilee Drive, Malvern, Worcestershire. WR13 6DW
Phone Number: 01684 540690
Details: allowed in the rooms and bar but not the restaurant

The Marlbank Inn

Address: Marlbank Road, Welland, Malvern, Worcestershire. WR13 6NA
Phone Number: 01684 310603
Details: allowed everywhere and have to be kept under control

The Railway Inn

Address: 78 Wells Rd, Malvern Wells, Malvern, Worcestershire. WR14 4PA
Phone Number: 01684 572168
Details: allowed in the bar but not in the restaurant and must be kept on a lead

The Wyche Inn

Address: 74 Wyche Road, Malvern, Worcestershire. WR14 4EQ
Phone Number: 01684 575396
Details: allowed in the bar but not the

dining area and preferably kept on a lead

The Chase Inn

Address: Chase Road, Upper Colwall, Worcestershire. WR13 6DJ
Phone Number: 01684 540 276
Details: allowed everywhere but not in the restaurant and kept under control

The Manor Arms

Address: Abberley Village, Abberley, Worcestershire. WR6 6BN
Phone Number: 01299 896 507
Details: allowed in the bar and preferably on a lead

Wellington Heifer

Address: Ainderby Steeple, Yorkshire, North. DL7 9PU
Phone Number: 01609 775542
Details: allowed everywhere except the restaurant

The Fox and Hound

Address: Ainthrope, Yorkshire, North. YO2 2LD
Phone Number: 01287 660 218
Details: allowed everywhere except the restaurant

Royal Dog & Duck Hotel

Address: Flamborough, Bridlington, Yorkshire, North. YO15 1NB
Phone Number: 01262 850 206
Details: allowed in the top bar and as long as they are kept under control

The Wheatsheaf Inn

Address: Carperby, Yorkshire, North. DL8 4DF
Phone Number: 01969 663216
Details: allowed in the bar & the bedrooms and kept under control

The White Lion

Address: Cray, Yorkshire, North. BD23 5JB
Phone Number: 01756 760262
Details: allowed in 3 of the bedrooms and allowed in the bar as long as they are kept under control and on a lead

The Blue Lion

Address: East Witton, Yorkshire, North. DL8 4SN
Phone Number: 01969 624273
Details: allowed in the courtyard rooms & the bar and must provide their own beds and be kept on a lead

The Cover Bridge Inn

Address: East Witton, Yorkshire, North. DL8 4SQ
Phone Number: 01969 623250
Details: allowed everywhere

The Three Tuns

Address: Murray Street, Filey, Yorkshire, North. YO14 9DG
Phone Number: 01723 512183
Details: allowed in the bar but not the dining area and kept under control

The Mason's Arms

Address: Marton Road, Gargrave, Yorkshire, North. BD23 3NL
Phone Number: 01756 749304
Details: allowed in the stone floor room and the bar and preferably on a lead

The Forrester's Arms

Address: Grassington High Street, Hengate, Yorkshire, North. HU17 8BL
Phone Number: 01482 861973
Details: allowed everywhere but not when serving food and must be on leads

www.dogfriendly.co.uk

The Craven Heifer

Address: Ingleton, Yorkshire, North.
Phone Number: 01524 242515
Details: allowed everywhere but must be near the bar when food is served an must be kept under control

The Wheatsheaf

Address: 22 High Street, Ingleton, Yorkshire, North. LA6 3AD
Phone Number: 01524 241275
Details: allowed everywhere but not the restaurant and have to be on a lead

The Lion Inn

Address: Blakey Ridge, Kirkbymoorside, Yorkshire, North. YO62 7LQ
Phone Number: 01751 417320
Details: allowed in the bar but not in the restaurant

The Kings Arms

Address: Askrigg, Leyburn, Yorkshire, North. DL8 3HQ
Phone Number: 01969 650817
Details: allowed in the pub and preferably on a lead

The Listers Arms Hotel

Address: Malham, Yorkshire, North. BD23 4DB
Phone Number: 01729 830330
Details: allowed in some of the bedrooms and are allowed in the pub where food is not being served and must be on a lead

The Black Swan

Address: Market Place, Middleham, Yorkshire, North. DL8 4NP
Phone Number: 01969 622221
Details: small dogs only an must be kept on a lead

The Black Swan Inn

Address: Olstead, Yorkshire, North. YO61 4BL
Phone Number: 01347 868387
Details: allowed in the bar and preferably on a lead

Mucky Duck Inn

Address: Pickering, Yorkshire, North. YO18 8QA
Phone Number: 01751 472505
Details: allowed everywhere except where food is being served and must be on a lead

The King's Arms

Address: Reeth, Yorkshire, North. DL11 6SY
Phone Number: 01748 884259
Details: allowed everywhere but must be on a lead

The Laurel Inn

Address: New Road, Robin Hoods BAY, Yorkshire, North. YO22 4SE
Phone Number: 01947 880400
Details: allowed everywhere as long as they are kept on a lead

The Rodley Barge

Address: Canal Rd, Rodley, Yorkshire, North. LS13
Phone Number: 0113 2574606
Details: allowed in the back room of the pub and have to be on lead

The Bull

Address: Skipton, Yorkshire, North. BB23 3AE

Phone Number: 01756 792065

Details: allowed everywhere as long as they are kept under control

The Narrow Boat

Address: 38 Victoria St, Skipton, Yorkshire, North. BD23 1JE

Phone Number: 01756 797922

Details: allowed everywhere as long as they are kept on a lead

The Old Hall Inn

Address: Threshfield, Yorkshire, North. BD23 5HB

Phone Number: 01756 752441

Details: allowed everywhere apart from the restaurant

Minster Inn

Address: 24 Marygate, York, Yorkshire, North. YO30 7BH

Phone Number: 01904 624499

Details: allowed everywhere must be kept under control

Strines Inn

Address: Mortimer Road, Bradfield, Yorkshire, South. S6 6JE

Phone Number: 01142 851247

Details: allowed everywhere providing they are kept under control

The Junction Inn

Address: 44 Bondgate, Otley, Yorkshire, South. LS21 1AD

Phone Number: 01943 463233

Details: allowed everywhere and

generally have to be kept on a lead

The Old Harrow Pub

Address: 165 Main Street, Grenoside, Sheffield, Yorkshire, South.

Phone Number: 0114 246 8801

Details: allowed everywhere and must be kept on a lead

The Sheaf View

Address: 25 Gleadless Road, Sheffield, Yorkshire, South. S2 3AA

Phone Number: 01142 496455

Details: allowed everywhere and have to be kept on a lead

The Sportsman

Address: Redmires Road, Sheffield, Yorkshire, South.

Phone Number: 01142 301 935

Details: allowed everywhere but must be on a lead

The Cricket Inn

Address: Penny Lane, Totley, Yorkshire, South. S17 3AZ

Phone Number: 0114 236 5256

Details: allowed everywhere but not allowed in the restaurant

The Rockingham Arms

Address: 8 Main Street, Wentworth, Yorkshire, South. S62 7TL

Phone Number: 01226 742075

Details: allowed everywhere but must be kept under control

The Red Rooster

Address: 113 Elland Road, Brookfoot, Yorkshire, West.

www.dogfriendly.co.uk

Phone Number: 01484 713737
Details: allowed everywhere and must be kept under control

Big Six

Address: 10 Horsefall St, Halifax, Yorkshire, West. HX1 3HG
Phone Number: 01422 350169
Details: allowed everywhere as long as they are kept under control

Falcon Inn

Address: 310-314 Salterhebble Hill, Halifax, Yorkshire, West. HX3 OQT
Phone Number: 01422 365077
Details: allowed everywhere but must be kept under control

The Shoulder of Mutton

Address: 36 New Road, Mytholmroyd, Halifax, Yorkshire, West. HX7 5DZ
Phone Number: 01422 883165
Details: allowed everywhere

Wheatsheaf

Address: 42 Mount Pelon Road, Halifax, Yorkshire, West. HX2 OEE
Phone Number: 01422 363080
Details: allowed everywhere

The Tunnel End Inn

Address: Waters Road, Marsden, Yorkshire, West. HD7 6MF
Phone Number: 01484 844636
Details: allowed every except in the dining areas

The Royalty

Address: Surprise View, Otley, Yorkshire, West.

Phone Number: 01943 461156
Details: only guide dogs in the dining room but all dogs allowed in the pub

Woodpecker

Address: 222 Rochdale Road, Shade, Yorkshire, West. OL14 7NU
Phone Number: 01706 816088
Details: allowed everywhere

Alma Inn

Address: Cottonstones, Sowerby Bridge, Yorkshire, West. HX6 4NS
Phone Number: 01422 823334
Details: allowed in the pub but not in the restaurant

Friendly Inn

Address: Burnley Rd, Friendly, Sowerby Bridge, Yorkshire, West. HX6 2UG
Phone Number: 01422 839159
Details: allowed everywhere preferably on a lead

Puzzle Hall Inn

Address: 21 Hollinsmill Lane, Sowerby Bridge, Yorkshire, West. HX6 2RF
Phone Number: 01422 835547
Details: allowed everywhere preferably on a lead

Travellers Rest

Address: Steep Lane, Sowerby, Yorkshire, West. HX6 IPE
Phone Number: 01422 832124
Details: allowed everywhere dog biscuits & water provided

Scotland

The Clachaig Inn

Address: Old Glencoe village road, Clachaig, Argyll. PH49 4HX
Phone Number: 01855 811252
Details: allowed everywhere in the bedrooms and bar area

The Golf Tavern

Address: 5 Links Road, Earlsferry, Fife. KY9 1AW
Phone Number: 01333 330610
Details: allowed in the bar but must be kept under control and on a lead

Victoria Inn

Address: The Brae, Auchendinny, Lothian. EH26 0QU
Phone Number: 01968 673088
Details: allowed everywhere and must be kept under control

The Auld Hoose

Address: 23-25 St. Leonards Street, Edinburgh, Lothian. EH8 9QN
Phone Number: 0131 6682934
Details: Dogs must be kept on a lead

The Halfway House

Address: 24 Fleshmarket Close, 199 High Street, Edinburgh, Lothian. EH1 1BX
Phone Number: 0131 225 7101
Details: must be kept under control

www.dogfriendly.co.uk

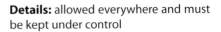

Scotland
Highlands

Failford Inn

Address: Failford, Ayrshire, The Highlands. KA5 5TF

Phone Number: 01292 540117

Details: allowed in the bar & lounge preferably on a lead

Munro Inn

Address: Main Street, Callender, The Highlands. FK18 8NA

Phone Number: 01877 384 333

Details: allowed in the pub and kept under control

The Clachaig Inn

Address: Glencoe, Ballachulish, Clachaig, The Highlands. PH49 4HX

Phone Number: 01855 811252

Details: allowed in the bar but not the restaurant and preferably kept on a lead

Benleva Hotel

Address: , The Highlands. IV63 6UH

Phone Number: 01456 4500 80

Details: allowed everywhere but need to be on a lead when food is being served

Killin

Address: Main St, Killin, The Highlands. FK21 8TP

Phone Number: 01567 820 270

Details: allowed everywhere and must be kept under control

The Coach House Coffee Shop

Address: Alexandria, Dunbartonshire, Luss, The Highlands. G83 8NN

Phone Number: 01436 860341

Details: preferably on a lead and can also use the garden

The Annandale Arms Hotel

Address: High Street, Moffat, The Highlands. DG10 9HF

Phone Number: 01683 220013

Details: allowed everywhere but not in the restaurant and have to be on a lead

The Heatherbrae

Address: Dell Road, Nethy Bridge, The Highlands. PH25 3DG

Phone Number: 01479 821345

Details: allowed everywhere preferably on a lead

Wales

The Star

Address: Dylife, Powis. SY19 7BW
Phone Number: 01650 521345
Details: allowed in the bar and must be kept on a lead

The Brown Cow

Address: 55 High St, Hinderwell, Swansea. TS13 5ET
Phone Number: 01947 840694
Details: allowed everywhere and have to be on a lead

The Oxwich Bay Hotel

Address: Oxwich, Swansea.
Phone Number: 01792 390329
Details: allowed in the cottages & by the tiled entrance in the bar

The Nags Head

Address: Boncath, Abercych, Wales. SA37 OHJ
Phone Number: 01239 841200
Details: allowed in the bar and must be kept on a lead

The Joiners Arms

Address: 50 Bishopston Rd, Bishopston, Wales. SA3 3EJ
Phone Number: 01792 232 658
Details: allowed everywhere and must be kept on leads

Gwaelod-y-Garth Inn

Address: Main Road, Gwaelod-y-Garth, Cardiff, Wales. CF15 9HH
Phone Number: 029 2081 0408
Details: allowed everywhere but not in the restaurant and must be on a lead

The Butchers Arms

Address: Llandaff Village, Cardiff, Wales. CF5
Phone Number: 0292 0227927
Details: allowed everywhere and must be kept under control

The Stag Inn

Address: High St, Anglesey, Cemaes Bay, Wales. LL67 OEW
Phone Number: 01407 710281
Details: allowed everywhere

The Bear Hotel

Address: Powys, Crickhowell, Wales. NP8 1BW
Phone Number: 01873 810408
Details: allowed everywhere but not in the restaurant

Worms Head Hotel

Address: Gower, Wales. SA3 1PP
Phone Number: 01792 390512
Details: allowed outside but not in the hotel

www.dogfriendly.co.uk

The Bluebell Inn

Address: Rhosesmor Rd, Holywell, Halkyn, Wales. CH8 8DL
Phone Number: 01352 780309
Details: allowed everywhere

The Farmers Arms

Address: Mathry, Haverfordwest, Wales. SA62 5HB
Phone Number: 01348 831284
Details: allowed in the main bar but not in the dining area preferably kept on a lead

The King's Head

Address: Llangennith, Wales.
Phone Number: 01792 386 212
Details: allowed in the bar and must be on a lead

The Duke of Edinburgh

Address: Newgale, Wales. SA62 6AS
Phone Number: 01437 720 586
Details: allowed in the bar and preferably to be on a lead

Oxwich Bay Hotel

Address: Oxwich BAY, Wales. SA3 1LS
Phone Number: 01792 390329
Details: dogs are allowed in the cottages and some of the hotel rooms preferably kept on a lead

Gower Inn

Address: Park Mill, Wales. SA3 2EQ
Phone Number: 01792 233116
Details: allowed in the bar preferably to be kept on a lead

Aberavon Beach Hotel

Address: Port Talbot, Wales. SA12 6QP
Phone Number: 01639 884949
Details: allowed in the bedrooms preferably to be kept on a lead

Alltyrodyn Arms

Address: Rhydowen, Wales. SA44 4QB
Phone Number: 01545 590319
Details: allowed in the bar and function room and must be kept under control

Ye Olde Anchor Inn

Address: Ruthin, Wales.
Phone Number: 01824 702813
Details: allowed in some of the bedrooms and they are allowed in the bar and must be on a lead

The Farmers

Address: 14 -16 Goat Street, St Davids, Wales.
Phone Number: 01437 721666
Details: allowed everywhere preferably kept on a lead

Lion Inn

Address: Trellech, Wales. NP5 4PA
Phone Number: 01600 860322
Details: allowed in the bar, doggie biscuits and water is provided

The Crown Hotel

Address: Ruthin Road, Llandegla, Wrexham, Wales. LL11 3AD
Phone Number: 01978 790228
Details: allowed in the bar and preferably to be on a lead

Beaches

Your comprehensive guide to dog friendly Beaches

Sun, Sea & Sand

www.dogfriendly.co.uk

Dog Friendly

Channel Islands

Channel Islands
Alderney

Beach: Arch Bay
Council Phone No. 01481 822811

Restrictions: Dogs are prohibited in the months of June, July, August and September at all other times they are permitted but must be kept on leads

Beach: Braye Bay
Council Phone No. 01481 822811

Restrictions: Dogs are prohibited in the months of June, July, August and September at all other times they are permitted but must be kept on leads

Beach: Clonque
Council Phone No. 01481 822811

Restrictions: Dogs are prohibited in the months of June, July, August and September at all other times they are permitted but must be kept on leads

Beach: Corblets
Council Phone No. 01481 822811

Restrictions: Dogs are prohibited in the months of June, July, August and September at all other times they are permitted but must be kept on leads

Beach: Longy Bay
Council Phone No. 01481 822811

Restrictions: Dogs are prohibited in the months of June, July, August and September at all other times they are permitted but must be kept on leads

Beach: Platte Saline
Council Phone No. 01481 822811

Restrictions: Dogs are prohibited in the months of June, July, August and September at all other times they are permitted but must be kept on leads

Beach: Saye
Council Phone No. 01481 822811

Restrictions: Dogs are prohibited in the months of June, July, August and September at all other times they are permitted but must be kept on leads

Beach: Portelet Bay

Council Phone No. 01481 723552

Restrictions: No dog restrictions, litter bins provided and beaches cleaned regularly

---

Beach: Saint's Bay

Council Phone No. 01481 723552

Restrictions: No dog restrictions, litter bins provided and beaches cleaned regularly

---

Beach: Vazon

Council Phone No. 01481 723552

Restrictions: Dogs are not permitted on beach 1st May to 30th Sep. Litter bins and dog bins are available.

Beach: Cobo Beach

Council Phone No. 01481 723552

Restrictions: Dogs are not permitted on beach 1st May to 30th Sep. Litter bins and dog bins are available.

Beach: Fermain

Council Phone No. 01481 723552

Restrictions: Dogs are not permitted on beach 1st May to 30th Sept. Litter bins and dog bins are available.

Beach: Grandes Rocques

Council Phone No. 01481 723552

Restrictions: No dog restrictions, litter bins provided and beaches cleaned regularly

---

Beach: Havelet Bay

Council Phone No. 01481 723552

Restrictions: No dog restrictions, litter bins provided and beaches cleaned regularly

---

Beach: L'eree

Council Phone No. 01481 723552

Restrictions: Dogs are not permitted on beach 1st May to 30th Sep. Litter bins and dog bins are available.

Beach: Pembroke Bay

Council Phone No. 01481 723552

Restrictions: Dogs are not permitted on beach 1st May to 30th Sep. Litter bins and dog bins are available.

Beach: Port Soif Bay

Council Phone No. 01481 723552

Restrictions: Dogs banned between 1st May - 30th September. Litter bins, dog bins are provided.

Beach: Bordeaux

Council Phone No. 01481 723552.

Restrictions: No dog restrictions, litter

www.dogfriendly.co.uk

bins provided and beaches cleaned regularly

Beach: Ladies Bay

Council Phone No. 01481 723552.

Restrictions: No dog restrictions., litter bins provided and beaches cleaned regularly

Beach: Petit Bot Bay

Council Phone No. 01481 726611

Restrictions: Dogs are banned from the beach 1 May - 30 September inclusive. Both litter bins and dog bins are provided.

Beach: Portelet

Council Phone No. 01534 445500

Restrictions: Dogs allowed all year round, but must be kept on a lead between 1st May - 30th September between 10.30am - 6pm, cleaned regularly and litter bins provided.

Beach: western

Council Phone No. 01534 445500

Restrictions: Dogs allowed all year round, but must be kept on a lead between 1st May - 30th September between 10.30am - 6pm, cleaned regularly and litter bins provided.

Beach: Beauport

Council Phone No. 01534 445500

Restrictions: Dogs allowed all year round, but must be kept on a lead between 1st May - 30th September between 10.30am - 6pm, cleaned regularly and litter bins provided.

Beach: Bonne Nuit

Council Phone No. 01534 445500

Restrictions: Dogs allowed all year round, but must be kept on a lead between 1st May - 30th September between 10.30am - 6pm, cleaned regularly and litter bins provided.

Beach: Greve De Lecq

Council Phone No. 01534 445500

Restrictions: Dogs allowed all year round, but must be kept on a lead between 1st May - 30th September between 10.30am - 6pm, cleaned regularly and litter bins provided.

Beach: Havre Des Pas

Council Phone No. 01534 445500

Restrictions: Dogs allowed all year round, but must be kept on a lead between 1st May - 30th September between 10.30am - 6pm, cleaned regularly and litter bins provided.

Beach: La Haule

Council Phone No. 01534 445500

Restrictions: Dogs allowed all year round, but must be kept on a lead between 1st May - 30th September between 10.30am - 6pm, cleaned regularly and litter bins provided.

Beach: Plemont

Council Phone No. 01534 445500

Restrictions: Dogs allowed all year round, but must be kept on a lead between 1st May - 30th September between 10.30am - 6pm, cleaned regularly and litter bins provided.

www.dogfriendly.co.uk

Beach: Victoria Pool

Council Phone No. 01534 445500

Restrictions: Dogs allowed all year round, but must be kept on a lead between 1st May - 30th September between 10.30am - 6pm, cleaned regularly and litter bins provided.

Beach: Bouley Bay

Council Phone No. 01534 445500

Restrictions: Dogs allowed all year round, but must be kept on a lead between 1st May - 30th September between 10.30am - 6pm, cleaned regularly and litter bins provided.

Beach: Green Island

Council Phone No. 01534 445500

Restrictions: Dogs allowed all year round, but must be kept on a lead between 1st May - 30th September between 10.30am - 6pm, cleaned regularly and litter bins provided.

Beach: Grouville

Council Phone No. 01534 445500

Restrictions: Dogs allowed all year round, but must be kept on a lead between 1st May - 30th September between 10.30am - 6pm, cleaned regularly and litter bins provided.

Beach: L'Archirondel

Council Phone No. 01534 445500

Restrictions: Dogs allowed all year round, but must be kept on a lead between 1st May - 30th September between 10.30am - 6pm, cleaned regularly and litter bins provided.

Beach: St. Brelades Bay

Council Phone No. 01534 445500

Restrictions: Dogs allowed all year round, but must be kept on a lead between 1st May - 30th September between 10.30am - 6pm, cleaned regularly and litter bins provided.

Beach: St. Ouens Bay - Le Brave

Council Phone No. 01534 445500

Restrictions: Dogs allowed all year round, but must be kept on a lead between 1st May - 30th September between 10.30am - 6pm, cleaned regularly and litter bins provided.

Beach: St. Ouens Bay - Watersplash

Council Phone No. 01534 445500

Restrictions: Dogs allowed all year round, but must be kept on a lead between 1st May - 30th September between 10.30am - 6pm, cleaned regularly and litter bins provided.

England
and the Isles around Britain

Cornwall

Beach: Greenaway Beach:

Council Phone No. 01208 893333

Restrictions: No dog restrictions.

Beach: Polzeath

Council Phone No. 01208 893333

Restrictions: There are litter bins on the beach. Dogs are banned from Easter to September

Beach: North Cliffs (Deadmans Cove)

Council Phone No. 01872 224400

Restrictions: No dog restriction.

Beach: Northcott

Council Phone No. 01208 893333

Restrictions: Dogs Allowed. Parking 200m

Beach: Black Rock

Council Phone No. 01208 893333

Restrictions: Dogs are allowed

Beach: Bude (Summerleaze)

Council Phone No. 01208 893333

Restrictions: Dogs allowed on lead between 10am and 6pm

Beach: Widemouth Bay (North Beach)

Council Phone No. 01208 893333

Restrictions: Dogs are banned North Beach . South Beach Dogs allowed

Beach: Cellars

Council Phone No. 01872 224400

Restrictions: Dogs Allowed

Beach: Porthcurnick

Council Phone No. 01872 224400

Restrictions: Dogs are allowed. Car parks. Toilets. Shops/café

Beach: Portscatho

Council Phone No. 01872 224400

Restrictions: No dog restrictions

Beach: St. Antonys Head

Council Phone No. 01872 224400

Restrictions: No dog restrictions

Beach: St. Mawes

Council Phone No. 01872 224400

Restrictions: Dogs are banned during the summer months

Beach: Hemmick

Council Phone No. 01726 223300

Restrictions: Dogs allowed. Use

National Trust car park at Penare, take footpath through fields or steep 10 min walk through country lanes

Beach: Maenporth

Council Phone No. 01872 224400

Restrictions: Dogs are not allowed from Easter to 1st October. Owners must remove their dog's waste during the rest of the year. Litter and Dog bins present.

Beach: Pentewan

Council Phone No. 01726 223300

Restrictions: Dogs banned all year

Beach: Swanpool

Council Phone No. 01872 224400

Restrictions: Dogs are banned from Easter Day - 1st Oct. litter and Dog bins provided.

Beach: Trefusis Beach at Flushing

Council Phone No. 01872 224400

Restrictions: No dog restrictions

Beach: Gyllyngvase Beach

Council Phone No. 01872 224400

Restrictions: Dogs are banned Easter Day - 1st Oct. Dog and litter bins provided.

Beach: Housel Bay

Council Phone No. 01209 614000

Restrictions: Dog Ban Easter to 1st Oct

Beach: Kenneggy Sand

Council Phone No. 01209 614000

Restrictions: Dogs are not recommended on this beach.

Beach: Kings Cove

Council Phone No. 01209 614000

Restrictions: Dogs are not recommended on this beach.

Beach: Lizard Church Cove

Phone No. 01326 565431

Restrictions: No dogs are allowed on beach from Easter to October.

Beach: Kynance Cove

Council Phone No. 01326 565431

Restrictions: Dogs are banned on the beach from Easter Day to October 1

Beach: Porthcew Rinsey

Council Phone No. 01326 565431

Restrictions: No dogs from Easter - 1st Oct

Beach: Bessy Cove

Council Phone No. 01326 565431

Restrictions: Dogs are tolerated on this beach all year round but owner must clean up mess after their dogs.

Beach: Cape Cornwall

Council Phone No. 01326 565431

Restrictions: Dog allowed all year round

www.dogfriendly.co.uk

Beach: Kennack Sands East

Council Phone No. 01209 614000

Restrictions: Dogs allowed. Swim with care. Shops. Parking. Toilets nearby. Kennack Sands West nr carpark dog ban easter to 1st Oct

Beach: Pollurian Cove

Council Phone No. 01209 614000

Restrictions: No dogs from easter-1st Oct

Beach: Polpeor

Council Phone No. 01209 614000

Restrictions: No dog restrictions. Shops, toilets, café.

Beach: Porthallow

Council Phone No. 01209 614000

Restrictions: Dogs allowed. Parking shops nearby. Swim with care

Beach: Porthleven - West

Council Phone No. 01209 614000

Restrictions: Dog Ban easter to 1st oct. (Porthleven East. Dogs allowed)

Beach: Portreath

Council Phone No. 01209 614000

Restrictions: Litter and dog bins are provided but dogs are not allowed on the beach from Easter Day to 1st October.

Beach: Praa Sands

Council Phone No. 01209 614000

Restrictions: Dogs are banned on the beach from Easter - end of October. Dog bins are provided.

Beach: Poldu Cove

Council Phone No. 01209 614000

Restrictions: Dog ban from Easter-1st Oct

Beach: Cadgwith East

Council Phone No. 01209 614000

Restrictions: Dogs allowed. Swim with care. Shops. Parking. Toilets nearby. Cadgwith Cove South dog ban easter to 1st Oct

Beach: Coverack

Council Phone No. 01209 614000

Restrictions: The beach is cleaned by Kerrier District Council as necessary. Dogs are allowed all year round. Litter bins present. Dog bins present.

Beach: Looe - East

Council Phone No. 01209 614000

Restrictions: All year Dog Ban

Beach: Talland Bay

Council Phone No. 01209 614000

Restrictions: Dogs allowed on lead only

Beach: Hannafore Point

Council Phone No. 01209 614000

Restrictions: Dogs allowed all year

Beach: Lansallos Beach:

Council Phone No. 01209 614000

Restrictions: Dogs allowed all year

Beach: Looe - Hannafore

Council Phone No. 01209 614000

Restrictions: No dog restrictions

Beach: Looe - Plaidy

Council Phone No. 01209 614000

Restrictions: Dogs allowed all year

Beach: Millendreath

Council Phone No. 01209 614000

Restrictions: Dogs are not allowed on the beach all year.

Beach: Seaton

Council Phone No. 01209 614000

Restrictions: Dogs allowed all year

Beach: Cawsand Beach

Council Phone No. 01579 341000

Restrictions: Dog Ban Easter to 1st Oct

Beach: Downderry

Council Phone No. 01579 341000

Restrictions: There are litter and dog bins on the beach and dogs are allowed throughout the year.

Beach: Crantock

Council Phone No. 01726 223300

Restrictions: Dogs are allowed all year round. Litter bins present. Car Park. Toilets. Shops. Café.

Beach: Fistral

Council Phone No. 01726 223300

Restrictions: Dogs allowed. Car Park. Toilets. Café. Shops.

Beach: Great Western

Council Phone No. 01726 223300

Restrictions: Dogs allowed. Car Park. Toilets. Cafe. Shops.

Beach: Holywell Bay

Council Phone No. 01872 224400

Restrictions: Dogs are allowed all year round. The beach is cleaned weekly by the National Trust but litter bins are not available.

Beach: Mawgan Porth

Council Phone No. 01726 223300

Restrictions: Dogs Allowed. Car park. Toilets. Cafe. Shops.

Beach: Newquay - Fistral

Council Phone No. 01726 223300

Restrictions: Dogs allowed. Shops, toilets, cafe, showers

Beach: Newquay - Great western Beach

Council Phone No. 01726 223300

Restrictions: Dogs allowed. Parking, toilets

Beach: Newquay - Towan

Council Phone No. 01726 223300

Restrictions: Dogs allowed

Beach: Porthcothan

Council Phone No. 01208 893333

Restrictions: Dogs allowed. Parking 150m. Toilets. Shops. Café.

Beach: Watergate Bay

Council Phone No. 01726 223300

Restrictions: Dogs Allowed. Car park. Toilets. Cafe. Shops.

Beach: Tolcarne

Council Phone No. 01726 223300

Restrictions: Dog Ban Easter to 1st Oct

Beach: Lusty Glaze

Council Phone No. 01726 223300

Restrictions: Dog ban 8am-7pm and whitsun to 1st September

Beach: Porth Beach

Council Phone No. 01726 223300

Restrictions: Dogs are not permitted from 1st April to the end of September.

Beach: Porthluney

Council Phone No. 01726 223300

Restrictions: Dogs allowed. Car Park. Toilets. Café. Shops.

Beach: Gorran Haven

Council Phone No. 01726 223300

Restrictions: Dogs allowed. Car Park. Toilets. Café. Shops.

Beach: Porthpean

Council Phone No. 01726 223300

Restrictions: Dogs banned Easter - September.

Beach: Lantic Bay

Council Phone No. 01579 341000

Restrictions: No dog restrictions

Beach: Readymoney

Council Phone No. 01726 223300

Restrictions: Dogs are banned between Easter and 30th September

Beach: Colona

Council Phone No. 01726 223300

Restrictions: Dogs allowed. Considerable walk along coastal path

Beach: Par

Council Phone No. 01726 223300

Restrictions: Dogs allowed. Car Park. Toilets. Café. Shops.

Beach: Polridmouth Beach

Council Phone No. 01726 223300

Restrictions: No dog restrictions. 15 mins walk from car park through farm

Beach: Port Mellon

Council Phone No. 01726 223300
Restrictions: Dogs allowed. Parking on street.

Beach: Trevaunance Cove

Council Phone No. 01872 224400
Restrictions: Dogs Allowed. Parking Toilets

Beach: Mousehole

Council Phone No. 01736 362341
Restrictions: Dog ban all year in harbour

Beach: Sennen Cove

Council Phone No. 01736 362341
Restrictions: Dog ban Easter to 1st Oct including harbour

Beach: St. Just Priests Cove

Council Phone No. 01736 362341
Restrictions: Dogs Allowed (Priests Cove)

Beach: Gwenver (Sennen)

Council Phone No. 01736 362341
Restrictions: Dogs Allowed

Beach: Mounts Bay - Heliport

Council Phone No. 01872 322000
Restrictions: Dogs Allowed

Beach: Mounts Bay - Little Hogus

Council Phone No. 01872 322000
Restrictions: Dogs Banned

Beach: Penzance Harbour

Council Phone No. 01872 322000
Restrictions: Dogs not allowed

Beach: Mounts Bay - Wherry Town

Council Phone No. 01872 322000
Restrictions: Dogs allowed

Beach: Porthcumo

Council Phone No. 01736 362341
Restrictions: Dogs are banned from Easter to October.

Beach: Porthgwarra

Council Phone No. 01736 362341
Restrictions: Dogs are banned from Easter to October.

Beach: Marazion

Council Phone No. 01736 362341
Restrictions: Dogs not allowed from Easter until 1st October. Chaple rock to long rock level crossing.

Beach: Godrevy

Council Phone No. 01736 362341
Restrictions: No dogs allowed. Red River to lighthouse

Beach: St Ives - Porthmeor

Council Phone No. 01736 362341
Restrictions: Dogs are banned from Easter Day until 1st October.

www.dogfriendly.co.uk

Beach: St Ives - Porthminster

Council Phone No. 01736 362341

Restrictions: Dogs are banned from Easter Day until 1st October

Beach: The Towans, Hayle

Council Phone No. 01736 362341

Restrictions: Dogs are banned from Easter - October. From Hayle River to Black Cliffs

Beach: Whitsand Bay

Council Phone No. 01736 362341

Restrictions: Dogs allowed

Beach: Kingsand Bay

Council Phone No. 01736 362341

Restrictions: No dog restrictions.

Beach: Portwrinkle

Council Phone No. 01736 362341

Restrictions: The beach is not cleaned but bins are available. Dogs are not allowed between Easter and October

Beach: Plymouth Hoe - East

Council Phone No. 01752 304140

Restrictions: No dog restrictions.

Beach: Tregonhawke Beach, Whitsand Bay

Council Phone No. 01752 304140

Restrictions: Dogs are allowed

Beach: Crackington Haven

Council Phone No. 01208 893333

Restrictions: Dogs are banned from April to 1st October. Litter bins present

Beach: Bossiney Haven

Phone No. 01840 250010

Restrictions: Dogs allowed All Year

Beach: Tintagel Haven

Council Phone No. 01840 250010

Restrictions: Dog Friendly

Beach: Trebarwith Strand

Council Phone No. 01208 893333

Restrictions: No dog restrictions. Parking 400m

Beach: Tregardock

Council Phone No. 01208 893333

Restrictions: No dog restrictions.

Beach: Constantine Bay

Council Phone No. 01208 893333

Restrictions: No dog restrictions.

Beach: Daymer Bay

Council Phone No. 01208 893333

Restrictions: Dogs are allowed but there are no dog bins. Parking. Toilets. Shops. Café

Beach: Mother Ivey's Bay

Council Phone No. 01208 893333

Restrictions: Dogs are welcome. But there are no dog or litter bins.

Beach: Port Isaac

Council Phone No. 01208 893333

Restrictions: No Dogs allowed

Beach: Roack

Council Phone No. 01208 893333

Restrictions: Dog Friendly allowed

Beach: Treyarnon Bay

Council Phone No. 01208 893333

Restrictions: No dog restrictions.

Beach: Boobys Bay

Council Phone No. 01208 893333

Restrictions: Dogs are allowed on beach must be kept under control and owners must clean up mess after dogs.

Beach: Trevon Bay

Council Phone No. 01208 893333

Restrictions: Dogs are not allowed on the beach from Easter to the end of September

Beach: Harlyn Bay

Council Phone No. 01208 893333

Restrictions: No dog restrictions.

Beach: Castle Beach

Council Phone No. 01208 893333

Restrictions: Dog Ban Easter to 1st Oct

Beach: Bedruthan steps

Council Phone No. 01208 893333

Restrictions: Dogs allowed

Beach: Carbis Bay

Council Phone No. 01736 362341

Restrictions: Dog Ban Easter to 1st Oct

Beach: Chapel Porth

Council Phone No. 01872 224400

Restrictions: Dog Ban Easter to 1st Oct

Beach: Gwithian

Council Phone No. 01736 362341

Restrictions: Dog Ban Easter to 1st Oct. Ceres Rock to Red River

Beach: Lamorna Cove

Council Phone No. 01872 224400

Restrictions: Rocky cove

Beach: Portholland

Council Phone No. 01726 223300

Restrictions: Dogs are allowed. Car parks. Toilets. Shops/café

Beach: Portloe

Council Phone No. 01872 274555

Restrictions: Rocky cove

www.dogfriendly.co.uk

111

Beach: Pendower - Carne Beach

Council Phone No. 01872 224400

Restrictions: Dogs are allowed on the beach but must be kept on the lead between May and September.

Beach: Pendower Beach

Council Phone No. 01872 224400

Restrictions: Dogs are allowed on the beach but must be kept on the lead between May and September

Beach: Carne

Council Phone No. 01872 224400

Restrictions: Dogs are allowed on the beach but must be kept on the lead between May and September.

Beach: Porthbeor

Council Phone No. 01872 274555

Restrictions: Dogs allowed

Beach: Towan Beach

Council Phone No. 01872 224400

Restrictions: No dog restrictions.

Beach: Polkerris

Council Phone No. 01726 223300

Restrictions: Dogs are banned from Easter Day until 1st October

Beach: Porthoustock

Council Phone No. 01209 614000

Restrictions: Dogs allowed. Parking. Shops. Swim with care

Beach: Whitsand Bay

Council Phone No. 01209 614000

Restrictions: All year dog friendly

Beach: Godrevy

Council Phone No. 01209 614000

Restrictions: Dog restrictions apply easter - September. Red River to Lighthouse

Beach: Polstreath

Council Phone No. 01726 223300

Restrictions: Dogs Allowed. Considerable walk through village and wooded valley

Beach: Sharrow Nr Whitsands

Council Phone No. 01503 262072

Restrictions: Dogs Allowed

Beach: Porthtowan

Council Phone No. 01872 224400

Restrictions: Litter bins provided. Dogs are banned between Easter and October. At other times dog litter bins provided.

Beach: Perran Sands

Council Phone No. 01872 224400

Restrictions: Beach litter and dog waste bins are provided and dogs are allowed onto the beach under control; please use a pooper scooper.

Beach: Perranporth - Penhale sands

Council Phone No. 01872 224400

Restrictions: Dogs on leads. Beach litter and dog waste bins are provided and dogs are allowed onto the beach under control; please use a pooper scooper.

Beach: Perranporth - Village

Council Phone No.

Restrictions: Beach litter and dog waste bins are provided and dogs are allowed onto the beach with lead.

Cumbria

Beach: Workington

Council Phone No. 01900 606699

Restrictions: No dog restrictions. Owners must clean up mess.

Beach: Bardsea

Council Phone No. 01229 587120

Restrictions: Dogs are allowed all year round. Litter bins are provided.

Beach: Ravenglass

Council Phone No. 01229 717278

Restrictions: Dogs are allowed all year round. Owners must clean up any mess from their dogs.

Beach: Millom

Council Phone No. 01229 774819

Restrictions: Dogs are allowed all year round. Owners must clean up any mess from their dogs.

Beach: Silecroft

Council Phone No. 01229 774819

Restrictions: Dogs are allowed all year round. Owners must clean up any mess from their dogs.

Beach: Newbiggin

Council Phone No. 01229 870156

Restrictions: Dogs are allowed all year round. Owners must clean up any mess from their dogs.

Beach: Aldingham

Council Phone No. 01229 894784

Restrictions: No dog restrictions.

Beach: Walney Island - West Shore

Council Phone No. 01229 894784

Restrictions: No dog restrictions., but advise to put dogs on lead at North tip or South tip of beach as goes into Nature Reserve.

Beach: Askam - in - Furness

Council Phone No. 01229 894784

Restrictions: No dog restrictions.

Beach: Roan Head

Council Phone No. 01229 894784

Restrictions: No dog restrictions., but advise to put dogs on lead as coming off beach as goes into Nature Reserve.

Beach: Walney Island - Sandy Gap

Council Phone No. 01229 894784

Restrictions: No dog restrictions., but advise to put dogs on lead at North tip or South tip of beach as goes into Nature Reserve.

Cumbria

Beach: Barrow - In - Furness

Council Phone No. 1229894900

Restrictions: No dog restriction. Litter bins are provided.

Beach: Arnside

Council Phone No. 015395 34026

Restrictions: Dogs not allowed on beach between April and Sept. No restrictions rest of year.

Beach: Grange over sands & Kents Bank

Council Phone No. 015395 34026

Restrictions: No dogs allowed between 1st May and 30th Sept. Dangerous beach has quick sand and advise not to take dogs all year.

Beach: Silloth

Council Phone No. 01900 606699

Restrictions: No dog restrictions. Owners must clean up mess.

Beach: Skinburness

Council Phone No. 01900 606699

Restrictions: No dog restrictions. Owners must clean up mess.

Beach: Siddick

Council Phone No. 01900 606699

Restrictions: No dog restrictions. Owners must clean up mess.

Beach: Allonby

Council Phone No. 01697 333055

Restrictions: Dogs are allowed all year round. Litter and Dog bins are available.

Beach: Allonby - South

Council Phone No. 01697 333055

Restrictions: Dogs are allowed all year round. Litter and Dog bins are available.

Beach: Maryport

Council Phone No. 01900 606699

Restrictions: Dogs are allowed all year round. No restrictions. Owners must clean up mess. Litter bins are provided.

Beach: Nethertown

Council Phone No. 01900 606699

Restrictions: No dog restrictions. Owners must clean up mess.

Beach: Braystones

Council Phone No. 01946 820693

Restrictions: Dogs are allowed all year round no restrictions .

Beach: Haverigg

Council Phone No. 01946 852761

Restrictions: No dog restrictions. but dogs must be kept under control or on a lead and owners must remember to clean up after their dogs

Beach: Seascale

Council Phone No. 01946 852761

Restrictions: No dog **restrictions.** but dogs must be kept under control or on

www.dogfriendly.co.uk

115

a lead and owners must remember to clean up after their dogs

Beach: St. Bees

Council Phone No. 01946 852761

Restrictions: No dog restrictions. but dogs must be kept under control or on a lead and owners must remember to clean up after their dogs

Beach: Parton

Council Phone No. 01946 598914

Restrictions: No dog restrictions. Doggy bags supplied at Tourist Office.

Beach: Whitehaven

Council Phone No. 01946 598914

Restrictions: No dog restrictions. Doggy bags supplied at Tourist Office. This is a Harbour rather than a beach.

Beach: Sandymere

Council Phone No. 01237 477676

Restrictions: Dogs are only allowed on part of the beach between 1st May and 30th Sept. Dogs are allowed on some parts of beach all year round.

Beach: Shipload Bay

Council Phone No. 01237 477676

Restrictions: Access is practically inaccessible.

Beach: Hartland Quay

Council Phone No. 01237 441218

Restrictions: Dogs not allowed on beach any time of year completely Dog Free Zone. There are walks along the cliffs where you can take dogs.

Beach: Instow

Council Phone No. 01237 477676

Restrictions: Dogs not allowed on middle part of beach between 1st May and 30th Sept. Dogs are allowed to the left and right sections all year round. Dogs have to be put on a lead by the cricket ground.

Beach: Welcombe Mouth

Council Phone No. 01237 477676/ 421853

Restrictions: No dog restrictions.

Beach: Clovelly

Council Phone No. 01237 431200

Restrictions: No dog restrictions. Owners must clean up mess. In village dogs must be kept on lead.

Beach: Westward Ho!

Council Phone No. 01237 477676

Restrictions: Dogs are not allowed on beach left of bridge between 1st May and 30th Sept. Dogs are allowed on beach all year round right of bridge. Owners must clear up mess from dog.

Beach: Putsborough Sands

Council Phone No. 01271 816 400

Restrictions: Dogs are only allowed to the right of the rocks on this beach all year round. Restricted areas are signposted. Litter bins are provided.

Beach: Croyde Bay

Council Phone No. 01271 816400

Restrictions: Dogs are not allowed on beach all year round.

Beach: Saunton Sands

Council Phone No. 01271 816400

Restrictions: Dogs are only allowed to the left of the beach all year round. Restricted areas are signposted. Litter bins are provided.

www.dogfriendly.co.uk

Beach: Ilfracombe - Capstone (Wildersmouth)

Council Phone No. 01271 863001

Restrictions: No dog restrictions. Litter bins are provided as you come off the beach .

Beach: Mortehoe - Rockham Bay

Council Phone No. 01271 870553

Restrictions: No dog restrictions. Litter bins are provided.

Beach: Woolacombe - Village

Council Phone No. 01271 816400

Restrictions: Dogs are only allowed to the left of the stream on the beach all year round. Restricted areas are signposted. Litter bins are provided.

Beach: Combe Martin

Council Phone No. 01271 883319

Restrictions: Dogs are not allowed on Main Beach between 1st May and 30th Sept (Seaside Award). Newbury side west of little stream dogs are allowed all year round, litter bins on this side and beach is cleaned most days.

Beach: Woolacombe - Barricane Bay

Council Phone No. 01271 870553

Restrictions: Dogs are not allowed on section from Esplanade to Stream between Apr and Oct. Dogs must be on leads from Stream to Mill between Apr and Oct. All other parts of beach are Dog Friendly all year round.

Beach: Beer

Council Phone No. 01297 21660

Restrictions: Dogs are not allowed opposite South West point below Charlie's Yard to the left of the beach between 1st May and 30th Sept. The restricted area will be signposted. Litter bins are available.

Beach: Branscombe

Council Phone No. 01297 21660

Restrictions: Dogs are not allowed 150m wide by café all year round.

Beach: Seaton - Devon

Council Phone No. 01297 21660

Restrictions: Dogs are not allowed on middle/main part of beach between 1st May and 30th Sept. They are allowed on far ends all year round. Litter bins are available.

Beach: Sandy Bay

Council Phone No. 01395 222299

Restrictions: No dogs allowed between 1st May and 30th Sept.

Beach: Exmouth

Council Phone No. 01395 222999

Restrictions: Dogs are allowed from the Docks to the Octagon Ice Cream and along far end from Orcombe Point to first breakwater only between 1st May and 30th Sept. Litter and Dog bins are provided. Beach is cleaned regularly.

Beach: Budleigh Salterton

Council Phone No. 01395 445275

Restrictions: Dogs are not allowed on the centre part of beach between 1st May and 30th Sept. There are sections at very ends of beach where dogs are allowed but must be kept on leads these areas are signposted. There are litter and dog bins provided.

Beach: Ladram Bay

Council Phone No. 01395 568398

Restrictions: Dogs are not allowed on the beach or slipway at all between 1st May and 30th Sept.

Beach: Sidmouth - Jacobs Ladder

Council Phone No. 01395 516441

Restrictions: Dogs are not allowed on most of the beach between 1st May and 30th Sept. There is a section at the very Western end where dogs are allowed.

Beach: Sidmouth - Town

Council Phone No. 01395 516441

Restrictions: Dogs are not allowed on most of the beach between 1st May and 30th Sept. There is a section at the very Eastern end where dogs are allowed.

Beach: Coryton Cove

Council Phone No. 01626 215665

Restrictions: Dogs are not allowed on this beach at any time.

Beach: Hope Cove

Council Phone No. 01626 215665

Restrictions: Dogs are allowed all year round.

Beach: Salcombe - North Sands

Council Phone No. 01548 843927

Restrictions: Dogs are allowed all year round. Litter and Dog bins are provided.

Beach: Gammonds Head

Council Phone No. 01548 853195

Restrictions: Dogs are allowed all year round.

Beach: Mill Bay

Council Phone No. 01548 843927

Restrictions: No dog restrictions a dog friendly Beach. Litter and Dog bins provided.

Beach: Redgate

Council Phone No. 01803 861234

Restrictions: Closed due to unstable cliff above

Beach: Salcombe - South Sands

Council Phone No. 01548 843927

Restrictions: No dogs allowed between 1st May and 30th Sept.

Beach: Soar Mill Cove

Council Phone No. 01548 843927

Restrictions: No dog restrictions. Litter bins are provided.

Beach: Abrahams Hole

Council Phone No. 01803 861234

Restrictions: Dogs are allowed but access is very difficult.

www.dogfriendly.co.uk

Beach: Beesands

Council Phone No. 01548 853195

Restrictions: Dogs are allowed all year round. Litter bins are available.

Beach: Great Mattiscombe

Council Phone No. 01548 853195

Restrictions: Dogs are allowed all year round.

Beach: Hallsands

Council Phone No. 01548 853195

Restrictions: Dogs are allowed all year round. Litter bins are available.

Beach: Bantham

Council Phone No. 01803 861234

Restrictions: Dogs are allowed on some parts of beach but there are restrictions on some sections between 1st May and 30th Sept. Restricted areas are signposted.

Beach: Sedgwell Cove

Council Phone No. 01548 830159

Restrictions: Dogs are allowed all year round to the left hand side at the bottom of slipway. Dogs are banned to the right hand side of the slipway to the Causeway, from 1st May to 30th September.

Beach: Thurlestone - North

Council Phone No. 01548 853195

Restrictions: Dogs are allowed all year round. Litter bins are available.

Beach: Thurlestone - South

Council Phone No. 01548 853195

Restrictions: Dogs are allowed all year round. Litter bins are provided.

Beach: Woody Bay

Council Phone No. 01598 752225

Restrictions: No dog restrictions.

Beach: Wringcliff

Council Phone No. 01598 752225

Restrictions: No dog restrictions., but access difficult as steps at bottom are not good.

Beach: Lynmouth

Council Phone No. 01598 752509

Restrictions: No dog restrictions.

Beach: Dawlish - Coryton Cove

Council Phone No. 01626 215665

Restrictions: Dogs are not allowed on this beach between 1st May and 30th Sept.

Beach: Dawlish - Town

Council Phone No. 01626 215665

Restrictions: Dogs are not allowed from boat cave to breakwater adjacent to The Lawn. Dogs are allowed to the left of railway arch only between 1st May and 30th Sept.

Beach: Dawlish - Warren

Council Phone No. 01626 215665

Restrictions: Dogs must be kept on

leads on Nature Reserve all year round. Dogs are not allowed beyond Groyne 9 towards Warren Point all year round. Dogs are allowed between Groynes 3 - 9 all year round. Dogs are not allowed between Langstone Rock and a point 230m to the SW of Langstone Rock and between lifeguard lookout and end of sea wall between Apr to Sept.

Beach: Holcombe Beach

Council Phone No. 01626 215666

Restrictions: Dogs are allowed all year round.

Beach: Teignmouth - Holcombe

Council Phone No. 01626 215666

Restrictions: Dogs are allowed on parts of the beach from Teignmouth Lido to Holcombe.

Beach: Teignmouth - Town

Council Phone No. 01626 215666

Restrictions: Dogs are not allowed on main beach between Slipway at East Cliff and Lighthouse between 1st May and 30th Sept.

Beach: Teignmouth - Back Beach

Council Phone No. 01626 215666

Restrictions: Dogs are allowed on beach all year round.

Beach: Shaldon

Council Phone No. 01626 873723

Restrictions: Dogs are not allowed from Clipper Quay and Steps from beach 410m to the South East of Clipper Quay between 1st May and 30th Sept.

Beach: Ness Cove

Council Phone No. 01626 873723

Restrictions: Dogs are allowed all year round.

Beach: Row Cove Beach (Stoke Beach)

Council Phone No. 01752 304849

Restrictions: Dogs are allowed all year round.

Beach: Wonwell Sands

Council Phone No. 01752 304849

Restrictions: Dogs are allowed all year round.

Beach: St Marys Bay

Council Phone No. 01803 201201

Restrictions: Dogs allowed all year and a 'poop scoop' law is in operation, dog wardens patrolling.

Beach: Anstey's Cove

Council Phone No. 01803 201201

Restrictions: Dogs allowed all year and a 'poop scoop' law is in operation, dog wardens patrolling.

Beach: Babbacombe Bay, Torquay

Council Phone No. 01803 201201

Restrictions: Dogs allowed all year and a 'poop scoop' law is in operation, dog wardens patrolling.

Beach: Maidencombe - Torbay

Council Phone No. 01803 201201

www.dogfriendly.co.uk

Restrictions: Dogs allowed all year and a 'poop scoop' law is in operation, dog wardens patrolling.

Beach: Meadfoot - Torbay

Council Phone No. 01803 201201

Restrictions: Dogs are banned from south western section between 1st May - 30th September. Dogs are allowed all year on North Eastern Section 'Poop Scoop' law in operation dog wardens patrolling.

Beach: Shoalstone Beach

Council Phone No. 01803 201201

Restrictions: The beach is cleaned daily during summer season. Dogs are allowed on beach all year but have to be kept on a lead on the promenade and pool area. 'Poop Scoop' law is in operation, dog wardens patrolling.

Beach: Beacon Cove

Council Phone No. 01803 297428

Restrictions: Dogs allowed all year and a 'poop scoop' law is in operation, dog wardens patrolling.

Beach: Elbury - Cove

Council Phone No. 01803 558383

Restrictions: Dogs allowed all year and a 'poop scoop' law is in operation, dog wardens patrolling.

Beach: Goodrington Sands

Council Phone No. 01803 558383

Restrictions: Dogs are allowed on North side but are banned on the South side from Apr to Sept.

Beach: Hollicombe

Council Phone No. 01803 558383

Restrictions: Dogs are not allowed from 1st May to 30th September. No dog ban rest of year.

Beach: Paignton - Paignton Sands

Council Phone No. 01803 558383

Restrictions: Dogs are not allowed from 1st May to 30th September. No dog ban rest of year.

Beach: Paignton - Preston Snads

Council Phone No. 01803 558383

Restrictions: Dogs are not allowed from 1st May to 30th September. No dog ban rest of year.

Beach: Leonards Cove

Council Phone No. 01803 770206

Restrictions: No access to beach tidal only.

Beach: Slapton Sands - Torcross

Council Phone No. 01803 834224

Restrictions: Dogs are allowed all year round.

Beach: Strete Gate Beach

Council Phone No. 01803 834224

Restrictions: Dogs are allowed all year round.

Beach: Bigbury on sea (North)

Council Phone No. 01803 861234

Restrictions: Dog restrictions from the 1st of May to the 30th September 2007. Partial Ban.

Beach: Bigbury on sea (South)

Council Phone No. 01803 861234

Restrictions: Dog restrictions from the 1st of May to the 30th September 2007. Partial Ban.

Beach: Blackpool Sand, Stoke Flemming

Council Phone No. 01803 861234

Restrictions: Private bans have been introduced by the owners which are signposted on the beach

Beach: Bovisand Bay

Council Phone No. 01803 861234

Restrictions: Private bans have been introduced by the owners which are signposted on the beach

Beach: Challaborough

Council Phone No. 01803 861234

Restrictions: Private bans have been introduced by the owners which are signposted on the beach

Beach: Mothecombe - Meadowsfoot & Coastguards Beach

Council Phone No. 01803 861234

Restrictions: Private bans have been introduced by the owners which are signposted on the beach

Beach: Mouthwell Sands

Council Phone No. 01803 861234

Restrictions: Dog restrictions from the 1st of May to the 30th September 2007.

Beach: Wembury

Council Phone No. 01803 861234

Restrictions: Private bans have been introduced by the owners which are signposted on the beach

Beach: Dartmouth Castle and Sugary Cove

Council Phone No. 01803 834224

Restrictions: Dogs are allowed all year round.

Beach: Ilfracombe - Hele Beach

Council Phone No. 01271 863001

Restrictions: Dogs are not allowed between 1st May and 30th Sept. Dogs are only allowed on Wilders Mouth and Harbour Beach. Litter bins are available.

Beach: Ilfracombe - Tunnels Beaches

Council Phone No. 0845 4583630

Restrictions: Dogs are not allowed between 1st May and 30th Sept. Dogs are only allowed on Wilders Mouth and Harbour Beach. Litter bins are available.

www.dogfriendly.co.uk

Plymouth

Beach: Mount Batten

Council Phone No. 01752 668000

Restrictions: Dogs are prohibited between the 1st of May and 30th of September on signposted areas

Beach: Bovisand

Council Phone No. 01752 668000

Restrictions: Dogs are prohibited between the 1st of May and 30th of September on signposted areas

Beach: Plymouth Hoe West

Council Phone No. 01752 668000

Restrictions: Dogs are prohibited between the 1st of May and 30th of September on signposted areas

Torbay

Beach: Oddicombe Beach

Council Phone No. 01803 201201

Restrictions: No dogs allowed from 1st May to 30th September. 'Poop Scoop' law is in operation.

Beach: Torre Abbey

Council Phone No. 01803 297428

Restrictions: The beach is cleaned regularly. Dogs are banned from the beach during the summer season. 1st May - 30th September. 'Poop Scoop' laws are in operation from Oct to April.

Beach: Broadsands Beach

Council Phone No. 01803 558383

Restrictions: The beach is cleaned regularly. Dogs are banned from the beach during the summer season. 1st May - 30th September. 'Poop Scoop' laws are in operation from Oct to April.

Beach: Churston Cove

Council Phone No. 0870 70 70 010

Restrictions: Dogs allowed all year round, 'poop scoop' law is in operation all year.

Beach: Watcombe

Council Phone No. 0870 70 70 010

Restrictions: Dogs allowed all year round, 'poop scoop' law is in operation all year.

Beach: Hengistbury Head Bournemouth

Council Phone No. 01202 451781

Restrictions: Dogs not allowed on the main beach between 1st May and 30th September they are allowed to the top of durley chine and east of fisherman's walk up to hengistbury

Beach: Poole - Canford Cliffs

Council Phone No. 01202 253253

Restrictions: Dogs are not allowed between 1st May and 30th Sept.

Beach: Poole - Harbour Lake

Council Phone No. 01202 253253

Restrictions: Dogs are allowed all year round. Litter and Dog bins are available.

Beach: Poole -Harbour rockley sand

Council Phone No. 01202 253253

Restrictions: Dogs are allowed all year round. Litter and Dog bins are available.

Beach: Poole - Harbour sandbanks

Council Phone No. 01202 253253

Restrictions: Dogs are not allowed on the main Beach between 1st May and 30th Sept. They are allowed East of Branksome Chimes and Western End of Sandbanks Promenade only these areas are signposted. Litter and Dog bins are available.

Beach: Poole Sandbanks Peninsular

Council Phone No. 01202 253253

Restrictions: Dogs are not allowed on the main beach between 1st May and 30th Sept. They are allowed East of Branksome Chimes and Western End of Sandbanks Promenade only these areas are signposted. Litter and Dog bins are available.

Beach: Poole - Shore road, Sandbanks

Council Phone No. 01202 253253

Restrictions: Dogs are not allowed on the main beach between 1st May and 30th Sept. They are allowed East of Branksome Chimes and Western End of Sandbanks Promenade only these areas are signposted. Litter and Dog bins are available.

Beach: Bournemouth - Alum Chine

Council Phone No. 01202 451781

Restrictions: Dog are allowed in some areas, must be kept on lead on promenade. No dogs allowed between Groyne 4 and 5 from 1st May - 30th September.

www.dogfriendly.co.uk

125

Beach: Bournemouth - Boscombe Pier

Council Phone No. 01202 451781

Restrictions: Dogs not allowed between 1st May - 30th September.

Beach: Bournemouth - Durley Chine

Council Phone No. 01202 451781

Restrictions: Between 1st May and 30th September -Dog allowed to the top of durley chine and east of fisherman's walk up to hengistbury head

Beach: Bournemouth - East Cliff

Council Phone No. 01202 451781

Restrictions: Dogs not allowed between 1st May - 30th September.

Beach: Bournemouth - Fisherman's walk

Council Phone No. 01202 451781

Restrictions: Dogs not allowed between 1st May - 30th September.

Beach: Bournemouth - Manor Steps

Council Phone No. 01202 451781

Restrictions: Dogs not allowed between 1st May - 30th September.

Beach: Bournemouth - Pier

Council Phone No. 01202 451781

Restrictions: Dogs not allowed between 1st May - 30th September.

Beach: Bournemouth - Southbourne

Council Phone No. 01202 451781

Restrictions: Dogs are allowed all year in certain areas of the beach . They must be kept on a lead on the promenade.

Beach: Christchurch - Mudeford Sandbank east

Council Phone No. 01202 471780

Restrictions: Dogs are allowed all year round but must be kept on a lead or under control.

Beach: Christchurch Avon Beach

Council Phone No. 01202 495070

Restrictions: Dogs prohibited between the 1st May and 30th September

Beach: Christchurch - Friars cliff

Council Phone No. 01202 495070

Restrictions: Between 1st may and 30th September no dogs between groynes H8 and H11. Dogs permitted between the wave wall at the end of Friars Cliff and groyne H8 at Highcliff Crows Nest

Beach: Christchurch - Highcliff castle

Council Phone No. 01202 495070

Restrictions: Dogs are allowed all year round. The beach is cleaned daily and litter bins are available.

Beach: Christchurch - Mudeford Quay

Council Phone No. 01202 495070

Restrictions: Dogs are allowed all year round but must be kept on a lead or under control.

Beach: Highcliffe

Council Phone No. 01202 495070

Restrictions: The beach is cleaned daily. There are litter and dog bins provided. Dogs are not allowed between groynes H8 - H11 from 1st May to 30th September and must be kept on a lead on the promenade.

Beach: Bournemouth - Hengistbury Head

Council Phone No. 01202 495070

Restrictions: Dogs are allowed all year round

Beach: Charmouth - East

Council Phone No. 01297 442138

Restrictions: Dogs are not allowed on beach during July and August from 10am to 6pm.

Beach: Charmouth - West

Council Phone No. 01297 442138

Restrictions: Dogs are not allowed on beach between 1st May and 30th September.

Beach: Lyme Regis - Church Beach

Council Phone No. 01297 442138

Restrictions: Dogs are allowed on beach all year round.

Beach: Lyme Regis - Cobb

Council Phone No. 01297 442138

Restrictions: Dogs are not allowed from Gate Car Park to Lifeboat slipway between 1st May and 30th Sept.

Beach: Lyme Regis - Monmouth Beach

Council Phone No. 01297 442138

Restrictions: Dogs are allowed on beach all year round.

Beach: RingStead Bay

Council Phone No. 01297 561900

Restrictions: Dogs are allowed on beach all year round.

Beach: Bowleaze Cove

Council Phone No. 01305 785747

Restrictions: Dogs are allowed all year, from Oasis Café downwards to Bowleaze Cove.

Beach: Church Hope cove

Council Phone No. 01305 785747

Restrictions: Dogs are allowed all year round.

Beach: Overcombe

Council Phone No. 01305 785747

Restrictions: Dog restrictions apply all year round. Restricted areas are signposted.

Beach: Portland Harbour - Castle Cove

Council Phone No. 01305 785747

Restrictions: Dogs are allowed all year round.

Beach: Portland Harbour - Sandsfoot Castle

Council Phone No. 01305 785747

Restrictions: Dogs are allowed all year round.

Beach: Weymouth - Central

Council Phone No. 01305 785747

Restrictions: No dogs on main beach between 1st May and 30th September - They are allowed all year round at the pavillion end of the beach and on preston beach.

Beach: Weymouth - Lodmoor

Council Phone No. 01305 785747

Restrictions: No dogs on main beach between 1st May and 30th September - They are allowed all year round at the pavillion end of the beach and on preston beach.

Beach: Weymouth - South

Council Phone No. 01305 785747

Restrictions: No dogs on main beach between 1st May and 30th September - They are allowed all year round at the pavillion end of the beach and on preston beach.

Beach: Lodmoor West

Council Phone No. 01305 785747

Restrictions: Dogs allowed all year past the groyne towards Bowleaze Cove. Litter bins are provided.

Beach: Chesil Cove

Council Phone No. 01305 785747

Restrictions: Dogs are allowed all year round.

Beach: Greenhill

Council Phone No. 01305 785747

Restrictions: Dogs are not allowed on **beach** between 1st May and 30th Sept.

Beach: Eypemouth

Council Phone No. 01308 424901

Restrictions: Dogs are allowed all year round.

Beach: Hive Beach, Burton bradstock

Council Phone No. 01308 424901

Restrictions: Dogs are not allowed on beach between 1st May and 30th Sept.

Beach: Sea Town

Council Phone No. 01308 424901

Restrictions: No dogs are allowed on this beach.

Beach: West Bay - East

Council Phone No. 01308 424901

Restrictions: Dogs are not allowed on beach between 1st May and 30th Sept.

Beach: West Bay - West

Council Phone No. 01308 424901

Restrictions: Dogs are not allow on beach between 1st May and 30th Sept.

Beach: Lulworth Cove

Council Phone No. 01929 400587

Restrictions: Dogs are allowed all year round but must be kept on a lead or under control

Beach: Shell Bay

Council Phone No. 01929 422885

Restrictions: Dogs are allowed as long as they are kept on a lead

Beach: Swanage- North

Council Phone No. 01929 422885

Restrictions: Dogs are prohibited between the 1st May and 30th September

Beach: Studland Knoll House

Council Phone No. 01929 422885

Restrictions: Dogs are allowed on Shell Bay and South Beach all year round. Dogs are not allowed on Middle Beach: and Knoll Beach: from 1st July to 2nd Sept.

Beach: Durdle Door - East

Council Phone No. 01929 552740

Restrictions: Dogs are allowed all year round.

Beach: Durdle Door - West

Council Phone No. 01929 552740

Restrictions: Dogs are allowed all year round.

Beach: Kimmeridge Bay

Council Phone No. 01929 552740

Restrictions: Dogs are allowed all year round.

Beach: Swanage - Central

Council Phone No. 0870 442 0680

Restrictions: Dogs not allowed at any time of year.

Beach: Swanage - South

Council Phone No. 0870 442 0680

Restrictions: Dogs allowed all year.

www.dogfriendly.co.uk

Durham

Beach: Blackhall

Council Phone No. 0191 527 0501

Restrictions: No dog restrictions. Dogs are welcome all year round but must be kept under control and owners must remember to clean up after their dog

Beach: Crimdon Park

Council Phone No. 0191 527 0501

Restrictions: No dog restrictions. Dogs are welcome all year round but must be kept under control and owners must remember to clean up after their dog

Beach: Crimdon - South

Council Phone No. 0191 527 0501

Restrictions: No dog restrictions. Dogs are welcome all year round but must be kept under control and owners must remember to clean up after their dog

Beach: Dalton Burn

Council Phone No. 0191 527 0501

Restrictions: No dog restrictions. Dogs are welcome all year round but must be kept under control and owners must remember to clean up after their dog

Beach: Denemouth south

Council Phone No. 0191 527 0501

Restrictions: No dog restrictions. Dogs are welcome all year round but must be kept under control and owners must remember to clean up after their dog

Beach: Easington

Council Phone No. 0191 527 0501

Restrictions: No dog restrictions. Dogs are welcome all year round but must be kept under control and owners must remember to clean up after their dog

Beach: Featherbed rocks

Council Phone No. 0191 527 0501

Restrictions: No dog restrictions. Dogs are welcome all year round but must be kept under control and owners must remember to clean up after their dog

Beach: Horden

Council Phone No. 0191 527 0501

Restrictions: No dog restrictions. Dogs are welcome all year round but must be kept under control and owners must remember to clean up after their dog

Beach: Seaham Beach:

Council Phone No. 0191 527 0501

Restrictions: No dog restrictions. Dogs are welcome all year round but must be kept under control and owners must remember to clean up after their dog

www.dogfriendly.co.uk

130

Beach: Seaham hall Beach (Remand house)

Council Phone No. 0191 527 0501

Restrictions: No dog restrictions. Dogs are welcome all year round but must be kept under control and owners must remember to clean up after their dog

Essex

Beach: Brightlingsea

Council Phone No. 01255 686868

Restrictions: Dogs prohibited between the 1st May and 30th September from West Marsh Point covering the paddling pool area and both beaches east of pool.

Beach: Canvey Island

Council Phone No. 01255 686868

Restrictions: No dog restrictions. but dogs must be kept under control or on a lead and owners must remember to clean up after their dogs

Beach: Canvey Island - Thorney Bay

Council Phone No. 01255 686868

Restrictions: No dog restrictions. but dogs must be kept under control or on a lead and owners must remember to clean up after their dogs

Beach: Clacton

Council Phone No. 01255 686868

Restrictions: Dogs are prohibited between the 1st of May and 30th of September on signposted areas

Beach: Clacton - North East

Council Phone No. 01255 686868

Restrictions: Dogs are prohibited between the 1st of May and 30th of September from opposite St Albans Road to Gun fleet Sailing Club, opposite Hazelmere Road.

Beach: Clacton - Martello Tower

Council Phone No. 01255 686868

Restrictions: Dogs are prohibited between the 1st of May and 30th of September from the pier to West Road out-fall pipe on Martello Bay

Beach: Dovercourt Bay

Council Phone No. 01255 686868

Restrictions: Dogs are prohibited between the 1st of May and 30th September from Mill Lane subway to end of promenade at Spa Cabins

Beach: Frinton - On - Sea

Council Phone No. 01255 686868

Restrictions: Dog are prohibited between the 1st of May and 30th of September from seafront warden station below connaught avenue to public conveniences below Cambridge road

Beach: Harwich - Beacon Hill

Council Phone No. 01255 686868

Restrictions: Dogs are prohibited between the 1st of May and 30th September from the Coast Guard building at Out part East to Low Lighthouse in front of Harbour Crescent.

www.dogfriendly.co.uk

132

Beach: Harwich - Sailing Club

Council Phone No. 01255 686868

Restrictions: Dogs are prohibited between the 1st of May and 30th of September on signposted areas

Beach: Holland-On-Sea - North East

Council Phone No. 01255 686868

Restrictions: Dogs are prohibited between the 1st of May and 30th September from cafe opposite Haven Avenue for 3 sections of beach south west

Beach: Holland-On-Sea - South West

Council Phone No. 01255 686868

Restrictions: Dogs are prohibited between the 1st of May and 30th of September from breakwater south west of Queensway to café north west of Queensway

Beach: Jaywick

Council Phone No. 01255 686868

Restrictions: Dogs are prohibited between the 1st of May and 30th of September on signposted areas

Beach: Southend - Waycliff Bay

Council Phone No. 01255 686868

Restrictions: Dogs are prohibited between the 1st of May and 30th of September on signposted areas

Beach: Walton-On-The-Naze - Central

Council Phone No. 01255 686868

Restrictions: Dogs are prohibited between the 1st of May and 30th September from the Pier to end of The Parade opposite Suffolk Street

Beach: Walton-On-The-Naze

Council Phone No. 01255 686868

Restrictions: Dogs are prohibited between the 1st Of may and 30th of September - North east from Percival Road to Naze Park Road

Beach: West Mersea

Council Phone No. 01255 686868

Restrictions: Dogs are allowed all year round but must be kept under control and on a lead.

Southend-on-sea

Beach: Shoebury East

Council Phone No. 01702 215000

Restrictions: Dogs are prohibited on signposted areas between the 1st of May and 30th of September every person who is in charge of a dog (except guide dogs) who permits a dog to enter or remain on the beach can be fined £100

Beach: Shoeburyness

Council Phone No. 01702 215000

Restrictions: Dogs are prohibited on signposted areas between the 1st of May and 30th of September every person who is in charge of a dog (except guide dogs) who permits a dog to enter or remain on the beach can be fined £100

Beach: Southend - Chalkwell Beach

Council Phone No. 01702 215000

Restrictions: Dogs are prohibited on signposted areas between the 1st of May and 30th of September every person who is in charge of a dog (except guide dogs) who permits a dog to enter or remain on the beach can be fined £100

Beach: Southend - Jubilee Beach

Council Phone No. 01702 215000

Restrictions: Dogs are prohibited between the 1st of May and 30th of september on signposted areas

Beach: Southend - Leigh bell wharf

Council Phone No. 01702 215000

Restrictions: Dogs are prohibited on signposted areas between the 1st of May and 30th of September every person who is in charge of a dog (except guide dogs) who permits a dog to enter or remain on the beach can be fined £100

Beach: Southend - Thorpe Bay

Council Phone No. 01702 215000

Restrictions: Dogs are prohibited between the 1st of May and 30th of september on signposted areas

Beach: Sourthend - Three shells

Council Phone No. 01702 215000

Restrictions: Dogs are prohibited on signposted areas between the 1st of May and 30th of September every person who is in charge of a dog (except guide dogs) who permits a dog to enter or remain on the beach can be fined £100

Beach: Eastney
Portsmouth

Council Phone No. 023 9283 4092

Restrictions: Allowed all year round on the beach but dogs must be kept under control and owners must remember to clean up after their dog

Beach: Old Portsmouth Beach
Portsmouth

Council Phone No. 023 9283 4092

Restrictions: Allowed all year round on the beach but dogs must be kept under control and owners must remember to clean up after their dog

Beach: Southsea
Portsmouth

Council Phone No. 023 9283 4092

Restrictions: Allowed all year round on the beach but dogs must be kept under control and owners must remember to clean up after their dog

Beach: Hillhead

Council Phone No. 01329 221342

Restrictions: Beach is cleaned all year round. and daily in the summer season. Litter bins are provided at this beach. Dogs are banned between May and September; dog litter bins are provided for other times.

Beach: Lepe

Council Phone No. 01590 689000

Restrictions: The beach is cleaned daily by Country Park staff. There are litter bins and dogs are banned from part of the beach all year round, these areas are signposted.

Beach: Burgh Island

Council Phone No. 01752 304849

Restrictions: Beach split into three sections. Middle section (Brigby) dogs are allowed in winter, but banned between 1stMay - 30th September. Either side of Brigby, dogs banned all year round. These areas are signposted.

Beach: Calshot

Council Phone No. 01590 689000

Restrictions: Dogs allowed all year round.

Beach: Christchurch Bay
(Barton - on - Sea)

Council Phone No. 01202 471780

Restrictions: During summer 1st Mat- 30th September dogs are not allowed most of the beach (these areas are signposted.) Are allowed in small area between wave wall and groyne 88. The beach is cleaned daily by hand in the summer and bins are provided.

www.dogfriendly.co.uk

135

Beach: Milford - On - Sea

Council Phone No. 01590 689000

Restrictions: The beach is cleaned daily in the summer. Dogs are allowed all year round.

Beach: Stokes Bay

Council Phone No. 023 9252 2944

Restrictions: The beach is manually cleaned which is permanently in place during the summer months. Dogs are not allowed in signed controlled areas between 1st May - 30th September. There are litter bins on the beach (dog bins available off season).

Beach: Lee On The Solent

Council Phone No. 023 9252 2944

Restrictions: The beach is manually cleaned which is permanently in place during the summer months. Dogs banned in signed controlled areas between 1st May - 30th September. Bins available

Beach: Solent Breezes

Council Phone No. 023 9282 6722

Restrictions: Not much of a beach, mainly mucd and stones! Dogs are allowed all year round, however must be kept on leads at all times, and mess must be cleared up after them.

Beach: Southsea
(300m West of Ec Site)

Council Phone No. 023 9282 8112

Restrictions: Dogs not allowed on beach from 1st March - 30th September.

These restricted areas cover most of the beach and are signposted.

Beach: Weston Hard Woolston

Council Phone No. 02380 223855

Restrictions: Dogs allowed on beach all year round

Beach: Hayling Island - West Hayling

Council Phone No. 02392 467111

Restrictions: Beaches cleaned daily from Easter to 30th September. Dogs are banned from 1st May - 30th September (these areas are signposted) except for between 'Ferry End' to the 'Golf club' where they are allowed. Dog bins are provided.

Beach: Hayling Island - West of Eastoke

Council Phone No. 02392 467111

Restrictions: Beach cleaned daily from Easter to 30th September. Dogs are banned from 1st May - 30th September on blueflag beaches (which are signposted). Dog bins are provided.

Hartlepool

Beach: Seaton Carew - North

Council Phone No. 01429 869706.

Restrictions: The beach is cleaned 3 times a week by Hartlepool Borough Council. There are dog bins on the beach . but dogs are not allowed from May to September.

Beach: Seaton Carew - North Gare

Council Phone No. 01429 869706.

Restrictions: The beach is cleaned 3 times a week by Hartlepool Borough Council. There are dog bins on the beach. but dogs are not allowed from May to September.

Beach: Seaton Carew Centre

Council Phone No. 01429 869706.

Restrictions: The beach is cleaned daily by the borough council. Dogs are banned from the beach between between May and September. Dog bins are present.

Beach: Hartlepool North Sands

Council Phone No. 01429 869706.

Restrictions: Dogs Not allowed on beaches from 1st May - 30th September

Beach: Lleiniog Beach, Penmon

Council Phone No. 01407 762622

Restrictions: Dogs not allowed on beach between 1st May - 30th September

Beach: Beaumaris

Council Phone No. 01407 762622

Restrictions: Dogs not allowed on beach between 1st May - 30th September

Beach: Benllech

Council Phone No. 01407 762622

Restrictions: Dogs not allowed on beach between 1st May - 30th September

Beach: Moelfre

Council Phone No. 01407 762622

Restrictions: No dog restrictions.

Beach: Rhosneigr - Treath Crigyll

Council Phone No. 01407 762622

Restrictions: No dog restrictions.

Beach: St. Georges Pier, Menai Bridge

Council Phone No. 01407 762622

Restrictions: No dog restrictions.

Beach: Cemlyn

Council Phone No. 01407 762622

Restrictions: Dogs not allowed on beach between 1st May - 30th September. The beach is cleaned daily by the local authority and litter bins are provided.

Beach: Church Bay

Council Phone No. 01407 762622

Restrictions: No dog restrictions.

Beach: Llanfaelog - Porth Nobla

Council Phone No. 01407 762622

Restrictions: No dog restrictions.

Beach: Porth Eilian, Amlwch

Council Phone No. 01407 762622

Restrictions: No dog restrictions.

Beach: Porth Trecastell

Council Phone No. 01407 762622

Restrictions: No dog restrictions.

Beach: Rhosneigr

Council Phone No. 01407 762622

Restrictions: The beach is cleaned weekly by the local council. Dogs are allowed on the beach .

www.dogfriendly.co.uk

Beach: St Davids, Benllech

Council Phone No. 01407 762622

Restrictions: Dogs are banned during summer. May 1st 30th September.

Beach: Porth Dafarch

Council Phone No. 01407 762622

Restrictions: Dogs are banned during summer. May 1st 30th September.

Beach: Porth trwyn Mawr (Sandy Beach)

Council Phone No. 01407 762622

Restrictions: Dogs are banned during summer. May 1st 30th September.

Beach: Rhoscolyn - Borth Wien

Council Phone No. 01407 762622

Restrictions: No dog restrictions.

Beach: Bull Bay

Council Phone No. 01407 762622

Restrictions: No dog restrictions.

Beach: Cemaes

Council Phone No. 01407 762622

Restrictions: Dogs are banned during summer. May 1st 30th September.

Beach: Cemaes - Traeth Bach

Council Phone No. 01407 762622

Restrictions: Dogs are banned during summer

Beach: Llanddona

Council Phone No. 01407 762622

Restrictions: Dog restrictions apple. Dogs banned from beach between 1st May - 30th September.

Beach: Llanddwyn Beach:

Council Phone No. 01407 762622

Restrictions: Dog restrictions apple. Dogs banned from beach between 1st May - 30th September. The beach is cleaned daily during the summer. Litter bins are provided in the car park

Beach: Llanfaelog - Porth Tyn Tywyn

Council Phone No. 01407 762622

Restrictions: No dog restrictions.

Beach: Llanfaelog - Cable Bay

Council Phone No. 01407 762622

Restrictions: No dog restrictions.

Beach: Newry Beach , Holyhead

Council Phone No. 01407 762622

Restrictions: No dog restrictions.

Beach: Pentraeth

Council Phone No. 01407 762622

Restrictions: No dog restrictions.

Beach: Porth Trwyn

Council Phone No. 01407 762622

Restrictions: No dog restrictions.

Beach: Red Wharf Bay

Council Phone No. 01407 762622

Restrictions: No dog restrictions.

Beach: Rhoscolyn - Silver Bay

Council Phone No. 01407 762622

Restrictions: No dog restrictions.

Beach: Treaddur Bay

Council Phone No. 01407 762622

Restrictions: Dogs are permitted on part of the beach at certain times of year, these small areas are signposted. But not allowed between May 1st - September 30th.

Beach: Traeth Lligwy

Council Phone No. 01407 762622.

Restrictions: No dog restrictions.

Beach: Aberffraw Bay (Traeth Mawr)

Council Phone No. 01407 762622.

Restrictions: No dog restrictions.

www.dogfriendly.co.uk

Isle of Man

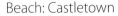

Beach: Castletown

Council Phone No. 01624 825005

Restrictions: Dogs allowed on beach all year round, as long as foul picked up after and kept under control.

Beach: Douglas - Broadway

Phone No. 01624 623021

Restrictions: Dogs allowed all year round, however between 1st May - 30th September, must be kept under 'effective control,' and should not foul, however if they do, must be cleaned up after. Phone number for updates on new laws.

Beach: Douglas - Central

Council Phone No. 01624 623021

Restrictions: Dogs allowed all year round, however between 1st May - 30th September, must be kept under 'effective control,' and should not foul, however if they do, must be cleaned up after. Phone number for updates on new laws.

Beach: Douglas - Summerhill

Council Phone No. 01624 623021

Restrictions: Dogs allowed all year round, however between 1st May - 30th September, must be kept under 'effective control,' and should not foul, however if they do, must be cleaned

up after. Phone number for updates on new laws.

Beach: Fenella Beach

Council Phone No. 01624 842341

Restrictions: Dogs allowed all year round, except for between 9am-9pm between 1st May - 30th September

Beach: Gansey Bay (Bay NY Carrickey)

Council Phone No. 01624 686801

Restrictions: Dogs allowed on beach all year round, but between 1st May - 30th September, must be kept under 'effective control.'

Beach: Garwick

Council Phone No. 01624 686801

Restrictions: Dogs allowed on beach all year round, but between 1st May - 30th September, must be kept under 'effective control.'

Beach: Jurby

Council Phone No. 01624 686801

Restrictions: No dog restrictions.

Beach: Kirk Michael

Council Phone No. 01624 878231

Restrictions: No dog restrictions.

Beach: Laxey

Council Phone No. 01624 861241

Restrictions: Dogs allowed on **beach** all year round but restricted from 'being at large' (must be kept under strict control) between 1st May - 30th September

Beach: Peel

Council Phone No. 01624 842341

Restrictions: Dogs allowed all year round, except for between 9am-9pm between 1st May - 30th September

Beach: Port Erin

Council Phone No. 01624 832298

Restrictions: Dogs banned from beaches between 1st May- 30th September between 9am - 6pm. Litter bins provided.

Beach: Port Soderick

Council Phone No. 01624 852808

Restrictions: No dog restrictions.

Beach: Port St Mary

Council Phone No. 01624 832101

Restrictions: Dogs banned on beaches from 1st May - 30th September 9am-6pm. Allowed on beach rest of the year.

Beach: Ramsey

Council Phone No. 01624 810100

Restrictions: Dogs allowed on beach all year round as long as kept under 'reasonable control' and dog mess is cleared up after. Litter bins provided.

Beach: White Strand

Council Phone No. 07624 494475

Restrictions: No dog restrictions.

Beach: Derbyhaven

Council Phone No. 07624 494475

Restrictions: Dogs allowed on beach all year round, but between 1st May - 30th September, must be kept under 'effective control.'

www.dogfriendly.co.uk

Isle of Wight

Beach: Ryde - West

Council Phone No. 01983 823362

Restrictions: Dogs banned between 1st May - 30th September. Notices of ban clearly displayed. Dog bins provided.

Beach: St. Helens

Council Phone No. 01983 741020

Restrictions: The beach is cleaned daily by the council. Dogs are allowed on the beach . dog bins are provided as are litter bins.

Beach: Compton Bay

Council Phone No. 01983 741020

Restrictions: No dogs allowed at any time.

Beach: Colwell Bay

Council Phone No. 01983 821000

Restrictions: No dogs allowed at any time.

Beach: Ryde - East

Council Phone No. 01983 823362

Restrictions: Dogs banned between 1st May - 3oth September. Notices of ban clearly displayed. Dog bins provided.

Beach: Gurnard

Council Phone No. 01983 823362

Restrictions: Dogs banned between 1st May - 3oth September. Notices of ban clearly displayed. Dog bins provided.

Beach: Bembridge

Council Phone No. 01983 821000

Restrictions: No dog restrictions.

Beach: Norton

Council Phone No. 01983 821000

Restrictions: Beach is dog friendly all year round. Dog litter bins are provided. Dog owners advised to keep dogs under control to prevent damage to the foliage on the dune.

Beach: Sandown - Yaverland

Council Phone No. 01983 823362

Restrictions: Dogs banned between 1st May - 3oth September. Notices of ban clearly displayed. Dog bins provided.

Beach: Seagrove

Council Phone No. 01983 821000

Restrictions: No dog restrictions.

Beach: Ventnor

Council Phone No. 01983 823362

Restrictions: Dogs banned between 1st May - 3oth September. Notices of ban clearly displayed. Dog bins provided.

Beach: Yarmouth

Council Phone No. 01983 823362

Restrictions: Dogs banned between 1st May - 3oth September. Notices of ban clearly displayed. Dog bins provided.

Beach: Cowes

Council Phone No. 01983 823362

Restrictions: The beach is cleaned and litter bins are present. Dog bins are provided but dogs are banned from May to September. Dog litter bins provided, beach cleaned at least every other day.

Beach: Cowes - East

Council Phone No. 01983 823362

Restrictions: The beach is cleaned and litter bins are present. Dog bins are provided but dogs are banned from May to September.

Beach: Ryde - Spring Vale

Council Phone No. 01983 823362

Restrictions: The beach is cleaned daily during the bathing season. There are both litter and dog bins on the beach . Dogs are allowed throughout the year except for 1st May - 30th Sept

Beach: Sandown

Council Phone No. 01983 823362

Restrictions: Dogs banned between 1st May - 3oth September. Notices of ban clearly displayed. Dog bins provided.

Beach: Shanklin

Council Phone No. 01983 823362

Restrictions: Dogs banned between 1st May - 3oth September. Notices of ban clearly displayed. Dog bins provided.

Beach: Shanklin - Welcome Beach

Council Phone No. 01983 823362

Restrictions: Dogs banned between 1st May - 3oth September. Notices of ban clearly displayed. Dog bins provided.

Beach: Totland Bay

Council Phone No. 01983 821000

Restrictions: Dog friendly throughout the year. Litter bins are also available. - dog litter bins are provided.

Beach: Whitecliff Bay

Council Phone No. 01983 821000

Restrictions: Dogs are not allowed on the **beach** at ANY time of the year

Isle of Wight

www.dogfriendly.co.uk

Kent

Beach: Reculver Beach:

Council Phone No. 01227 266719

Restrictions: Dogs allowed all year round on the 14 1/2 mile stretch coast line except for in Herne bay, Lane end to William street, and Tankerton bay (only restricted between 1stMay-30thSept). Litter bins. Cleaned on an as and when basis.

Beach: Hampton Pier - West

Council Phone No. 01227 275482

Restrictions: No dog restrictions. on beach unless it states they need to be on a lead (signposted.) There are litter bins. Cleaned on an as and when basis - Blue flag award for cleanliness

Beach: Whitstable West Beach

Council Phone No. 01227 275482

Restrictions: No dog restrictions. on beach unless it states they need to be on a lead (signposted.) There are litter bins. Cleaned on an as and when basis - Blue flag award for cleanliness

Beach: Herne Bay

Council Phone No. 01227 361911

Restrictions: Dogs are permitted on 7 mile stretch of beach except for between Lane end and William Street (only restricted between 1stMay - 30thSept). There are litter bins

Beach: Herne Bay - Central

Council Phone No. 01227 361911

Restrictions: Dogs are permitted on 7 mile stretch of beach except for between Lane end and William Street (only restricted between 1stMay - 30thSept). There are litter bins

Beach: Hampton Pier - East

Council Phone No. 01227 361911

Restrictions: Dogs are permitted on beach all year round. There are litter bins

Beach: St. Marys Bay

Council Phone No. 01271 336020.

Restrictions: Dogs allowed all year round. There are litter bins

Beach: Folkestone - The Warren

Council Phone No. 01303 850388

Restrictions: No dog restrictions. except for between East pier to Promenade 1st May - 30th September, this area is signposted.

Beach: Folkestone

Council Phone No. 01303 850388

Restrictions: The beach is cleaned daily by the lifeguards and cleansing operatives. Dogs are banned from 1st May - 30 thOctober from East pier - Promenade, this area is signposted.

Beach: Hythe Bay

Council Phone No. 01303 850388

Restrictions: Dogs allowed except for between 1st May - 30th september, from St Leonard road to Twiss road, this area is signposted. The beach is cleaned daily and there are litter bins on the promenade which are emptied regularly.

Beach: Sandgate - Town Centre

Council Phone No. 01303 850388

Restrictions: Dogs allowed except for between 1st May - 30th september, from Sea Road - Sandgate Castle, this area is signposted.

Beach: Sandgate Beach

Council Phone No. 01303 850388

Restrictions: Dogs allowed except for between 1st May - 30th september, from Sea Road - Sandgate Castle, this area is signposted.

Beach: Dover Harbour

Council Phone No. 01304 205108.

Restrictions: The Harbour Board is responsible for the maintenance of the beach . It is cleaned daily and there are litter bins available. Dogs are banned from the beach all year round. The beach suffers from occasional litter.

Beach: St. Margaret's Bay

Council Phone No. 01304 205108.

Restrictions: Cleaned manually on a daily basis by SITA (GB) Ltd on behalf of Dover District Council. Dogs

are banned from 1st Mat - 30th September, But must be kept on a lead at all other times.

Beach: Kingsdown Beach

Council Phone No. 01304 369576

Restrictions: Dogs are allowed all year round, except for a 2mile stretch between April and October (1 mile either side of the pier) but this is signposted. Lots of litter and specific 'Dog' Bins.

Beach: Deal Castle

Council Phone No. 01304 374 726

Restrictions: The beach is manually cleaned daily in the summer months and bins are available for Beach: users. Dogs are also banned in the summer months (April - October) 1 mile either side of the pier, these areas are signposted; dog litter bins are provided for other times.

Beach: Shakespeare Beach

Council Phone No. 01304 821199

Restrictions: The beach is the responsibility of the Dover Harbour Board. Some volunteer Beach: cleans also take place. Dogs are allowed on the beach but there are no dog bins provided. The beach occasionally suffers pollution from tar.

Beach: Sandwich Bay

Council Phone No. 01304 612061

Restrictions: Dogs allowed all year round. Dog bins are provided. Beach cleaned regularly.

Beach: Minster Leas

Council Phone No. 01795 667015

Restrictions: Dogs are banned from 1st May to 30th September from the beach . However are allowed the rest of the year. Dog litter bins are provided. Beach is cleaned on a daily basis.

Beach: Leysdown - On - Sea

Council Phone No. 01795 424341

Restrictions: The beach is cleaned daily during summer. A dog ban is also enforced.

Beach: Sheerness Beach:

Council Phone No. 01795 424341

Restrictions: The beach is cleaned daily during the summer season. Dogs are banned from beach but are allowed on promenade if kept on lead.

Beach: Tankerton beach

Council Phone No. 01227 266719

Restrictions: The beach is cleaned regularly by hand. three days per week low season and daily in high summer. Dogs restricted at Tankerton bay (only restricted between 1stMay-30thSept). Litter bins provided

Beach: Greatstone Beach:

Council Phone No. 01303 850388

Restrictions: Dogs allowed except for between Seaview Road and the car park, this area is clearly signposted litter bins are provided.

Beach: Littlestone

Council Phone No. 01303 850388

Restrictions: No dog restrictions. except for between Clark Road and Madeira Road also clearly signposted. Litter bins are provided.

Beach: DymChurch

Council Phone No. 01303 850388

Restrictions: The beach is cleaned daily and litter bins are provided. Dogs are banned between High Knock and Shipclose all year round (this area is clearly signposted); however dog litter bins are still present

Beach: Dymchurch - Hythe Road

Council Phone No. 01303 850388

Restrictions: The beach is cleaned daily and litter bins are provided. Dogs are banned between High Knock and Shipclose all year round (this area is clearly signposted); however dog litter bins are still present.

Beach: Dymchurch - Redoubt

Council Phone No. 01303 850388

Restrictions: The beach is cleaned daily and litter bins are provided. Dogs are banned between High Knock and Shipclose all year round (this area is clearly signposted); however dog litter bins are still present.

Beach: Margate - Fulsam Rock

Council Phone No. 01843 577000

Restrictions: Beach is cleaned regularly during summer. Dogs allowed on beach all year round.

Beach: Minnis Bay

Council Phone No. 01843 577671

Restrictions: The beach is cleaned daily in the summer daily and weekly in the winter by the Council. There are litter and dog bins but dogs are not allowed on the beach from 1st May to 30th September

Beach: Ramsgate

Council Phone No. 01843 583333.

Restrictions: The **beach** is cleaned daily between May - September and litter bins are available. Dogs are banned between May and September but dog litter bins are provided.

Beach: Ramsgate Main Sands

Council Phone No. 01843 583333.

Restrictions: The beach is cleaned daily between May - September and litter bins are available. Dogs are banned between May and September but dog litter bins are provided.

Beach: Palm Bay

Council Phone No. 01843 583334

Restrictions: Dogs banned between 1st May - 30th September. Litter bins provided

Beach: Westbrook Bay

Council Phone No. 01843 583334

Restrictions: Dogs banned from 15th May to 15th Sept from 10am to 6pm. The beach is cleaned regularly.

Beach: Westgate Bay

Council Phone No. 01843 583334

Restrictions: Dog banned from 15th May to 15th Sept from 10am to 6pm. There is a dog exercise area however.

Beach: Margate - The Bay

Council Phone No. 01843 583334

Restrictions: Dogs banned are in place 1st May - 30th September. 10.00am & 6.00pm

Beach: St. Mildred's Bay

Council Phone No. 01843 583334

Restrictions: Dogs banned from 15th May to 15th Sept from 10am to 6pm.

Beach: Walpole Bay

Council Phone No. 01843 583334

Restrictions: Dog banned apply 1st May - 30th September 10.00am & 6.00pm

Beach: Broadstairs - Main Beach

Council Phone No. 01843 865650

Restrictions: Dogs banned between 1st May - 30th September 10.00am & 6.00pm

Beach: Botany Bay

Council Phone No. 01843 865650

Restrictions: No dog restrictions.

Beach: Broadstairs - East Cliff

Council Phone No. 01843 865650

Restrictions: No dog restrictions.

Beach: Stone Bay

Council Phone No. 01843 865650

Restrictions: Dog ban from 15 May - 15 September between 10.00am & 6.00pm

Beach: Joss Bay

Council Phone No. 0870 2646111

Restrictions: Dogs allowed all year.

The Medway Towns

Beach: Allhallows

Council Phone No. 0800 521 178

Restrictions: Privately owned Beach can pay for day or use if staying at caravan site. No restrictions dogs allowed all year round but owners must clean up after their dog. Beach cleaned regularly.

Beach: Bispham Blackpool

Council Phone No. 01253 477477

Restrictions: Dogs are not allowed south and north pier from the 1st May - 5th november also dogs only need to be on a lead when the tide is near sea wall

Beach: Blackpool- Central

Council Phone No. 01253 477477

Restrictions: No dogs allowed south and north pier from 1st may - 5th november

Beach: Blackpool - North

Council Phone No. 01253 477477

Restrictions: Dogs are not allowed south and north pier from the 1st May - 5th november also dogs only need to be on a lead when the tide is near sea wall

Beach: Blackpool - South

Council Phone No. 01253 477477

Restrictions: Dogs are not allowed south and north pier from the 1st May - 5th november also dogs only need to be on a lead when the tide is near sea wall

Beach: St. Annes

Council Phone No. 01253 478456

Restrictions: Dogs are not allowed on section of beach from toilets at North End of North Car Park & South to Slipway at New Lifeboat Station between 1st May and 30th Sept. Dogs must be on a lead on promenade. Litter bins are provided.

Beach: St. Annes - North

Council Phone No. 01253 478456

Restrictions: Dogs are not allowed on section of **beach** from toilets at North End of North Car Park & South to Slipway at New Lifeboat Station between 1st May and 30th Sept. Dogs must be on a lead on promenade. Litter bins are provided.

Beach: Fleetwood

Council Phone No. 01253 891000

Restrictions: Dogs are only allowed on parts of the beach from 1st May to 30th Sept. Restrictions are signposted.

Beach: Pilling Sands

Council Phone No. 01253 773953

Restrictions: No dog restrictions.

Beach: Cleveleys

Council Phone No. 01253 891000

Restrictions: Dogs are only allowed on parts of the beach from 1st May to 30th Sept. Restrictions are signposted. Beach is undergoing major works at moment and is not open.

www.dogfriendly.co.uk

Beach: Hest Bank

Council Phone No. 01524 582757

Restrictions: Dogs allowed all year round. No restrictions. Litter bins are provided and beach cleaned once a week.

Beach: Morecambe - North

Council Phone No. 01524 582757

Restrictions: Dogs are prohibited from Bubbles Breakwater to Green Street Breakwater between 1st May to 30th Sept. Litter bins are provided and beach is cleaned daily, twice a week with a machine during the summer.

Beach: Morecambe - South

Council Phone No. 01524 582757

Restrictions: Dogs are prohibited from Battery Breakwater to Stone Jetty Breakwater between 1st May to 30th Sept. Litter bins are provided and beach is cleaned daily, twice a week with a machine during the summer.

Beach: Heysham (Half Moon Bay)

Council Phone No. 01524 582757

Restrictions: Dogs allowed all year round. No restrictions. Litter bins are provided and beach cleaned once a week.

Beach: Cleethorpes

Council Phone No. 01472 323111

Restrictions: Dogs are not allowed on main stretch of beach from Leisure Centre to end of North Promenade from Easter to End Sept. Litter bins are provided and beach cleaned daily.

Beach: Sutton - On - Sea

Council Phone No. 01507 441373

Restrictions: Dogs are not allowed on section of beach that is Blue Flag (from Bohemia to just below Council Chalets). The vast areas in between they are allowed, this restriction applies from 1st May to 30th Sept. Owners must clean up any mess.

Beach: Moggs Eye (Huttoft Beach)

Council Phone No. 01507 474939

Restrictions: Dogs are allowed on the beach all year round. There are dog and litter bins provided.

Beach: Mablethorpe Town

Council Phone No. 01507 474939

Restrictions: Dogs are not allowed on main part of the beach from 1st May - 30th Sept this is signposted. There are vast areas where there are No restrictions. Litter and dog bins

provided beaches are cleaned daily in peak season.

Beach: Anderby

Council Phone No. 01754 899887

Restrictions: Dogs are allowed on some parts of the beach but there are some Restrictions from 1st May to 30th Sept these will be signposted. Litter and dog bins are provided. Beach is cleaned daily during peak season.

Beach: Ingoldmells south

Council Phone No. 01754 899887

Restrictions: Dogs are allowed on some parts of the beach but there are some Restrictions from 1st May to 30th Sept these will be signposted. Litter and dog bins are provided. Beach is cleaned daily during peak season.

Beach: Skegness

Council Phone No. 01754 899887

Restrictions: Dogs are allowed on some parts of the beach but there are some Restrictions from 1st May to 30th Sept these will be signposted. Litter and dog bins are provided. Beach is cleaned daily during peak season.

Beach: Chapel St. Leonards

Council Phone No. 01754 899887

Restrictions: Dogs are allowed on some parts of the beach but there are

www.dogfriendly.co.uk

some Restrictions from 1st May to 30th Sept these will be signposted. Litter and dog bins are provided. Beach is cleaned daily during peak season.

Beach: Tempel Town Louth

Council Phone No. 00353 429 33 5484

Restrictions: Dogs are allowed on beach all year round.

Beach: West Runton

Council Phone No. 01263 516168

Restrictions: Dogs are not allowed on some parts of the beach between 1st May to 30th Sept. These areas are signposted.

Beach: Cromer

Council Phone No. 01263 516168

Restrictions: Dogs are not allowed on some parts of the beach between 1st May to 30th Sept. These areas are signposted. Dogs must be on a lead on the promenade. They are litter bins provided.

Beach: Mundesley

Council Phone No. 01263 721070

Restrictions: Dogs are not allowed on main part of the beach between 1st May to 30th Sept. There are designated areas where dogs can go and they are signposted. Litter bins are provided and it is a Blue Flag Beach.

Beach: Sheringham

Council Phone No. 01263 516168

Restrictions: Dogs are not allowed on the main Beach between 1st May and 30th Sept. Dogs are allowed on far ends of West and East Beach: only it is signposted. They are litter bins provided and it is Blue Flag.

Beach: Cley Beach

Council Phone No. 01263 824329

Restrictions: Dogs are not allowed on beach between 1st May and 30th Sept. Dogs are banned from the Reserve all year round. Dogs are allowed to walk on footpath all year round on a lead.

Beach: Wells

Council Phone No. 01328 710885

Restrictions: Dogs are allowed on parts of the beach all year round. Dogs are not allowed near the beach huts have to go through gate at far right hand corner of car park along right hand path, through pine woods, up second steps to far end of beach huts. Litter bins are provided on path.

Beach: Hunstanton - Main Beach

Council Phone No. 01553 692722

Restrictions: Dogs are allowed on the beach all year round. Dogs are not allowed from the Bandstand to the Sea Life Sanctuary between 1st May and 30th Sept. Dogs must be kept on a lead on the Promenade, the Green and the Esplanade Gardens.

Beach: Hunstanton - South

Council Phone No. 01553 692722

Restrictions: Dogs are allowed on the beach all year round. Dogs are not allowed from the Bandstand to the Sea Life Sanctuary between 1st May and 30th Sept. Dogs must be kept on a

www.dogfriendly.co.uk

lead on the Promenade, the Green and the Esplanade Gardens.

Beach: Hunstanton beach

Council Phone No. 01553 692722

Restrictions: Dogs are allowed on the **beach** all year round. Dogs are not allowed from the Bandstand to the Sea Life Sanctuary between 1st May and 30th Sept. Dogs must be kept on a lead on the Promenade, the Green and the Esplanade Gardens.

Beach: Caister Point

Council Phone No. 01493 842195

Restrictions: Dogs are not allowed on parts of the beach from 1st May to 30th Sept. The restricted area is marked with flags. Dogs can go either side of the flagged area.

Beach: Great Yarmouth - Power Station

Council Phone No. 01493 842195

Restrictions: Dogs are allowed on the beach all year round. No restrictions.

Beach: Great Yarmouth - S. denes

Council Phone No. 01493 842195

Restrictions: Dogs are allowed on the beach all year round. No restrictions.

Beach: Great Yarmouth - Pier (Marina Leisure Centre)

Council Phone No. 01493 842195

Restrictions: No dogs allowed at any time.

Beach: Great Yarmouth - South

Council Phone No. 01493 842195

Restrictions: Dogs are allowed on the beach all year round. No restrictions.

Beach: Overstrand

Council Phone No. 01493 842195

Restrictions: Dogs are not allowed on some parts of the beach between 1st May and 30th Sept These areas are signposted.

Beach: Scratby Beach:

Council Phone No. 01493 842195

Restrictions: Dogs are not allowed on parts of the beach from 1st May to 30th Sept. The restricted area is marked with flags. Dogs can go either side of the flagged area.

Beach: Gorleston beach

Council Phone No. 01493 846345

Restrictions: Dogs are allowed on some parts of the beach all year round. They are not allowed from Harbours Mouth to Ravine at any time.

Beach: Great Yarmouth - North

Council Phone No. 01493 846345

Restrictions: Dogs are allowed on the beach all year round. No restrictions.

Beach: Hemsby

Council Phone No. 01493 846345

Restrictions: Dogs are not allowed on parts of the beach from 1st May to 30th

Sept. The restricted area is marked with flags. Dogs can go either side of the flagged area.

Beach: Heacham - S. Sands Club

Council Phone No. 01553 616661

Restrictions: Dogs are allowed all year round. Owners must clear up any mess. Litter and dog bins are provided and are emptied 2/3 times a week.

Beach: Heacham - South Beach

Council Phone No. 01553 616661

Restrictions: Dogs are allowed all year round. Owners must clear up any mess. Litter and dog bins are provided and are emptied 2/3 times a week.

Beach: Snettisham Beach

Council Phone No. 01485 543721

Restrictions: Dogs are allowed all year round. Dog bins are available.

Beach: Sea Palling

Council Phone No. 01263 513811

Restrictions: Dogs are not allowed on main part of the **beach** between 1st May to 30th Sept. Dogs are allowed past the Lifeboat Station until the last groyne on other side at any time. Litter bins are provided in some areas.

www.dogfriendly.co.uk

Northumberland

Beach: Bamburgh Castle

Council Phone No. 01289 330733

Restrictions: Dogs are allowed all year round. Owners must clean up any mess from their dogs. A Spring clean is done at beginning of the Summer season.

Beach: Beadnell Bay

Council Phone No. 01289 301734

Restrictions: Dogs allowed on all year round.

Beach: Berwick-Upon-Tweed

Council Phone No. 01289 301734

Restrictions: Dogs allowed on all year round.

Beach: Fisherman's Haven

Council Phone No. 01289 301734

Restrictions: Dogs allowed on all year round.

Beach: Holy Island (Lindisfarne)

Council Phone No. 01289 301734

Restrictions: Dogs allowed on all year round.

Beach: Spittal

Council Phone No. 01289 330044

Restrictions: Dogs allowed all year round. Owners must clean up any mess from their dogs. A Spring Clean is done at beginning of Summer season.

Beach: Spittal - Quay

Council Phone No. 01289 330044

Restrictions: Dogs allowed all year round. Owners must clean up any mess from their dogs. A Spring Clean is done at beginning of Summer season.

Beach: Cocklawburn Beach

Council Phone No. 01289 330044

Restrictions: Dogs allowed all year round No restrictions.

Beach: Longhoughton Steel

Council Phone No. 01289 330044

Restrictions: Dogs allowed all year round No restrictions.

Beach: Alnmouth

Council Phone No. 01289 330044

Restrictions: Dogs allowed all year round No restrictions.

Beach: Druridge Bay

Council Phone No. 01289 330044

Restrictions: Dogs allowed all year round No restrictions.

Beach: Druridge Bay North (Adj Visitors Centre)

Northumberland

www.dogfriendly.co.uk

158

Council Phone No. 01289 330044

Restrictions: Dogs allowed all year round No restrictions.

Beach: Druridge Bay South (North cresswell)

Council Phone No. 01289 330044

Restrictions: Dogs allowed all year round No restrictions.

Beach: Low newton, newton haven

Council Phone No. 01289 330044

Restrictions: Dogs allowed all year round No restrictions.

Beach: Seahouses North

Council Phone No. 01289 330044

Restrictions: Dogs allowed all year round. Owners must clean up any mess from their dogs. A Spring clean is done at beginning of Summer season.

Beach: Craster

Council Phone No. 01665 576007

Restrictions: Dogs allowed but do have to be kept on a lead.

Beach: Warkworth

Council Phone No. 01665 712313

Restrictions: Dogs allowed on beach all year round. Dog bins are provided.

Beach: Amble Links

Council Phone No. 01665 712313

Restrictions: Dogs allowed on beach all year round.

Beach: Cresswell

Council Phone No. 01670 500700

Restrictions: Dogs are allowed all year round owners must clean up mess from their dogs.

Beach: Newbiggin - South

Council Phone No. 01670 511323

Restrictions: No dog restrictions.

Beach: Newbiggin - North

Council Phone No. 0191 261 0610

Restrictions: Dogs are not allowed between 1st May and 30th Sept.

Beach: Blyth South Beach

Council Phone No. 01670 542325

Restrictions: Dog are allowed on the beach all year round at the moment but looking to change that shortly.

Beach: Cambois - North

Council Phone No. 01670 532200

Restrictions: No dog restrictions.

Beach: Cambois - South

Council Phone No. 01670 532200

Restrictions: No dog restrictions.

Redcar and Cleveland

Beach: Redcar- Coatham

Council Phone No. 01642 471921

Restrictions: Dogs are prohibited between the 1st May and 30th September on signposted areas

Beach: Redcar - Granville

Council Phone No. 01642 471921

Restrictions: Dogs are prohibited between the 1st May and 30th September on signposted area

Beach: Recar- Lifeboat station

Council Phone No. 01642 471921

Restrictions: Dogs are prohibited between the 1st May and 30th September on signposted areas

Beach: Redcar- Stray

Council Phone No. 01642 471921

Restrictions: Dogs are prohibited between the 1st May and 30th September on signposted areas

Beach: Saltburn

Council Phone No. 01642 471921

Restrictions: Dogs are prohibited between the 1st May and 30th September the area at Saltburn stretches from the Pier to Hazelgrove

Beach: Sea At Marske Sands

Council Phone No. 01642 471921

Restrictions: Dogs are prohibited between the 1st May and 30th September on signposted areas

Beach: Skinnigrove (Cattersty Sands)

Council Phone No. 01642 471921

Restrictions: Dogs are prohibited between the 1st May and 30th September on signposted areas

Beach: Ainsdale

Council Phone No. 0845 140 0845

Restrictions: Dogs are prohibited between the 1st of May and 30th of september on signposted areas

Beach: Blundellsands

Council Phone No. 0845 140 0845

Restrictions: No restrictions dogs allowed all year round but must be under control or on a lead

Beach: Formby

Council Phone No. 0845 140 0845

Restrictions: No restrictions dogs allowed all year round but must be under control or on a lead

Beach: Formby - Lifeboat Road

Council Phone No. 0845 140 0845

Restrictions: No restrictions dogs allowed all year round but must be under control or on a lead

Beach: Formby - Victoria Road

Council Phone No. 0845 140 0845

Restrictions: No restrictions dogs allowed all year round but must be under control or on a lead

Beach: Hall Road West, Crosby

Council Phone No. 0845 140 0845

Restrictions: No restrictions dogs allowed all year round but must be under control or on a lead

Beach: Hightown

Council Phone No. 0845 140 0845

Restrictions: No restrictions dogs allowed all year round but must be under control or on a lead

Beach: Mariners Road, Crosby

Council Phone No. 0845 140 0845

Restrictions: No restrictions dogs allowed all year round but must be under control or on a lead

Beach: Southport

Council Phone No. 0845 140 0845

Restrictions: Dogs are prohibited between the 1st of May and 30th of september on signposted areas

www.dogfriendly.co.uk

Beach: Clevedon Bay

Council Phone No. 01934 634882

Restrictions: No Dogs are allowed on this beach from 1st May - 30th Sept. Dogs are allowed on the main promenade but must be kept on a lead at all times all year round, there are litter bins on the promenade. Dogs are banned from the Marine Lake area lower walkway all year round.

Beach: Clevedon beach

Council Phone No. 01934 634882

Restrictions: No Dogs are allowed on this beach from 1st May - 30th Sept. Dogs are allowed on the main promenade but must be kept on a lead at all times all year round, there are litter bins on the promenade. Dogs are banned from the Marine Lake area lower walkway all year round.

Beach: Weston- Super-Mare - Grand Pier

Council Phone No. 01934 888800

Restrictions: Dogs are allowed on far side if facing the pier to the right hand side up to Marine Lake all year round, it is signposted. Beach: cleaned daily during Summer months and litter bins provided.

Beach: Weston- Super-Mare - Main Beach

Council Phone No. 01934 888800

Restrictions: No dogs allowed all year round from left of pier to Royal Sands (most of beach). Beach: cleaned daily during Summer months and litter bins provided.

Beach: Weston- Super-Mare - Nr. Marine Lake

Council Phone No. 01934 888800

Restrictions: No dogs allowed all year round. Beach cleaned daily during Summer months and litter bins provided.

Beach: Weston- Super-Mare - Sanatorium

Council Phone No. 01934 888800

Restrictions: Dogs are allowed all year round, No restrictions.

Beach: Weston- Super-Mare - Uphill Slipway

Council Phone No. 01934 888800

Restrictions: Dogs are allowed all year round, No restrictions.

www.dogfriendly.co.uk

163

Suffolk

Beach: Dunwich

Council Phone No. 01394 383789

Restrictions: Dogs are allowed on the beach all year round.

Beach: Aldeburgh

Council Phone No. 01502 405000

Restrictions: Dogs are prohibited on signposted areas between the 1st of May and 30th of September

Beach: Felixstowe - North

Council Phone No. 01502 405000

Restrictions: Dogs are prohibited on signposted areas between the 1st of May and 30th of September

Beach: Felixstowe - South

Council Phone No. 01502 405000

Restrictions: Dogs are prohibited on signposted areas between the 1st of May and 30th of September

Beach: Kessingland

Council Phone No. 01502 533600

Restrictions: No restrictions dogs allowed all year round.

Beach: Lowestoft - South of claremont pier

Council Phone No. 01502 533600

Restrictions: The beach is cleaned manually on a daily basis in the summer by Waveney District Council. Litter bins are provided. Dogs are banned from the beach from 1st May to 30th September.

Beach: Lowestoft - North of claremont pier

Council Phone No. 01502 533600

Restrictions: The beach is cleaned manually on a daily basis in the summer by Waveney District Council. Litter bins are provided. Dogs are banned from the beach from 1st May to 30th September.

Beach: Lowestoft - Gunton Denes

Council Phone No. 01502 533600

Restrictions: No restrictions dogs are allowed all year round.

Beach: Southwold - The Denes

Council Phone No. 01502 724729

Restrictions: No dog restrictions.

Beach: Southwold - The Pier

Council Phone No. 01502 724729

Restrictions: No dogs allowed North of the beach huts from 1st May to 30th Sept.

www.dogfriendly.co.uk

164

Beach: Grangetown

Council Phone No. 0191 520 5555

Restrictions: Dogs allowed on the beach all year round but must be kept on a lead or under control and owners must remember to clean up after their dog

Beach: Roker (Whitburn South)

Council Phone No. 0191 520 5555

Restrictions: Dogs are prohibited between 1st of May and 30th of September from the pier to Roker revine

Beach: Ryhope East Beach:

Council Phone No. 0191 520 5555

Restrictions: Dogs allowed on the beach all year round but must be kept on a lead or under control and owners must remember to clean up after their dog

Beach: Ryhope South

Council Phone No. 0191 520 5555

Restrictions: Dogs allowed on the beach all year round but must be kept on a lead or under control and owners must remember to clean up after their dog

Beach: Sunderland - City

Council Phone No. 0191 520 5555

Restrictions: Dogs allowed on the beach all year round but must be kept on a lead or under control and owners must remember to clean up after their dog

Beach: Sunderland - Hendon South

Council Phone No. 0191 520 5555

Restrictions: Dogs allowed on the beach all year round but must be kept on a lead or under control and owners must remember to clean up after their dog

www.dogfriendly.co.uk

Sussex

East Sussex

Beach: Saltdean

Council Phone No. 01273 290000

Restrictions: The beach is cleaned regularly. It is cleaned daily in the summer. Dogs are banned on 2 of the 4 beaches from 1st May until 30th September. Bins are available. Very well marked

Beach: Southwick

Council Phone No. 01273 263000

Restrictions: Dogs are allowed on the beach and dog bins are provided.

Beach: Newhaven

Council Phone No. 01273 471 600

Restrictions: Dogs are allowed all year no restrictions . Dog bins and 'Poop Scoop' bins available.

Beach: Newhaven West Quay

Council Phone No. 01273 471 600

Restrictions: Dogs are allowed all year no restrictions. Dog bins and 'Poop Scoop' bins available.

Beach: Brighton - Kemp Town

Council Phone No. 01273 290000

Restrictions: Beaches cleaned daily. Dogs allowed all year round

Beach: Brighton - Palace Pier

Council Phone No. 01273 290000

Restrictions: Beaches cleaned daily. Dogs restricted during summer months 1st May - 30th September.

Beach: Brighton - Portobello

Council Phone No. 09067 112255

Restrictions: 1st May- 30th September, dogs not allowed between the two piers. Either side of the piers, dogs are allowed on the whole. However any areas of restriction are clearly signposted.

Beach: Hove

Council Phone No. 01273 290000

Restrictions: The beach is cleaned daily. There are areas where gods are allowed and dogs are restricted. Dogs are banned 1st may- 30th sept. banned areas are signposted. Both litter and dog bins are provided.

Beach: Birling Gap

Council Phone No. 01323 443322

Restrictions: No dog restrictions.

Beach: Pevensey Bay

Council Phone No. 01323 443322

Restrictions: No dog restrictions.

Beach: Eastbourne

Council Phone No. 01323 411400

Restrictions: dogs are prohibited

www.dogfriendly.co.uk

between the 1st May and 30th September on signposted areas but are allowed on other areas but they must be on a lead

Beach: Eastbourne - East of Pier

Council Phone No. 01323 411400

Restrictions: dogs are prohibited between the 1st May and 30th September on signposted areas but are allowed on other areas but they must be on a lead

Beach: Eastbourne - Western Parade

Council Phone No. 01323 411400

Restrictions: dogs are prohibited between the 1st May and 30th September on signposted areas but are allowed on other areas but they must be on a lead

Beach: Cuckmere Haven Beach

Council Phone No. 01323 443322

Restrictions: No dog restrictions.

Beach: Seaford Bay

Council Phone No. 01273 471 600

Restrictions: Pebble beach 'Poop and Scoop' there are no breakwaters. Maps and signs indicate where dogs may not be off lead during 1st May and 30th Sept dogs not allowed between promenade and ice cream kiosk. Benwicks Kennels accept dogs for one day. Dogs have to be on lead on the promenade. Recent dog thefts advised to keep close eye on dogs.

Beach: Seaford Dane

Council Phone No. 01273 471 600

Restrictions: Pebble beach 'Poop and Scoop' there are no breakwaters. Maps and signs indicate where dogs may not be off lead during 1st May and 30th Sept dogs not allowed between promenade and ice cream kiosk. Benwicks Kennels accept dogs for one day. Dogs have to be on lead on the promenade. Recent dog thefts advised to keep close eye on dogs.

Beach: Bexhill

Council Phone No. 01424 787878

Restrictions: Dogs restricted in certain signposted areas between 1stMay - 30th September. These areas are clearly signpsoted. Dog bins provided, beach cleaned everyday between April - September.

Beach: Cooden Beach

Council Phone No. 01424 787878

Restrictions: Dogs restricted in certain signposted areas between 1stMay - 30th September. These areas are clearly signpsoted. The beach is cleaned 4 times a week during the summer season. dog bins are provided. as are litter bins.

Beach: Normans Bay

Council Phone No. 01424 787878

Restrictions: Dogs restricted in certain signposted areas between 1stMay - 30th September. These areas are clearly signpsoted. Cleaned twice a week, dog bins provided.

www.dogfriendly.co.uk

Beach: Hastings

Council Phone No. 01424 781111

Restrictions: The beach is cleaned daily during summer and there are dog free zones between the pier and the harbour arm - these areas are signposted all year round.

Beach: Hastings - Bulverhythe

Council Phone No. 01424 781111

Restrictions: The beach is cleaned daily during summer and there are dog free zones between the pier and the harbour arm - these areas are signposted all year round.

Beach: Hastings - Fairlight Glen

Council Phone No. 01424 781111

Restrictions: The beach is cleaned daily during summer and there are dog free zones between the pier and the harbour arm - these areas are signposted all year round.

Beach: Brighton - Broomhill Sands

Council Phone No. 01797 226488

Restrictions: Dogs allowed on beach, but always must be kept on leads. Mainly a car park, not much of a beach.

Beach: Camber

Council Phone No. 01797 226696

Restrictions: Dog & litter bins are provided. Dogs are allowed between 1st May and 30th September but must be on a lead and restricted between Zones F & H on the beach. And where permitted must be kept

on leads. Areas of dog bans are signposted.

Beach: Winchelsea

Council Phone No. 01797 226696

Restrictions: No dog restrictions.

Beach: St Leonards

Council Phone No. 0845 2741001

Restrictions: Dogs restricted from 1st May - 30th September. (guide and signposts as to where dogs are aren't allowed.)

West Sussex

Beach: Bracklesham Bay

Council Phone No. 01243 785166

Restrictions: Dogs are allowed on beach all year round but they are prohibited from designated areas (between groynes A22 & A29) between 1st May and 30th Sept. Must be kept on lead on the sea wall.

Beach: Selsey

Council Phone No. 01243 785166

Restrictions: Dogs are allowed on beach all year round but they are prohibited from designated areas (between groynes E26 & E33) between 1st May and 30th Sept. Must be kept on lead on the sea wall.

Beach: Selsey - Hillfield Road

Council Phone No. 01243 785166

Restrictions: Dogs are allowed on

beach all year round but they are prohibited from designated areas (between groynes E26 & E33) between 1st May and 30th Sept. Must be kept on lead on the sea wall.

Beach: West Wittering

Council Phone No. 01243 539434

Restrictions: Dogs are allowed on beach all year round there are No restrictions.

Beach: West Wittering - East Head

Council Phone No. 01243 514143

Restrictions: Dogs are not allowed by area in front of the beach huts (groynes 14a to 18) between 1st May and 30th Sept. Blue Flag Beach.

Beach: East Wittering

Council Phone No. 01243 785166

Restrictions: Dogs are allowed on beach all year round but they are prohibited from designated areas (between groynes A49 & S1) between 1st May and 30th Sept. Must be kept on lead on the sea wall.

Beach: Bognor Regis

Council Phone No. 01903 737826

Restrictions: Dogs are not allowed on beach from Gloucester Road to Park Terrace from 1st May to 30th Sept.

Beach: Bognor Regis - East

Council Phone No. 01903 737826

Restrictions: Dogs are not allowed on beach from Gloucester Road to Park Terrace from 1st May to 30th Sept.

Beach: Bognor Regis - Pier

Council Phone No. 01903 737826

Restrictions: Dogs are not allowed on beach from Gloucester Road to Park Terrace from 1st May to 30th Sept.

Beach: Felpham Beach

Council Phone No. 01903 737826

Restrictions: Dogs are not allowed from Canning Road to Felpham Sailing Club from 1st May to 30th Sept.

Beach: Middleton-on-sea

Council Phone No. 01903 737826

Restrictions: No dog restrictions.

Beach: Pagham

Council Phone No. 01903 737826

Restrictions: No dog restrictions.

Beach: South Lancing

Council Phone No. 01903 753355

Restrictions: No restrictions dogs allowed all year round owners have to clean up after their dog.

Beach: Shoreham - Kingston Beach

Council Phone No. 01273 263000

Restrictions: No dog restrictions. but owners must clean up after their dogs.

Beach: Shoreham- by - sea Beach

Council Phone No. 01273 263000

Restrictions: No dog restrictions. but owners must clean up after their dogs.

Beach: Goring Beach

Council Phone No. 01903 221234

Restrictions: No dogs allowed from High Tide Mark to Low Tide Mark between Sea Place and Allinora Park from 1st May to 30th Sept.

Beach: Worthing

Council Phone No. 01903 238977

Restrictions: No dogs allowed from Flashpoint to Heene Road from 1st May to 30th Sept. Dogs can walk on leads only on the promenade.

Beach: Worthing - East Pier

Council Phone No. 01903 238977

Restrictions: Dogs are allowed all year round on East Splashpoint but owners must clean up after them. No dogs allowed from 1st May - 30th Sept in Yacht Club Slip or Allinora Slip.

Beach: Littlehampton

Council Phone No. 01903 721866

Restrictions: The beach is cleaned regularly and there are litter bins. Dog access is restricted to certain areas of the beach from 1st May to 30th Sept and dogs must be kept on leads on the promenade

Beach: Littlehampton - norfolk road

Council Phone No. 01903 721866

Restrictions: The beach is cleaned regularly and there are litter bins. Dog access is restricted to certain areas of the beach from 1st May to 30th Sept and dogs must be kept on leads on the promenade

Beach: Littlehampton - Coastguard station

Council Phone No. 01903 721866

Restrictions: The beach is cleaned regularly and there are litter bins. Dog access is restricted to certain areas of the beach from 1st May to 30th Sept and dogs must be kept on leads on the promenade

Beach: Coldingham Bay

Council Phone No. 01361 882600

Restrictions: No restrictions dogs allowed all year round but 'Poop Scoop' laws are in operation all year.

Beach: St. Abbs

Council Phone No. 01361 882600

Restrictions: No restrictions dogs allowed all year round but 'Poop Scoop' laws are in operation all year.

Beach: Pease Bay

Council Phone No. 01368 830206

Restrictions: No restrictions dogs allowed all year round but owners must clean up after their dogs.

Beach: Eyemouth

Council Phone No. 01361 882600

Restrictions: No restrictions dogs allowed all year round but 'Poop Scoop' laws are in operation all year.

www.dogfriendly.co.uk

Tyneside

North Tyneside

Beach: Tynemouth -
Long Sands North

Council Phone No. 0191 219 2389

Restrictions: Dogs are allowed all year round.

Beach: Seaton Sluice

Council Phone No. 0191 200 8535

Restrictions: Dogs are allowed all year round.

Beach: Tynemouth -
Long Sands **South**

Council Phone No. 0191 2008535

Restrictions: Dogs are banned from 1st May to 30th September. No dog ban rest of year.

Beach: Whitley Bay

Council Phone No. 0191 2008535

Restrictions: Dogs are not allowed from Rendevouz Café south to Whitley Bay from 1st May - 30th Sept. No dog ban rest of year.

Beach: Tynemouth - Cullercoats

Council Phone No. 0191 261 0610

Restrictions: No dogs allowed from 1st May to 30th September.

Beach: Seaburn Beach
(Whitburn North)

Council Phone No. 0191 553 2830

Restrictions: Dogs are not allowed from the concrete structure (the outfall pipe) area to just South of little Italy from 1st May to 30th Sept. Dogs allowed North of little Italy all year round. Restrictions: signposted on railings and on the beach . Litter and Dog bins provided. Cleaned every day.

Beach: Tynemouth,
King Edwards Bay

Council Phone No. 0191 2008535

Restrictions: Dogs are not allowed from 1st May to 30th September. No dog ban rest of year.

South Tyneside

Beach: Marsden

Council Phone No. 0191 455 6313

Restrictions: Dogs are allowed all year round. Litter bins are available.

Tyne and Wear

Beach: South Shields

Council Phone No. 0191 454 6612

Restrictions: Dogs are allowed on parts of beach they are not allowed in some areas that are signposted between 1st Mar - 31 Oct. Beach cleaned every night, litter bins provided.

Beach: Meols

Council Phone No. 0151 647 8799

Restrictions: No restrictions dogs allowed all year round but must be under control

Beach: Moreton

Council Phone No. 0151 647 8799

Restrictions: No restrictions dogs allowed all year round but must be under control

Beach: New Brighton (Wallasey)

Council Phone No. 0151 647 8799

Restrictions: No restrictions dogs allowed all year round but must be under control

Beach: West Kirby

Council Phone No. 0151 647 8799

Restrictions: No restrictions dogs allowed all year round but must be under control

www.dogfriendly.co.uk

Yorkshire

Beach: Fraisthorpe

Council Phone No. 01904 707961

Restrictions: No restrictions dogs allowed all year round but must be under control or on a lead

Beach: Hornsea

Council Phone No. 01904 707961

Restrictions: No restrictions dogs allowed all year round but must be under control or on a lead

Beach: Tunstall

Council Phone No. 01904 707961

Restrictions: No restrictions dogs allowed all year round but must be under control or on a lead

East Riding of Yorkshire

Beach: Barmston

Council Phone No. 01262 670594

Restrictions: No dog restrictions. but they must be kept under control or on a lead and owners must clean up after their dog

Beach: Bridlington - North Beach

Council Phone No. 01262 670594

Restrictions: dogs are prohibited between the 1st May and 30th September on signposted areas but are allowed on other areas but they must be on a lead

Beach: Bridlington - South Beach

Council Phone No. 01262 670594

Restrictions: dogs are prohibited between the 1st May and 30th September on signposted areas but are allowed on other areas but they must be on a lead

Beach: Earls Dyke

Council Phone No. 01262 670594

Restrictions: No dog restrictions. but they must be kept under control and owners must clean up after their dog

Beach: Flamborough - Danes Dyke

Council Phone No. 01262 670594

Restrictions: No dog restrictions. but they must be kept under control and owners must clean up after their dog

Beach: Flamborough - North landing

Council Phone No. 01262 670594

Restrictions: No dog restrictions. but they must be kept under control and owners must clean up after their dog

Beach: Flamborough - South Landing

Council Phone No. 01262 670594

Restrictions: No dog restrictions. but they must be kept under control and owners must clean up after their dog

Beach: Flamborough - North West Beach

Council Phone No. 01262 670594

Restrictions: No dog restrictions. but they must be kept under control and owners must clean up after their dog

Beach: Hornsea - South Beach

Council Phone No. 01262 670594

Restrictions: dogs are prohibited between the 1st May and 30th September on signposted areas but are allowed on other areas but they must be on a lead

Beach: Skipsea

Council Phone No. 01262 670594

Restrictions: No dog restrictions. but they must be kept under control and owners must clean up after their dog

Beach: Thornwick Bay

Council Phone No. 01262 670594

Restrictions: No dog restrictions. but they must be kept under control and owners must clean up after their dog

Beach: Wilsthorpe

Council Phone No. 01262 670594

Restrictions: No dog restrictions. but they must be kept under control and owners must clean up after their dog

Beach: Withernsea

Council Phone No. 01262 670594

Restrictions: dogs are prohibited between the 1st May and 30th September on signposted areas but are allowed on other areas but they must be on a lead

North Yorkshire

Beach: Cayton Bay

Council Phone No. 01723 232323

Restrictions: Dogs allowed all year round No restrictions. Litter bins provided.

Beach: Filey

Council Phone No. 01723 232323

Restrictions: Dogs are not allowed between Lifeboat station and the beach chalets at opposite end and in front of promenade from 1st May and 30th Sept.

Beach: Reighton

Council Phone No. 01723 232323

Restrictions: Dogs allowed all year round No restrictions.

Beach: Robin Hoods Bay

Council Phone No. 01723 232323

Restrictions: Dogs allowed all year round No restrictions.

www.dogfriendly.co.uk

Beach: Runswick Bay

Council Phone No. 01723 232323

Restrictions: Dogs allowed all year round No restrictions.

Beach: Sandsend

Council Phone No. 01723 232323

Restrictions: Dogs are not allowed between Bank at bottom of car park to Sands Hill dog between 1st May and 30th Sept. All restricted areas are signposted.

Beach: Scarborough - South Bay

Council Phone No. 01723 232323

Restrictions: Dogs are not allowed from Life boat house and the Spa Foot Bridge between 1st May and 30th Sept. No dog ban rest of year.

Beach: Scarborough - South no. 2

Council Phone No. 01723 232323

Restrictions: Dog are prohibited between the 1st May and 30th September

Beach: Scarborough - North Bay

Council Phone No. 01723 232323

Restrictions: Dogs are not allowed from Peasholm Gap to Sea Life Centre between 1st May and 30th Sept. No dog ban rest of year.

Beach: Staithes

Council Phone No. 01723 232323

Restrictions: Dogs allowed all year round No **restrictions**.

Beach: Whit by

Council Phone No. 01723 232323

Restrictions: Dogs are not allowed from West Pier to just past Beach Chalets between 1st May and 30th Sept. No dog ban rest of year.

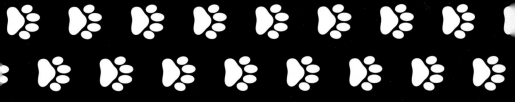

Northern Ireland

Antrim

Beach: Cushendall

Council Phone No. 028 2177 1180

Restrictions: Dogs allowed all year but you have to clean up dog waste

Beach: Cushendun

Council Phone No. 028 2177 1180

Restrictions: Owned by National Trust. Dogs are allowed but to be kept preferably on a lead.

Beach: Ballycastle

Council Phone No. 028 9446 3113

Restrictions: No dogs from May - Sept. Blue Flag Beach

Beach: Carnlough

Council Phone No. 028 9446 3113

Restrictions: Dogs allowed

Beach: Waterfoot

Council Phone No. 028 9446 3113

Restrictions: Dogs allowed all year but you have to clean up dog waste

Beach: Ballygally

Council Phone No. 0282826 0088

Restrictions: Dogs Not allowed on part of Beach from May to Sept. There is a section dogs are allowed.

Beach: Browns Bay

Council Phone No. 0282826 0088

Restrictions: Dogs Not allowed on part of beach from May to Sept. There is a section dogs are allowed.

Beach: Glenarm

Council Phone No. 0282826 0088

Restrictions: Dogs Allowed

Beach: Portrush - Mill (West) Strand

Council Phone No. 0287034 7034

Restrictions: Dogs are only permitted on certain areas of beach which are sign posted. Litter bins on beach

Beach: Portrush - Curran (East) Strand

Council Phone No. 0287034 7034

Restrictions: Dogs are only permitted on certain areas of Beach which are sign posted. Litter bins on Beach

Coleraine

Beach: Porthrush, Whiterocks

Council Phone No. 028 7034 7234

Restrictions: Dog restrictions from the 1st of May to the 30th September 2007, signposted to say where dogs are allowed during this time

www.dogfriendly.co.uk

Northern Ireland

Beach: Tyrella Beach (Clough) County Down

Council Phone No. 028 4461 0800

Restrictions: Dogs are not allowed on the beach all year round

Beach: Nicholson's Strand, cranfield

Council Phone No. 028 303 13170

Restrictions: Blue Flag Beach dogs are not allowed at any time.

Beach: Warrenpoint

Council Phone No. 028 303 13170

Restrictions: Dogs are allowed on beach all year round but must be kept on a lead.

Beach: Cranfield Bay

Council Phone No. 028 4176. 2525

Restrictions: Dogs are allowed on beach all year round.

Beach: Millisle Lagoon

Council Phone No. 028 9182 4000

Restrictions: Dogs are not allowed on enclosed area around lagoon or surrounding grass at any time. Dogs are allowed on rest of beach all year round.

Beach: Groomsport

Council Phone No. 028 91270371

Restrictions: Dogs are allowed on beach all year round, must be restrained and no more than two dogs off leads when walking through promenade, pier or marine gardens. Laws are changing in next few weeks.

Beach: Ballyholme

Council Phone No. 028 91270371

Restrictions: Dogs are allowed on beach all year round, must be restrained and no more than two dogs off leads when walking through promenade, pier or marine gardens. Laws are changing in next few weeks.

Beach: Murlough (Tyrella), Newcastle

Council Phone No. 028437 22222

Restrictions: Dogs are allowed on beach all year round.

Beach: Newcastle

Council Phone No. 028437 22222

Restrictions: Dogs are allowed on beach all year round.

Beach: Rossglass

Council Phone No. 028 446 12233

Restrictions: No dog restrictions.

www.dogfriendly.co.uk

Beach: Crawfordsburn, Banhor

Council Phone No. 028 91270371

Restrictions: Dogs are allowed on beach all year round, must be restrained and no more than two dogs off leads when walking through promenade, pier or marine gardens. Laws are changing in next few weeks.

Beach: Helen's Bay

Council Phone No. 028 91270371

Restrictions: Dogs are allowed on beach all year round, must be restrained and no more than two dogs off leads when walking through promenade, pier or marine gardens. Laws are changing in next few weeks.

Beach: Ballyhalbert

Council Phone No. 0289182 6846

Restrictions: Dogs are allowed on beach all year round, owners must clean up mess after their dog.

Beach: Ballywalter

Council Phone No. 0289182 6846

Restrictions: Dogs are allowed on beach all year round, owners must clean up mess after their dog.

Beach: Megillian - Downhill

Council Phone No. 028 7032 7720

Restrictions: Dogs are allowed on some parts of the beach all year round. There are restricted areas between 1st May and 30th Sept, these are signposted. There are litter and dog bins provided and the beach is cleaned daily during peak season.

Beach: Castlerock

Council Phone No. 028 7034 4723

Restrictions: Dogs are allowed on the beach all year round but must be kept under control or on a lead. There are some Restrictions to the left hand side of beach between 1st May to 30th Sept. Litter bins are provided and beach is cleaned mechanically daily during summer.

Beach: Portstewart (The Strand)

Council Phone No. 02870 823333

Restrictions: Dogs are allowed all year round but have to be kept on a lead. There are litter and dog bins provided.

Beach: Megillian Strand - Benone

Council Phone No. 028777 60307

Restrictions: Dogs are allowed on some parts of the beach all year round. There are restricted areas between 1st May and 30th Sept these are signposted. There are litter and dog bins provided and the beach is cleaned daily during peak season.

www.dogfriendly.co.uk

Republic of Ireland
Wicklow

Beach: Brittas Bay North

Council Phone No. 00353 404 20070

Restrictions: Dogs allowed all year round. Fly's the Blue Flag so all litter must be cleaned up.

Beach: Greystones South

Council Phone No. 00353 404 20070

Restrictions: Dogs allowed all year round. Fly's the Blue Flag so all litter must be cleaned up.

Scotland

Scotland
Aberdeenshire

Beach: Footdee

Council Phone No. 01224 522000

Restrictions: Dog restrictions from the 1st of May to the 30th September 2007, signposted to say where dogs are allowed during this time

Beach: Banff Bridge

Council Phone No. 01261 813200
Banff and Buchan:

Restrictions: No regulations - Allowed all year round don't have to be kept on a lead just have to be kept under control

Beach: Collieston

Council Phone No. 01261 813200
Banff and Buchan:

Restrictions: No regulations - Allowed all year round don't have to be kept on a lead just have to be kept under control

Beach: Cruden Bay

Council Phone No. 01779 483 812

Restrictions: No regulations - Allowed all year round don't have to be kept on a lead just have to be kept under control

Beach: Fraserburgh

Council Phone No. 01779 483 812

Restrictions: No regulations - Allowed all year round don't have to be kept on a lead just have to be kept under control

Beach: Fraserburgh Philorth

Council Phone No. 01779 483 812

Restrictions: No regulations - Allowed all year round don't have to be kept on a lead just have to be kept under control

Beach: Inverbervie

Council Phone No. 01779 483 812

Restrictions: No regulations - Allowed all year round don't have to be kept on a lead just have to be kept under control

Beach: Inverboyndie

Council Phone No. 01779 483 812

Restrictions: No regulations - Allowed all year round don't have to be kept on a lead just have to be kept under control

www.dogfriendly.co.uk

Beach: Muchalls

Council Phone No. 01779 483 812

Restrictions: No regulations - Allowed all year round don't have to be kept on a lead just have to be kept under control

Beach: Newburgh

Council Phone No. 01779 483 812

Restrictions: No regulations - Allowed all year round don't have to be kept on a lead just have to be kept under control

Beach: Peterhead Lido

Council Phone No. 01779 483 812

Restrictions: No regulations - Allowed all year round don't have to be kept on a lead just have to be kept under control

Beach: Rosehearty

Council Phone No. 01779 483 812

Restrictions: No regulations - Allowed all year round don't have to be kept on a lead just have to be kept under control

Beach: Sandend Bay

Council Phone No. 01779 483 812

Restrictions: No regulations - Allowed all year round don't have to be kept on a lead just have to be kept under control

Beach: St. Combs

Council Phone No. 01779 483 812

Restrictions: No regulations - Allowed all year round don't have to be kept on a lead just have to be kept under control

Beach: St. Cyrus

Council Phone No. 01779 483 812

Restrictions: No regulations - Allowed all year round don't have to be kept on a lead just have to be kept under control

Beach: Stonehaven - Carron

Council Phone No. 08456 081207

Restrictions: Dogs are welcome all year round but must be kept under control or on a lead and owners must remember to clean up after their dog

Beach: Stonehaven - Cowie

Council Phone No. 08456 081207

Restrictions: Dogs are welcome all year round but must be kept under control or on a lead and owners must remember to clean up after their dog

Beach: Balmedie Country Park

Council Phone No. Contact Ian Tillet

Restrictions: No regulations - Allowed all year round don't have to be kept on a lead just have to be kept under control

Scotland

www.dogfriendly.co.uk

North Ayrshire

Beach: Largs - Pencil

Council Phone No. 01294 324339

Restrictions: Dogs are allowed all year round. Owners must clear up any mess.

Beach: Irvine - Gailes (New Town)

Council Phone No. 01294 324339

Restrictions: Dogs are allowed all year round. Owners must clear up any mess.

Beach: Largs

Council Phone No. 01294 324339

Restrictions: Dogs are allowed all year round. Owners must clear up any mess.

Beach: Largs - Main

Council Phone No. 01294 324339

Restrictions: Dogs are allowed all year round. Owners must clear up any mess.

Beach: Millport, Cumbrae

Council Phone No. 01294 324339

Restrictions: Dogs are allowed all year round. Owners must clear up any mess.

Beach: Saltcoats

Council Phone No. 01294 324339

Restrictions: Dogs are allowed all year

round. Owners must clear up any mess.

Beach: Stevenston

Council Phone No. 01294 324339

Restrictions: Dogs are allowed all year round. Owners must clear up any mess.

Beach: Cardwell Bay

Council Phone No. 01475 712607

Restrictions: Dogs are allowed all year round but not suitable for walking dogs. Park next door called Battery Park good for walking dogs. Owners must clean up wardens patrolling.

Beach: Ardrossan (Boydston)

Council Phone No. 01294 324339

Restrictions: Dogs are allowed all year round. Owners must clear up any mess.

Beach: Seamill

Council Phone No. 01294 324339

Restrictions: Dogs are allowed all year round. Owners must clear up any mess.

Beach: Fairlie

Council Phone No. 01294 324339

Restrictions: Dogs are allowed all year round. Owners must clear up any mess.

Beach: Brodick Bay

Council Phone No. 01294 324339

Restrictions: Dogs are allowed all year round. Owners must clear up any mess.

Beach: Whiting Bay

Council Phone No. 01294 324339

Restrictions: Dogs are allowed all year round. Owners must clear up any mess.

Beach: Lunderston Bay

Council Phone No. 01475 712607

Restrictions: Dogs are allowed all year round but not in picnic area or childrens play area.

Beach: Prestwick Beach

Council Phone No. 01292 618222

Restrictions: No dog restrictions. but they must be kept under control

Beach: Culzean

Council Phone No. 01292 618222

Restrictions: No dog restrictions. but they must be kept under control

Beach: Troon-South

Council Phone No. 01292 618222

Restrictions: No dog restrictions. but they must be kept under control

South Ayrshire

Beach: Ayr Beach

Council Phone No. 01292 618222

Restrictions: No dog restrictions. but they must be kept under control

www.dogfriendly.co.uk

Scotland
Angus

Beach: Arbroath - West Links

Council Phone No. 08452 777 778

Restrictions: Dogs are permitted all year round as long as they are kept on leads

Beach: Montrose

Council Phone No. 08452 777 778

Restrictions: Blue flag award: Dogs allowed but must be held under control

Beach: Arbroath - Victoria Park

Council Phone No. 08452 777 778

Restrictions: Dogs are permitted all year round but must be kept on a lead

Beach: Westhaven

Council Phone No. 08452 777 778

Restrictions: Dogs are permitted all year round but must be kept on a lead

Beach: Carnoustie

Council Phone No. 08452 777 778

Restrictions: Dogs allowed but must be held under control

Beach: Easthaven

Council Phone No. 08452 777 778

Restrictions: Dogs are permitted all year round but must be kept on a lead

Beach: Lunan Bay

Council Phone No. 08452 777 778

Restrictions: Dogs are permitted all year round but must be kept on a lead

Beach: Monifieth

Council Phone No. 08452 777 778

Restrictions: Dogs are permitted all year round but must be kept on a lead

www.dogfriendly.co.uk

Edinburgh

Beach: Silverknowes

Council Phone No. 0131 200 2323

Restrictions: Dogs allowed on the beach all year round but must be kept on a lead or under control

---

Beach: Cramond

Council Phone No. 0131 529 3030

Restrictions: Dogs allowed on the beach all year round but must be kept on a lead or under control

---

Beach: Portobello

Council Phone No. 0131 529 3030

Restrictions: Dogs allowed on the beach all year round but must be kept on a lead or under control

---

Beach: Portobello West (King's Road)

Council Phone No. 0131 529 3030

Restrictions: Dogs allowed on the beach all year round but must be kept on a lead or under control

---

Beach: Portobello Central (James Street)

Council Phone No. 0131 529 3030

Restrictions: Dogs allowed on the beach all year round but must be kept on a lead or under control

---

Dumfries and Galloway

Beach: Carrick Bay

Council Phone No. 01557 814212

Restrictions: Dogs are allowed on beach all year round.

Dundee

Beach: Broughty Ferry

Council Phone No. 01382 432128

Restrictions: Dogs are not allowed on section from Castle to Brook Sea between April to Sept but are allowed on rest of beach.

---

www.dogfriendly.co.uk

Beach: Dunbar - Belhaven

Council Phone No. 01620 827827

Restrictions: No dog restrictions. but they must be kept under control or on a lead and owners must clean up after their dog

Beach: Dunbar - East

Council Phone No. 01620 827827

Restrictions: No dog restrictions. but they must be kept under control or on a lead and owners must clean up after their dog

Beach: Dunglass

Council Phone No. 01620 827827

Restrictions: No dog restrictions. but they must be kept under control or on a lead and owners must clean up after their dog

Beach: Fisherrow - East

Council Phone No. 01620 827827

Restrictions: No dog restrictions. but they must be kept under control or on a lead and owners must clean up after their dog

Beach: Fisherrow - West

Council Phone No. 01620 827827

Restrictions: No dog restrictions. but they must be kept under control or on a lead and owners must clean up after their dog

Beach: Gosford Sands

Council Phone No. 01620 827827

Restrictions: No dog restrictions. but they must be kept under control or on a lead and owners must clean up after their dog

Beach: Gullane

Council Phone No. 01620 827827

Restrictions: No dog restrictions. but they must be kept under control or on a lead and owners must clean up after their dog

Beach: Longniddry

Council Phone No. 01620 827827

Restrictions: No dog restrictions. but they must be kept under control or on a lead and owners must clean up after their dog

Beach: North Berwick - Milsey Bay

Council Phone No. 01620 827827

Restrictions: No dog restrictions. but they must be kept under control or on a lead and owners must clean up after their dog

Beach: North Berwick - West Bay

Council Phone No. 01620 827827

Restrictions: No dog restrictions. but they must be kept under control or on a lead and owners must clean up after their dog

Beach: Peffersands

Council Phone No. 01620 827827

Restrictions: No dog restrictions. but they must be kept under control or on a lead and owners must clean up after their dog

Beach: Port Seton

Council Phone No. 01620 827827

Restrictions: No dog restrictions. but they must be kept under control or on a lead and owners must clean up after their dog

Beach: Seacliff

Council Phone No. 01620 827827

Restrictions: No dog restrictions. but they must be kept under control or on a lead and owners must clean up after their dog

Beach: Seton Sands, Longniddry

Council Phone No. 01620 827827

Restrictions: No dog restrictions. but they must be kept under control or on a lead and owners must clean up after their dog

Beach: Thorntonloch

Council Phone No. 01620 827827

Restrictions: No dog restrictions. but they must be kept under control or on a lead and owners must clean up after their dog

Beach: Whitesands Bay

Council Phone No. 01620 827827

Restrictions: No dog restrictions. but they must be kept under control or on a lead and owners must clean up after their dog

Beach: Yellowcraigs (Broad Sands Bay)

Council Phone No. 01620 827827

Restrictions: No dog restrictions. but they must be kept under control or on a lead and owners must clean up after their dog

www.dogfriendly.co.uk

Beach: Aberdour - Harbour

Council Phone No. 08451 55 00 00

Restrictions: No dog restrictions. but dogs must be kept under control or on a lead and owners must remember to clean up after their dogs

Beach: Aberdour - Silver Sands

Council Phone No. 08451 55 00 00

Restrictions: Dogs are prohibited on the beach between the 1st of May and 30th September but there is plenty of areas near the beach where dogs can walk.

Beach: Anstruther, Billow ness

Council Phone No. 08451 55 00 00

Restrictions: No dog restrictions. but dogs must be kept under control or on a lead and owners must remember to clean up after their dogs

Beach: Burnt Island

Council Phone No. 08451 55 00 00

Restrictions: Dogs are prohibited on the beach between the 1st of May and 30th September but there is plenty of areas near the beach where dogs can walk.

Beach: Dalgety Bay (Yatch Club)

Council Phone No. 08451 55 00 00

Restrictions: No dog restrictions. but dogs must be kept under control or on a lead and owners must remember to clean up after their dogs

Beach: Earls ferry

Council Phone No. 08451 55 00 00

Restrictions: No dog restrictions. but dogs must be kept under control or on a lead and owners must remember to clean up after their dogs

Beach: Elie. Earlsferry Beach and Shell Bay

Council Phone No. 08451 55 00 00

Restrictions: Dogs are prohibited on the beach between the 1st of May and 30th September but there is plenty of areas near the beach where dogs can walk.

Beach: Kinghorn - Harbour

Council Phone No. 08451 55 00 00

Restrictions: No dog restrictions. but dogs must be kept under control or on a lead and owners must remember to clean up after their dogs

Beach: Kinghorn - Pettycur

Council Phone No. 08451 55 00 00

Restrictions: No dog restrictions. but dogs must be kept under control or on a lead and owners must remember to clean up after their dogs

Beach: Kingsbarns

Council Phone No. 08451 55 00 00

Restrictions: No dog restrictions. but dogs must be kept under control or on a lead and owners must remember to clean up after their dogs

Beach: Kirkcaldy - Linktown

Council Phone No. 08451 55 00 00

Restrictions: No dog restrictions. but dogs must be kept under control or on a lead and owners must remember to clean up after their dogs

Beach: Kirkcaldy - Seafield

Council Phone No. 08451 55 00 00

Restrictions: No dog restrictions. but dogs must be kept under control or on a lead and owners must remember to clean up after their dogs

Beach: Largo East

Council Phone No. 08451 55 00 00

Restrictions: No dog restrictions. but dogs must be kept under control or on a lead and owners must remember to clean up after their dogs

Beach: Leven East

Council Phone No. 08451 55 00 00

Restrictions: No dog restrictions. but dogs must be kept under control or on a lead and owners must remember to clean up after their dogs

Beach: Leven - West

Council Phone No. 08451 55 00 00

Restrictions: No dog restrictions. but dogs must be kept under control or on a lead and owners must remember to clean up after their dogs

Beach: Lower Largo

Council Phone No. 08451 55 00 00

Restrictions: No dog restrictions. but dogs must be kept under control or on a lead and owners must remember to clean up after their dogs

Beach: Lundin Links

Council Phone No. 08451 55 00 00

Restrictions: No dog restrictions. but dogs must be kept under control or on a lead and owners must remember to clean up after their dogs

Beach: Pathhead Sands

Council Phone No. 08451 55 00 00

Restrictions: No dog restrictions. but dogs must be kept under control or on a lead and owners must remember to clean up after their dogs

Beach: Pittenweem

Council Phone No. 08451 55 00 00

Restrictions: No dog restrictions. but dogs must be kept under control or on a lead and owners must remember to clean up after their dogs

Beach: Roome Bay, Crail

Council Phone No. 08451 55 00 00

Restrictions: No dog restrictions. but dogs must be kept under control or on a lead and owners must remember to clean up after their dogs

www.dogfriendly.co.uk

193

Beach: Shell Bay, earlsferry

Council Phone No. 08451 55 00 00

Restrictions: No dog restrictions. but dogs must be kept under control or on a lead and owners must remember to clean up after their dogs

Beach: St. Andrews - West Sands

Council Phone No. 08451 55 00 00

Restrictions: Dogs are prohibited on the beach between the 1st of May and 30th September but there is plenty of areas near the beach where dogs can walk.

Beach: St. Andrews - East Sands

Council Phone No. 08451 55 00 00

Restrictions: Dogs are prohibited on the beach between the 1st of May and 30th September but there is plenty of areas near the beach where dogs can walk.

Beach: Tayport

Council Phone No. 08451 55 00 00

Restrictions: No dog restrictions. but dogs must be kept under control or on a lead and owners must remember to clean up after their dogs

Beach: Tentsmuir Sands

Council Phone No. 08451 55 00 00

Restrictions: No dog **restrictions.** but dogs must be kept under control or on a lead and owners must remember to clean up after their dogs

Beach: Findhorn

Council Phone No. 01786 471333

Restrictions: Dogs allowed all year round. Dog foul must be cleared up. bins are provided

Beach: Loch Linnhe (Underwater Centre Pier)

Council Phone No. 01786 471333

Restrictions: Dogs allowed all year round. Dog foul must be cleared up. Dog bins are provided. Beach cleaned regularly.

Beach: Gruinard Beach:

Council Phone No. 01786 471333

Restrictions: Dogs allowed all year round. Dog bins are provided. Beach cleaned regularly.

Beach: Gairloch

Council Phone No. 01786 471333

Restrictions: Dogs allowed all year round. Dog bins are provided. Beach cleaned regularly.

Beach: Gairloch - Big Sand

Council Phone No. 01786 471333

Restrictions: Dogs allowed all year round. Dog bins are provided. beach cleaned regularly.

Beach: Gairloch - Redpoint North

Council Phone No. 01786 471333

Restrictions: Dogs allowed all year round. Dog bins are provided. Beach cleaned regularly.

Beach: Mellon Udrigle, Laide

Council Phone No. 01786 471333

Restrictions: Dogs allowed all year round. Dog bins are provided. Beach cleaned regularly.

Beach: Rosemarkie North

Council Phone No. 01786 471333

Restrictions: Dogs allowed all year round. Dog foul must be cleared up. bins are provided

Beach: Avoch

Council Phone No. 01786 471333

Restrictions: Dogs allowed all year round. Dog bins are provided. Beach cleaned regularly.

Beach: Cromarty

Council Phone No. 01786 471333

Restrictions: Dogs allowed all year round. Dog bins are provided. Beach cleaned regularly.

Beach: Fortrose

Council Phone No. 01786 471333

www.dogfriendly.co.uk

Restrictions: Dogs allowed all year round. Dog bins are provided. Beach cleaned regularly.

Beach: Golspie - North

Council Phone No.

Restrictions: Dogs allowed all year round. Dog foul must be cleared up. Dog bins are provided

Beach: Sandside Bay

Council Phone No.

Restrictions: Dogs allowed all year round. Dog foul must be cleared up. Dog bins are provided

Beach: Thurso Bay Central

Council Phone No.

Restrictions: Dogs allowed all year round. Dog foul must be cleared up. Dog bins are provided

Beach: Dornoch (Caravan Park)

Council Phone No. 01786 471333

Restrictions: Areas of this beach dogs are restricted during the summer (1st May - 30th September) these areas are signposted.

Beach: Dornoch - Burn Mouth

Council Phone No. 01786 471333

Restrictions: Areas of this beach dogs are restricted during the summer (1st May - 30th September) these areas are signposted.

Beach: Embo Beach:

Council Phone No. 01786 471333

Restrictions: Dogs allowed all year round. Dog bins are provided. Beach cleaned regularly.

Beach: Portmahomack

Council Phone No. 01786 471333

Restrictions: Dogs allowed all year round. Dog bins are provided. Beach cleaned regularly.

Beach: Dunnet Bay - Caslehill

Council Phone No. 01786 471333

Restrictions: Dogs allowed all year round. Dog bins are provided. Beach cleaned regularly.

Beach: Dunnet Bay - Murkle Bay/ Dunnet

Council Phone No. 01786 471333

Restrictions: Dogs allowed all year round. Dog bins are provided. Beach cleaned regularly.

Beach: Sinclairs Bay - Keiss

Council Phone No. 01786 471333

Restrictions: Dogs allowed all year round. Dog bins are provided. Beach cleaned regularly.

Beach: Sinclairs Bay - Reiss Golf Course

Council Phone No. 01786 471333

Restrictions: Dogs allowed all year

round. Dog bins are provided. Beach cleaned regularly.

Beach: Sango Bay, Durness

Council Phone No. 01786 471333

Restrictions: Dogs allowed all year round. Dog bins are provided. Beach cleaned regularly.

Beach: Scourie

Council Phone No. 01786 471333

Restrictions: Dogs allowed all year round. Dog bins are provided. Beach cleaned regularly.

Beach: Achmelvich Bay

Council Phone No. 01786 471333

Restrictions: Dogs allowed all year round. Dog bins are provided. Beach cleaned regularly.

Beach: Findhorn Family Beach

Council Phone No. 01786 471333

Restrictions: Dogs allowed all year round. Dog bins are provided. Beach cleaned regularly.

Beach: Firemoore,Poolewe

Council Phone No. 01786 471333

Restrictions: Dogs allowed all year round. Dog bins are provided. Beach cleaned regularly.

Beach: Golspie - South

Council Phone No. 01786 471333

Restrictions: Dogs allowed all year round. Dog bins are provided. Beach cleaned regularly.

Beach: Morar Beach:

Council Phone No. 01786 471333

Restrictions: Dogs allowed all year round. Dog bins are provided. Beach cleaned regularly.

Beach: Shandwick Bay

Council Phone No. 01786 471333

Restrictions: Dogs allowed all year round. Dog bins are provided. Beach cleaned regularly.

Beach: Strathy Bay

Council Phone No. 01786 471333

Restrictions: Dogs allowed all year round. Dog bins are provided. Beach cleaned regularly.

Beach: Brora Beach:

Council Phone No. 01786 471333

Restrictions: Dogs allowed all year round. Dog bins are provided. Beach cleaned regularly.

Inverclyde

Beach: Gourock West Bay

Council Phone No. 0141 204 4400

Restrictions: No dog restrictions.

Scotland
Moray

Beach: Buckie, Strathlene

Council Phone No. 01224 288828

Restrictions: No dog restrictions.

Beach: Burghead

Council Phone No. 01343 542666

Restrictions: No dog restrictions.

Beach: Findochty

Council Phone No. 01343 552075

Restrictions: No dog restrictions.

Beach: Hopeman East

Council Phone No. 01343 552075

Restrictions: No dog restrictions.

Beach: Lossiemouth - East

Council Phone No. 01343 552075

Restrictions: No dog restrictions.

Beach: Lossiemouth - Silversands

Council Phone No. 01343 552075

Restrictions: No dog restrictions.

Beach: Cullen

Council Phone No. 01343 543451

Restrictions: No dog restrictions.

Beach: Nairn - Central

Council Phone No. 01342 563345

Restrictions: No dog restrictions.

Beach: Nairn East

Council Phone No. 01667 452753

Restrictions: No dog **restrictions.**

Wales

Beach: Sker Beach

Council Phone No. 01656 643643

Restrictions: Dogs are permitted throughout the year - but dog owners are reminded that if they do not clean up after their pet, they could face a £75 instant fine and if prosecuted, a max fine of £1,000

Beach: Porthcawl - Trecco Bay

Council Phone No. 01656 643643

Restrictions: Dogs are not allowed between may and September

Beach: Newton Beach

Council Phone No. 01656 643643

Restrictions: Dogs are permitted throughout the year - but dog owners are reminded that if they do not clean up after their pet, they could face a £75 instant fine and if prosecuted, a max fine of £1,000

Beach: Porthcawl - Coney Beach

Council Phone No. 01656 643643

Restrictions: Dogs are not allowed between may and September

Beach: Porthcawl - Rest Bay

Council Phone No. 01656 643643

Restrictions: Dogs are not allowed between may and September

Beach: Sandy Bay

Council Phone No. 01656 643643

Restrictions: Dogs are not allowed between may and September

Beach: Pink Bay

Council Phone No. 01656 643663

Restrictions: Dogs are permitted throughout the year - but dog owners are reminded that if they do not clean up after their pet, they could face a £75 instant fine and if prosecuted, a max fine of £1,000

Beach: Porthcawl - Town Beach

Council Phone No. 01656 643663

Restrictions: Dogs are not allowed between may and September

www.dogfriendly.co.uk

Beach: Ferryside Beach

Council Phone No. 0845 658 0445

Restrictions: no restrictions allowed throughout the year don't have to be on a lead but must be kept under control

Beach: Llanelli & Loughor Estuary (Fourth Groyne)

Council Phone No. 0845 658 0445

Restrictions: no restrictions allowed throughout the year don't have to be on a lead but must be kept under control

Beach: Llanstephan & Tywi Estuary

Council Phone No. 0845 658 0445

Restrictions: no restrictions allowed throughout the year don't have to be on a lead but must be kept under control

Beach: Morfa Bychan (Pendine)

Council Phone No. 0845 658 0445

Restrictions: no restrictions allowed throughout the year don't have to be on a lead but must be kept under control

Beach: Pembrey Beach Llanelli (Cefn Sidan)

Council Phone No. 0845 658 0445

Restrictions:

Dog ban on half a mile on this beach well signposted the ban is from 1st may - 30th September dogs don't have to be on a lead but must be kept under control

Beach: Pendine Sands

Council Phone No. 0845 658 0445

Restrictions: dog ban on a small area it is well signposted from 1st may - 30th September dogs don't have to be kept on a lead but must be under control

Beach: St. Ishmael, Kidwelly

Council Phone No. 0845 658 0445

Restrictions: no restrictions allowed throughout the year don't have to be on a lead but must be kept under control

www.dogfriendly.co.uk

201

Wales
Ceredigion

Beach: Aberaeron Harbour (Fourth Groyne North)

Council Phone No. 01545 570881

Restrictions: Dogs need to be kept on a lead and are prohibited between the 1st of May and the 30th of September

Beach: Aberaeron North (North of Groynes)

Council Phone No. 01545 570881

Restrictions: Dogs need to be kept on a lead and are prohibited between the 1st of May and the 30th of September

Beach: Aberaeron North Beach

Council Phone No. 01545 570881

Restrictions: Dogs need to be kept on a lead and are prohibited between the 1st of May and the 30th of September

Beach: Aberaeron South (Northern Groyne)

Council Phone No. 01545 570881

Restrictions: Dogs need to be kept on a lead and are prohibited between the 1st of May and the 30th of September

Beach: Aberarth

Council Phone No. 01545 570881

Restrictions: Dogs need to be kept on a lead and are prohibited between the 1st of May and the 30th of September

Beach: Aberporth

Council Phone No. 01545 570881

Restrictions: Dolwen beach dogs are banned between 1st may and 30th September and must be kept under control

Beach: Aberporth - Traeth-y-Dyffryn

Council Phone No. 01545 570881

Restrictions: dogs are permitted all year round but must be kept on a lead

Beach: Aberystwyth - Harbour

Council Phone No. 01545 570881

Restrictions: dogs are permitted but must be kept on a lead

Beach: Aberystwyth - North

Council Phone No. 01545 570881

Restrictions: Dogs are prohibited from North Beach between the north side of the Landing Stage and the extreme northern end of the beach at Craig Glais between the 1st May and 30th September inclusive

Beach: Aberystwyth - South

Council Phone No. 01545 570881

Restrictions: Dogs are prohibited from South Beach between Castle Headland (northern limit) and the first groyne at the end of South Marine Terrace

www.dogfriendly.co.uk

(southern limit) between the 1st May and 30th September inclusive

Beach: Aberystwyth - Tanybwich Beach

Council Phone No. 01545 570881

Restrictions: Dogs are prohibited between the 1st of may and 30th of September

Beach: Borth

Council Phone No. 01545 570881

Restrictions: Prohibited on the beach area from slipway at the lifeboat station to the club house opposite the youth hostel on the high street.

Beach: Cilborth

Council Phone No. 01545 570881

Restrictions: Dogs are allowed all year round but must be kept under control

Beach: Clarach - North

Council Phone No. 01545 570881

Restrictions: prohibited on the beach area which runs parallel with the breakwater between 1st of may and 30th September

Beach: Clarach - South

Council Phone No. 01545 570881

Restrictions: Dogs are allowed on the beach but not between the 1st may and 30th September they must also be on a lead

Beach: Cwmtydu

Council Phone No. 01545 570881

Restrictions: Dogs are allowed all year round but must be kept on a lead

Beach: Gilfach Yr Halen

Council Phone No. 01545 570881

Restrictions: dogs allowed but must be kept on a lead

Beach: Gwbert-on-sea at craig y gwent

Council Phone No. 01545 570881

Restrictions: Dogs allowed on the beach as long as they are kept on a lead

Beach: Little Quay (Cei Bach)

Council Phone No. 01545 570881

Restrictions: Dogs allowed all year round but must be kept on a lead

Beach: Llangrannog

Council Phone No. 01545 570881

Restrictions: Beach area dogs are prohibited between Nant Hawen and Ren Rhip between the 1st may and 30th September

Beach: Llanina

Council Phone No. 01545 570881

Restrictions: Dogs are allowed all year round but must be kept on a lead

Beach: Llanon (Slipway)

Council Phone No. 01545 570881

Restrictions: dogs permitted all year round but me kept on a lead

Beach: Llanrhystyd - South
Council Phone No. 01545 570881
Restrictions: dogs are permitted throughout the year as long as they are kept on a lead

Beach: Llansantffraid
Council Phone No. 01545 570881
Restrictions: dogs are permitted all year round but must be kept on a lead

Beach: Morfa Bychan (Slipway)
Council Phone No. 01545 570881
Restrictions: Dogs are permitted all year round but must be kept under control and on a lead

Beach: mwnt
Council Phone No. 01545 570881
Restrictions: Prohibited on the beach between 1st may and 30th September

Beach: New quay - North Beach
Council Phone No. 01545 570881
Restrictions: Dogs are prohibited from the beach between the Pier and Penpolion between the 1st May and 30th September inclusive

Beach: New Quay - South
Council Phone No. 01545 570881
Restrictions: Dogs are prohibited from the beach between the Pier and Penpolion between the 1st May and 30th September inclusive

Beach: New Quay - Traeth Gwyn
Council Phone No. 01545 570881
Restrictions: Dogs are prohibited from the beach between the Pier and Penpolion between the 1st May and 30th September inclusive

Beach: New Quay - Harbour Beach
Council Phone No. 01545 570881
Restrictions: Dogs are prohibited from the beach between the Pier and Penpolion between the 1st May and 30th September inclusive

Beach: Patch
Council Phone No. 01545 570881
Restrictions: Dogs are permitted all year round as long as they are kept on a lead

Beach: Penbryn
Council Phone No. 01545 570881
Restrictions: Prohibited on the beach area south of Nant Hoffnant between the 1st may and 30th September

Beach: Tresaith
Council Phone No. 01545 570881
Restrictions: Prohibited on the southern beach area between the access steps and carreg Ddafad (left hand side) between the 1st may and 30th September

Beach: Ynyslas - Northern Groyne (Sea)

Council Phone No. 01545 570881

Restrictions: dogs are permitted throughout the year but dogs must be kept on a lead

Beach: Ynyslas - Twyni Bach (Estuary)

Council Phone No. 01545 570881

Restrictions: Dog allowed all year round providing that they are kept on a lead

Beach: Ballroom

Council Phone No. 01224 522000

Restrictions: Dog restrictions from the 1st of May to the 30th September 2007, signposted to say where dogs are allowed during this time

Wales
Conwy

Beach: Colwyn Bay - Cayley Promenade

Council Phone No. 01492 530478

Restrictions: Dog restrictions

Beach: Colwyn Bay - Marine Road

Council Phone No. 01492 530478

Restrictions: Dog Restrictions

Beach: Colwyn Bay - Rhos on sea

Council Phone No. 01492 530478

Restrictions: Dogs allowed

Beach: Llanddulas

Council Phone No. 01492 530478

Restrictions: Dogs allowed in restricted areas

Beach: Llandudno - North Shore

Council Phone No. 01492 530478

Restrictions: Dogs are permitted between the paddling pool and the little Orme

Beach: Llandudno - West Shore

Council Phone No. 01492 530478

Restrictions: Dogs are permitted between the two brake waters

Beach: Old Conwyn

Council Phone No. 01492 530478

Restrictions: Dogs allowed

Beach: Penmaenmawr

Council Phone No. 01492 531731

Restrictions: Dog restrictions apply. There is a dog exercise area.

Beach: Abergele - Pensarn

Council Phone No. 01492 574000

Restrictions: Dog restrictions

Beach: Penrhyn Bay

Council Phone No. 01492 574000

Restrictions: Dogs allowed

Beach: Llanfairfechan

Council Phone No. 01492 574000.

Restrictions: Dogs allowed

Beach: Kinmel Bay (Sandy Cove)

Council Phone No. 01492 574000.

Restrictions: Dogs allowed

Beach: Conwy Morfa

Council Phone No. 01492 592 248

Restrictions: Dogs allowed

www.dogfriendly.co.uk

www.dogfriendly.co.uk

Beach: Deganwy North

Council Phone No. 01492 592 248
Restrictions: Dogs allowed

Beach: Abergele - Towyn

Council Phone No. 01745 833242
Restrictions: Dogs allowed

Beach: Barkby Beach, Prestatyn

Council Phone No. 01824 706101

Restrictions: Dog restriction from the 1st of May to the 30th September 2007, signposted to say where dogs are allowed during this time

Beach: Ffrith, Preststyn

Council Phone No. 01824 706101

Restrictions: dogs allowed on the beach but must be kept under control or on a lead. Dogs are prohibited between the 1st of May and 30th September 2007

Beach: Gronant

Council Phone No. 01824 706101

Restrictions: Dog restrictions from the 1st of May to the 30th September 2007, signposted to say where dogs are allowed during this time

Beach: Prestatyn

Council Phone No. 01824 706101

Restrictions: Dog restrictions from the 1st of May to the 30th September 2007, signposted to say where dogs are allowed during this time

Beach: Rhyl

Council Phone No. 01824 706101

Restrictions: Dog restrictions from the 1st of May to the 30th September 2007, signposted to say where dogs are allowed during this time

Beach: Splash Point, Rhyl

Council Phone No. 01824 706101

Restrictions: Dog **restrictions** from the 1st of May to the 30th September 2007, signposted to say where dogs are allowed during this time

Flintshire

Beach: Point Of Ayr, Talacre

Council Phone No. 01352 752121

Restrictions: Dogs allowed on beach all year round. However there are areas of the beach where the dogs need to be put on leads, these areas are signposted. Bins provided on beach, and beach cleaned daily.

www.dogfriendly.co.uk

Beach: Dyffryn

Council Phone No. 01286 672255

Restrictions: Dogs banned from beach between 1st May - 30th September, these are blue flag areas, which are clearly signposted and maps placed on notice boards visible on beach/promenade. Dogs allowed either side of these blue flag areas throughout year.

Beach: Plas Menai

Council Phone No. 01286 672255

Restrictions: No dog restrictions. Litter bins provided

Beach: Dinas Dinlle

Council Phone No. 01286 672255

Restrictions: No dog restrictions. Litter bins provided

Beach: Pontllyfni

Council Phone No. 01286 672255

Restrictions: No dog restrictions. Litter bins provided

Beach: Port Dinorwic Sailing Club, Felinheli

Council Phone No. 01286 672255

Restrictions: Dogs banned from beach between 1st May - 30th September, these are blue flag areas, which are clearly signposted and maps placed on notice boards visible on beach/promenade. Dogs allowed either side of these blue flag areas throughout year.

Beach: Llwyngwril

Council Phone No. 01286 672255

Restrictions: Dogs banned from beach between 1st May - 30th September, these are blue flag areas, which are clearly signposted and maps placed on notice boards visible on beach/promenade. Dogs allowed either side of these blue flag areas throughout year.

Beach: Tal - Y - Bont

Council Phone No. 01286 672255

Restrictions: Dogs banned from beach between 1st May - 30th September, these are blue flag areas, which are clearly signposted and maps placed on notice boards visible on beach/promenade. Dogs allowed either side of these blue flag areas throughout year.

Beach: Barmouth

Council Phone No. 01286 672255

Restrictions: Dogs banned from beach between 1st May - 30th September, these are blue flag areas, which are clearly signposted and maps placed on notice boards visible on beach/promenade. Dogs allowed either side of these blue flag areas throughout year.

Beach: Fairbourne

Council Phone No. 01286 672255

Restrictions: Dogs banned from beach between 1st May - 30th September, these are blue flag areas, which are clearly signposted and maps placed on notice boards visible on beach/promenade. Dogs allowed either side of these blue flag areas throughout year.

Beach: Tywyn

Council Phone No. 01286 672255

Restrictions: Dogs banned from beach between 1st May - 30th September, these are blue flag areas, which are clearly signposted and maps placed on notice boards visible on beach/promenade. Dogs allowed either side of these blue flag areas throughout year.

Beach: Aberdyfi

Council Phone No. 01286 672255

Restrictions: Dogs banned from beach between 1st May - 30th September, these are blue flag areas, which are clearly signposted and maps placed on notice boards visible on beach/promenade. Dogs allowed either side of these blue flag areas throughout year.

Beach: Machroes

Council Phone No. 01286 672255

Restrictions: Dogs banned from beach between 1st May - 30th

September, these are blue flag areas, which are clearly signposted and maps placed on notice boards visible on beach/promenade. Dogs allowed either side of these blue flag areas throughout year.

Beach: Afon Wen

Council Phone No. 01286 672255

Restrictions: No dog restrictions. Litter bins provided

Beach: Porthor (oer)

Council Phone No. 01286 672255

Restrictions: Dogs banned from beach between 1st May - 30th September, these are blue flag areas, which are clearly signposted and maps placed on notice boards visible on beach/promenade. Dogs allowed either side of these blue flag areas throughout year.

Beach: Rhos-y-llan

Council Phone No. 01286 672255

Restrictions: No dog **restrictions.** Litter bins provided

Beach: Porth Dinllaen

Council Phone No. 01286 672255

Restrictions: Dogs banned from beach between 1st May - 30th September, these are blue flag areas, which are clearly signposted and maps placed on notice boards visible on beach/promenade. Dogs allowed either side of these blue flag areas throughout year.

www.dogfriendly.co.uk

Beach: Porth Nefyn

Council Phone No. 01286 672255

Restrictions: Dogs banned from beach between 1st May - 30th September, these are blue flag areas, which are clearly signposted and maps placed on notice boards visible on beach/promenade. Dogs allowed either side of these blue flag areas throughout year.

Beach: Abersoch

Council Phone No. 01286 672255

Restrictions: Dogs banned from beach between 1st May - 30th September, these are blue flag areas, which are clearly signposted and maps placed on notice boards visible on beach/promenade. Dogs allowed either side of these blue flag areas throughout year.

Beach: Trefor

Council Phone No. 01286 672255

Restrictions: No dog **restrictions.** Litter bins provided

Beach: Llanbedrog

Council Phone No. 01286 672255

Restrictions: No dog restrictions. Litter bins provided

Beach: Aberdaron beach

Council Phone No. 01286 672255

Restrictions: Dogs banned from beach between 1st May - 30th September, these are blue flag areas, which are clearly signposted and maps placed on notice boards visible on beach/promenade. Dogs allowed either side of these blue flag areas throughout year.

Beach: Pwllheli

Council Phone No. 01286 672255

Restrictions: Dogs banned from beach between 1st May - 30th September, these are blue flag areas, which are clearly signposted and maps placed on notice boards visible on beach/promenade. Dogs allowed either side of these blue flag areas throughout year.

Beach: Abererch

Council Phone No. 01286 672255

Restrictions: Dogs banned from beach between 1st May - 30th September, these are blue flag areas, which are clearly signposted and maps placed on notice boards visible on beach/promenade. Dogs allowed either side of these blue flag areas throughout year.

Beach: Porth Neigwl

Council Phone No. 01286 672255

Restrictions: No dog restrictions. Litter bins provided

Beach: Llanbedrog Beach North

Council Phone No. 01286 672255

Restrictions: No dog restrictions. Litter bins provided

www.dogfriendly.co.uk

Beach: Carreg Wen

Council Phone No. 01286 672255

Restrictions: No dog restrictions. Litter bins provided

Beach: Criccieth

Council Phone No. 01286 672255

Restrictions: Dogs banned from beach between 1st May - 30th September, these are blue flag areas, which are clearly signposted and maps placed on notice boards visible on beach/promenade. Dogs allowed either side of these blue flag areas throughout year.

Beach: Criccieth - West End

Council Phone No. 01286 672255

Restrictions: Dogs banned from beach between 1st May - 30th September, these are blue flag areas, which are clearly signposted and maps placed on notice boards visible on beach/promenade. Dogs allowed either side of these blue flag areas throughout year.

Beach: Morfa Bychan

Council Phone No. 01286 672255

Restrictions: Dogs banned from beach between 1st May - 30th September, these are blue flag areas, which are clearly signposted and maps placed on notice boards visible on beach/promenade. Dogs allowed either side of these blue flag areas throughout year.

Beach: Morfa Bychan - Black Rock Sands

Council Phone No. 01286 672255

Restrictions: Dogs banned from beach between 1st May - 30th September, these are blue flag areas, which are clearly signposted and maps placed on notice boards visible on beach/promenade. Dogs allowed either side of these blue flag areas throughout year.

Beach: Harlech

Council Phone No. 01286 672255

Restrictions: Dogs banned from beach between 1st May - 30th September, these are blue flag areas, which are clearly signposted and maps placed on notice boards visible on beach/promenade. Dogs allowed either side of these blue flag areas throughout year.

Beach: Llandanwg

Council Phone No. 01286 672255

Restrictions: Dogs banned from beach between 1st May - 30th September, these are blue flag areas, which are clearly signposted and maps placed on notice boards visible on beach/promenade. Dogs allowed either side of these blue flag areas throughout year.

www.dogfriendly.co.uk

Wales
Pembrokeshire

Beach: Aber Mawr Bay

Council Phone No. 01437 764551

Restrictions: No dog restrictions. but must be kept under control

Beach: Abercastle

Council Phone No. 01437 764551

Restrictions: No restrictions dogs allowed all year round

Beach: Abereiddy Bay - Slipway

Council Phone No. 01437 764551

Restrictions: No restrictions dogs allowed all year round

Beach: Amroth

Council Phone No. 01437 764551

Restrictions: Dogs are prohibited between the 1st May and 30th September on signposted areas but are allowed on the promenade but they must be on a lead

Beach: Barfundle Bay

Council Phone No. 01437 764551

Restrictions: No dog restrictions. but must be kept under control

Beach: Blue Lagoon - Abereiddy Bay

Council Phone No. 01437 764551

Restrictions: No dog restrictions. but must be kept under control

Beach: Broadhaven

Council Phone No. 01437 764551

Restrictions: Dog are prohibited between the 1st May and 30th September

Beach: Broadhaven South

Council Phone No. 01437 764551

Restrictions: Dogs are allowed on the beach and promenade but be kept on a lead and under control

Beach: Caerfai Bay

Council Phone No. 01437 764551

Restrictions: Dogs are allowed all year round but must be kept under control

Beach: Coppet Hall

Council Phone No. 01437 764551

Restrictions: Dogs are prohibited between 1st May and 30th September on signposted areas

Beach: Cwm Yr Eglwys

Council Phone No. 01437 764551

Restrictions: No restrictions dogs allowed all year round but must be under control or on a lead

Beach: Dale

Council Phone No. 01437 764551

Restrictions: Dog are prohibited between the 1st May and 30th September on signposted areas but are allowed on other signposted areas but must be on a lead

Beach: Druidstone Haven

Council Phone No. 01437 764551

Restrictions: No restrictions dogs allowed all year round but must be under control or on a lead

Beach: Freshwater East

Council Phone No. 01437 764551

Restrictions: No restrictions dogs allowed all year round but must be under control or on a lead

Beach: Freshwater West

Council Phone No. 01437 764551

Restrictions: No restrictions dogs allowed all year round but must be under control or on a lead

Beach: Gelliswick, Milford Haven

Council Phone No. 01437 764551

Restrictions: No restrictions dogs allowed all year round but must be under control or on a lead

Beach: Glen Beach

Council Phone No. 01437 764551

Restrictions: No restrictions dogs allowed all year round but must be under control or on a lead

Beach: Goodwick - Harbour South

Council Phone No. 01437 764551

Restrictions: No restrictions dogs allowed all year round but must be under control or on a lead

Beach: Goodwick Sands

Council Phone No. 01437 764551

Restrictions: No restrictions dogs allowed all year round but must be under control or on a lead

Beach: Little Haven

Council Phone No. 01437 764551

Restrictions: No restrictions dogs allowed all year round but must be under control or on a lead

Beach: Lydstep Haven

Council Phone No. 01437 764551

Restrictions: Dogs are prohibited between the 1st May and 30th September on signposted areas

Beach: Manorbier Bay

Council Phone No. 01437 764551

Restrictions: Dog are allowed all year round providing they are kept under control

Beach: Marloes Sands

Council Phone No. 01437 764551

Restrictions: No restrictions dogs allowed all year round but must be under control or on a lead

www.dogfriendly.co.uk

Beach: Martins Haven

Council Phone No. 01437 764551

Restrictions: No restrictions dogs allowed all year round but must be under control or on a lead

Beach: Monkstone Beach (Near Tenby)

Council Phone No. 01437 764551

Restrictions: No restrictions dogs allowed all year round but must be under control or on a lead

Beach: Newgale sands

Council Phone No. 01437 764551

Restrictions: Dog ban between the 1st May and 30th September but there are signposted areas along the promenade where dogs are allowed but must be on leads

Beach: Newport - Car Park Slip

Council Phone No. 01437 764551

Restrictions: No restrictions dogs allowed all year round but must be under control or on a lead

Beach: Newport Sands - North

Council Phone No. 01437 764551

Restrictions: Dogs allowed all year round but must be kept under control or on a lead

Beach: Newport Sands - South

Council Phone No. 01437 764551

Restrictions: Dogs are allowed on the **beach** all year round providing they are kept under control

Beach: Neyland Slip

Council Phone No. 01437 764551

Restrictions: Dogs are allowed on the beach all year round providing they are kept under control or on a lead

Beach: Nolton Haven

Council Phone No. 01437 764551

Restrictions: Dogs are allowed all year round but must be kept under control or on a lead

Beach: Penally

Council Phone No. 01437 764551

Restrictions: No restrictions dogs allowed all year round but must be under control or on a lead

Beach: Poppit Sands - East

Council Phone No. 01437 764551

Restrictions: No restrictions but dogs must be kept under control or a lead

Beach: Poppit Sands - West

Council Phone No. 01437 764551

Restrictions: Dogs are prohibited between the 1st May and 30th September

Beach: Porthclais

Council Phone No. 01437 764551

Restrictions: No dog restrictions. but they must be kept under control or on a lead

Beach: Porthselau

Council Phone No. 01437 764551

Restrictions: dogs allowed all year round but must be kept under control or on a lead

Beach: Priory Bay, Caldy Island

Council Phone No. 01437 764551

Restrictions: Dogs are allowed but must be on a lead at all times and owners must clean up after their dogs or they will be fined

Beach: Pwllgwaelod

Council Phone No. 01437 764551

Restrictions: No restrictions dogs allowed all year round but must be under control or on a lead

Beach: Sandy Haven

Council Phone No. 01437 764551

Restrictions: No restrictions dogs allowed all year round but must be under control or on a lead

Beach: Saundersfoot

Council Phone No. 01437 764551

Restrictions: dogs are prohibited between the 1st May and 30th September on signposted areas but are allowed on other areas but they must be on a lead

Beach: Skrinkle

Council Phone No. 01437 764551

Restrictions: No restrictions dogs

allowed all year round but must be under control or on a lead

Beach: St. Brides Haven

Council Phone No. 01437 764551

Restrictions: Dogs are allowed all year round but must be kept under control

Beach: St. Dogmaels Slipway

Council Phone No. 01437 764551

Restrictions: No restrictions

Beach: St Ishmaels (Lindsway Bay)

Council Phone No. 01437 764551

Restrictions: Dogs are allowed all year round but must be kept under control or on a lead

Beach: Swanlake Bay

Council Phone No. 01437 764551

Restrictions: No restrictions

Beach: Tenby Castle Beach

Council Phone No. 01437 764551

Restrictions: Dogs are prohibited between 1st May and 30th September

Beach: Tenby North

Council Phone No. 01437 764551

Restrictions: Dogs are allowed on signposted areas but be kept on a lead

Beach: Tenby South

Council Phone No. 01437 764551

Restrictions: Dogs are allowed on the

www.dogfriendly.co.uk

beach all year round but must be kept under control or on a lead

Beach: Traeth llyn

Council Phone No. 01437 764551

Restrictions: No restrictions

Beach: Waterwynch

Council Phone No. 01437 764551

Restrictions: No dog restrictions. but must be kept under control or on a lead

Beach: Watwick

Council Phone No. 01437 764551

Restrictions: No dog restrictions. but they must be kept under control or on a lead

Beach: West Angle Bay

Council Phone No. 01437 764551

Restrictions: No dog restrictions. but they must be kept under control or on a lead

Beach: Westdale

Council Phone No. 01437 764551

Restrictions: No dog restrictions. but they must be kept under control

Beach: White Sands

Council Phone No. 01437 764551

Restrictions: Dogs are prohibited between the 1st May and 30th September

Beach: Wisemands Bridge

Council Phone No. 01437 764551

Restrictions: No dog restrictions. but they must be kept under control

www.dogfriendly.co.uk

Beach: Bracelet Bay

Council Phone No. 01792 635600

Restrictions: Dogs prohibited between the 1st of May and 30th of September on signposted areas

Beach: Brandy Cove

Council Phone No. 01792 635600

Restrictions: Dogs prohibited between the 1st of May and 30th of September on signposted areas

Beach: Broughton Bay

Council Phone No. 01792 635600

Restrictions: No restrictions dogs allowed all year round but must be under control or on a lead

Beach: Caswell Bay

Council Phone No. 01792 635600

Restrictions: Dogs prohibited between the 1st of May and 30th of September on signposted areas

Beach: Fall Bay

Council Phone No. 01792 635600

Restrictions: Dogs prohibited between the 1st of May and 30th of September on signposted areas

Beach: Horton Bay

Council Phone No. 01792 635600

Restrictions: No restrictions dogs allowed all year round but must be under control or on a lead

Beach: Langland Bay

Council Phone No. 01792 635600

Restrictions: Dogs prohibited between the 1st of May and 30th of September on signposted areas

Beach: Limeslade Bay

Council Phone No. 01792 635600

Restrictions: Dogs prohibited between the 1st of May and 30th of September on signposted areas

Beach: Llangennith

Council Phone No. 01792 635600

Restrictions: No restrictions dogs allowed all year round but must be under control or on a lead

Beach: Mewslade Bay East

Council Phone No. 01792 635600

Restrictions: No restrictions dogs allowed all year round but must be under control or on a lead

Beach: Oxwich Bay

Council Phone No. 01792 635600

Restrictions: No restrictions dogs allowed all year round but must be

www.dogfriendly.co.uk

under control or on a lead

Beach: Port Eynon

Council Phone No. 01792 635600

Restrictions: Dogs prohibited between the 1st of May and 30th of September from the eastern edge of the steps to Port Eynon beach to the eastern edge of Horton beach access

Beach: Pobbles Bay

Council Phone No. 01792 635600

Restrictions: No restrictions dogs allowed all year round but must be under control or on a lead

Beach: Pwlldu Bay

Council Phone No. 01792 635600

Restrictions: No restrictions dogs allowed all year round but must be under control or on a lead

Beach: Rhossili

Council Phone No. 01792 635600

Restrictions: No restrictions dogs allowed all year round but must be under control or on a lead

Beach: Rhossili Bay - Hillend

Council Phone No. 01792 635600

Restrictions: No restrictions dogs allowed all year round but must be under control or on a lead

Beach: Rotherslade Bay

Council Phone No. 01792 635600

Restrictions: Dogs prohibited between

the 1st of May and 30th of September on signposted areas

Beach: Swansea Bay - County Hall

Council Phone No. 01792 635600

Restrictions: No restrictions dogs allowed all year round but must be under control or on a lead

Beach: Swansea Bay - Mumbles Head

Council Phone No. 01792 635600

Restrictions: No restrictions dogs allowed all year round but must be under control or on a lead

Beach: Swansea Bay - opp. Norton Road

Council Phone No. 01792 635600

Restrictions: No restrictions dogs allowed all year round but must be under control or on a lead

Beach: Swansea Bay - Opp Black Pill Rock

Council Phone No. 01792 635600

Restrictions: No restrictions dogs allowed all year round but must be under control or on a lead

Beach: Swansea Bay - Sketty Lane

Council Phone No. 01792 635600

Restrictions: Dogs are prohibited between the 1st of May and 30th of September from the beach opposite Sketty Lane to the Northern edge of the slip opposite the West Cross Inn

www.dogfriendly.co.uk

Beach: Swansea Bay - Slip

Council Phone No. 01792 635600

Restrictions: Dogs prohibited between the 1st of May and 30th of September on signposted areas

Beach: Swansea Bay - West Cross

Council Phone No. 01792 635600

Restrictions: No restrictions dogs allowed all year round but must be under control or on a lead

Beach: Swansea Bay - Knab Rock

Council Phone No. 01792 635600

Restrictions: No restrictions dogs allowed all year round but must be under control or on a lead

Beach: Three Cliffs Bay

Council Phone No. 01792 635600

Restrictions: No restrictions dogs allowed all year round but must be under control or on a lead

Beach: Torbay, Crawley Woods

Council Phone No. 01792 635600

Restrictions: No restrictions dogs allowed all year round but must be under control or on a lead

Beach: Whitford Sands

Council Phone No. 01792 635600

Restrictions: No restrictions dogs allowed all year round but must be under control or on a lead

www.dogfriendly.co.uk

Vale of Glamorgan

Beach: Ogmore Central

Council Phone No. 01446 700111

Restrictions: No restrictions dogs allowed all year round but must be under control or on a lead

Beach: Barry - Little Island Bay

Council Phone No. 01446 709325

Restrictions: Dogs prohibited between the 1st of May and 30th of September

Beach: Barry - Watch House Bay

Council Phone No. 01446 709325

Restrictions: Dogs prohibited between the 1st of May and 30th of September

Beach: Bendricks Beach:

Council Phone No. 01446 709325

Restrictions: Dogs prohibited between the 1st of May and 30th of September

Beach: Cold Knap, Barry

Council Phone No. 01446 709325

Restrictions: Dogs prohibited between the 1st of May and 30th of September

Beach: Fontygary Bay

Council Phone No. 01446 709325

Restrictions: Dogs prohibited between the 1st of May and 30th of September

Beach: Limpert Bay, Alberthaw

Council Phone No. 01446 709325

Restrictions: Dogs prohibited between the 1st of May and 30th of September

Beach: Llantwit Major Beach

Council Phone No. 01446 709325

Restrictions: Dogs prohibited between the 1st of May and 30th of September

Beach: Penarth

Council Phone No. 01446 709325

Restrictions: Dogs prohibited between the 1st of May and 30th of September

Beach: Southerndown

Council Phone No. 01446 709325

Restrictions: Dogs prohibited between the 1st of May and 30th of September

Beach: St. Marys Well Bay, Barry

Council Phone No. 01446 709325

Restrictions: Dogs prohibited between the 1st of May and 30th of September

Beach: Tresilian Bay

Council Phone No. 01446 709325

Restrictions: Dogs prohibited between the 1st of May and 30th of September

Beach: Whitmore Bay, Barry

Council Phone No. 01446 709325

Restrictions: Dogs prohibited between the 1st of May and 30th of September

Beach: Burry Port Beach: - East

Council Phone No. 0845 6580445

Restrictions: No restrictions dogs allowed all year round but must be under control or on a lead

Beach: Jacksons Bay, Barry

Council Phone No. 01446 700111

Restrictions: No restrictions dogs allowed all year round but must be under control or on a lead

Western Isles

Beach: Isle Of Harris

Council Phone No. 01859 502011

Restrictions: No restrictions dogs allowed all year round

www.dogfriendly.co.uk

Days Out

Your comprehensive guide to dog friendly Days Out

www.dogfriendly.co.uk

Dog Friendly

Bedfordshire

Dunstable Downs

Address: Dunstable Road, Whipsnade, Bedfordshire LU6 2GY

Activities: Outstanding views over the vale of Aylesbury and Chiltern Ridge. Chalk grassland offers a wildlife haven. Kite flying hotspot. Highest point in the East of England

Restrictions: Dogs-Under close control, on leads near livestock. Please clear up dog waste and dispose of it sensibly.

Car Parking: Parking off B4540 Bison Hill & B4541 Dunstable Downs

Opening Times: Open all year

Telephone: 01582 608489

Website: www.nationaltrust.org.uk

Whipsnade Tree Cathedral

Address: 4ml South of Dunstable, off B4540 (in centre of Whipsnade)

Activities: Trees, hedges and shrubs planted in the form of a medieval cathedral. Covers a tranquil 9 ½ acres.

Restrictions: Dogs under close control. Please remember to clear up dog waste and dispose of it sensibly

Car Parking: Pay & Display. Car park locked at dusk or 7

Opening Times: Open all year

Telephone: 01582 872406

Website: www.nationaltrust.org.uk

www.dogfriendly.co.uk

Donnington Castle

Address: One mile north of Newbury, off the B4494.

Activities: The striking twin-towered 14th- century gate-house of this castle, later the focus of a Civil War siege and battle, survives amid impressive earthworks. Exterior viewing only

Restrictions: The castle is at the top of a fairly steep grassy hill. Dogs allowed on a leads.

Car Parking: Parking available

Opening Times: Open all year

Telephone: 0845 3010008

Website: www.castlexplorer.co.uk

Wellington Country Park

Address: Odiham Road. Riseley. Reading. RG7 1SP

Activities: Set in 350 acres of Parkland, Wellington Country Park is an ideal destination for all the family, and has all the ingredients for a fantastic day out.

Restrictions: Dogs are very welcome.

Car Parking: Free parking

Opening Times: Open March - Nov

Telephone: 0118 9326 444

Website: www.wellington-country-park.co.uk

www.dogfriendly.co.uk

Bristol

Ashton Court

Address: Long Ashton, Bristol BS41 9JN

Activities: The magnificent estate of Ashton Court covers 850 acres of woods and grassland with breathtaking views over the city of Bristol.

Restrictions: Dogs are very welcome, but please on a lead through Deer Park.

Car Parking: Free parking

Opening Times: Open all year

Telephone: 0117 963 9176

Website: www.forestofavon.org.uk

HorseWorld Bristol

Address: Staunton Lane, Whitchurch. Bristol, BS14 0QJ

Activities: Set in beautiful stone farm-buildings HorseWorld is a Quality Assured Attraction that offers a great day out for everyone.

Restrictions: We welcome any well behaved Dogs on leads, however, dogs are not allowed in the buildings.

Car Parking: Free parking

Opening Times: Open all year

Telephone: 01275 540173

Website: www.horseworld.org.uk

Bucks Goat Centre

Address: Layby Farm, Stoke Mandeville, Buckinghamshire, HP22 5XJ

Activities: Children's miniature zoo featuring a wide range of animals, including llamas, wallabies, birds, reptiles, pigs, donkeys and every breed of domestic goat found in Britain.

Restrictions: Dogs on leads are welcome

Car Parking: Free parking

Opening Times: Open daily throughout the year

Telephone: 01296 612983

Website: www.bucksgoatcentre.co.uk

Hughenden Manor garden

Address: High Wycombe, Bucks, HP14 4LA

Activities: Take a stroll through the beautiful gardens and take in some of the superb views to be had throughout the surrounding park and woodland.

Restrictions: Dogs on leads are welcome

Car Parking: Free parking

Opening Times: 3 Mar to 28 Oct, Wed-Sun, 1-16 Dec, Sat & Sun

Telephone: 01494 755573

Website: www.britainsfinest.co.uk

Chiltern Open Air Museum

Address: Newland Park, Gorelands Lane, Chalfont St Giles, Buckinghamshire, HP8 4AB

Activities: Chiltern Open Air Museum is home to a collection of historic buildings rescued from in and around Buckinghamshire, Berkshire, Oxfordshire and Hertfordshire and re-erected on the 45 acre parkland site.

Restrictions: Dogs on leads are welcome

Car Parking: Free parking

Opening Times: 30 March - 31 October

Telephone: 01494 871 117

Website: www.coam.org.uk

Stowe Landscape Gardens

Address: Stowe, Buckingham, MK18 5EH

Activities: Stowe Landscape Gardens is an extraordinary, living, breathing work of art. With its ornamental lakes, glorious open spaces, wooded valleys and adorned with over 40 monument temples

Restrictions: Dogs on leads are welcome

Car Parking: Free parking

Opening Times: 1 Mar to 4 Nov, Wed-Sun, 10 Nov to 24 Sat & Sun

Telephone: 01280 822850

Website: www.britainsfinest.co.uk

www.dogfriendly.co.uk

Cambridgeshire

Wicken Fen National Nature Reserve

Address: Lode Lane. Wicken. Cambridgeshire. CB7 5XP

Activities: A unique fragment of the wilderness that once covered East Anglia. The Fen is a haven for birds, plants, insects and mammals alike, including a boardwalk nature trail.

Restrictions: Dogs on leads only. Please clear up dog waste and dispose of it sensibly.

Car Parking: Parking, 120 yds, £2

Opening Times: Open all year

Telephone: 01353 720274

Website: www.nationaltrust.org.uk

Arley Hall & Gardens

Address: Arley, Northwich, Cheshire, CW9 6NA

Activities: Arley is a place of enormous character, charm and interest.The Gardens, are amongst the finest in Britain. The Hall is an impressive example of a Victorian country house

Restrictions: Dogs are very, very welcome

Car Parking: Free parking

Opening Times: Open March - Sept

Telephone: 01565 777353

Website: www.arleyhallandgardens.com

Beeston Castle

Address: Tarporley, Cheshire, CW6 9TX

Activities: Climb to the top of the formidable Castle of the Rock with incredible views over eight counties. There are acres of unspoilt woodland trails to explore, and wildlife to see.

Restrictions: Dogs very welcome on leads

Car Parking: Free parking

Opening Times: Open April-End Sept

Telephone: 01829 260464

Website: www.english-heritage.org.uk

Cholmondeley Castle Garden

Address: Malpas. Cheshire. SY14 8AH

Activities: Cholmondeley Castle has extensive ornamental gardens set in idyllic parkland and lake dominated by the romantic Gothic Castle.

Restrictions: Dogs are very welcome and can be off the lead in certain areas

Car Parking: Free parking

Opening Times: Open April - Sept

Telephone: 01829 720383

Website: www.britainsfinest.co.uk

Lyme Park Garden

Address: Disley. Cheshire. SK12 2NX

Activities: Lyme Park is a 17 acre high-Victorian garden. The garden is surrounded by a medieval deer park of almost 1400 acres of moorland, woodland and parkland

Restrictions: Dogs must be kept on a lead in main car park. In the park etc they must be under close control in case of wandering livestock.

Car Parking: Pay & Display

Opening Times: Open all year

Telephone: 01663 762023

Website: www.britainsfinest.co.uk

Rode Hall Garden

Address: Church Lane. Scholar Green. Cheshire. ST7 3QP

Activities: A beautiful country house with extensive gardens. There is an Italian garden in the ruins of the old Tenents´ Hall.Vegetables and fruit are grown in the walled kitchen garden

Restrictions: Dogs very welcome on leads

Car Parking: Free parking

www.dogfriendly.co.uk

Opening Times: Open April - Sept
Telephone: 01270 873237
Website: www.rodehall.co.uk

Tatton Park

Address: Tatton Park, Knutsford, Cheshire, WA16 6QN

Activities: One of the UK's most complete historic estates. The Mansion, Gardens, Farm, Old Hall, 1,000 acre deer park and speciality shops offer something for everyone

Restrictions: Dogs are welcome. Please on a lead in the farm and near livestock. Dogs are not allowed in the formal gardens.

Car Parking: Pay & Display

Opening Times: Open all year

Telephone: 01625 374400

Website: www.tattonpark.org.uk

Bodmin and Wenford Railway

Address: General Station, PL31 1AQ

Activities: Cornwall's only standard guage steam railway. Come and enjoy a 13 mile round trip on this steeply graded line through the beautiful countryside.

Restrictions: Bowl of water on station. Dogs carried free on all trains except dining trains. Please keep them on the floor not on the furniture.

Car Parking: Free parking and Pay & Display

Opening Times: Open all year

Telephone: 01208 73666

Website: www.bodminandwenford railway.co.uk

Brocklands Adventure Park

Address: West Street Kilkhampton, Near Bude, Cornwall, EX23 9QW

Activities: For younger children

Restrictions: Dogs welcome on leads.

Car Parking:

Opening Times: Open from Feb on Sat, Sun, Tues, Wed, Thurs

Telephone: 01288 321920

Website: www.brocklands.com

Carn Euny Ancient Village

Address: 1 1/4 miles South West of Sancreed off A30

Activities: Among the best preserved ancient villages in the South-West, occupied from Iron Age until late Roman times. The foundations of stone houses & an underground passage.

Restrictions: Dogs on leads welcome

Car Parking: Parking (600 metres (660 yards) away in Brane).

Opening Times: Open all year

Telephone: 0870 333 1181

Website: www.megalithic.co.uk

Chysauster Ancient Village

Address: Newmill. Penzance. TR20 8XA

Activities: English Heritage - Iron Age settlement was originally occupied almost 2,000 years ago

Restrictions: Dogs welcome on leads.

Car Parking: Free parking: quarter mile away

Opening Times: Open April - End Oct

Telephone: 07831 757934

Website: www.english-heritage.org.uk

Colliford Lake Park

Address: Bolventor. Bodmin Moor. Cornwall. PL14 6PZ

Activities: Over 58 acres of woodland, wetland and moorland nature walks. You're guaranteed a fantastic day out.

Restrictions: Dogs welcome on leads

www.dogfriendly.co.uk

Car Parking: Free parking

Opening Times: Open Easter - End Oct

Telephone: 01208 821469

Website: www.collifordlakepark.com

Fal River Links

Address: Truro, Falmouth & Helford area

Activities: Spend the day serenely travelling between each of the many activities and attractions that the river Fal has to offer. Wonderful woodland walks and scenery

Restrictions: Dogs are welcome on all ferries and itinerary walks. Dogs are permitted on National Trust Woodland Walks but not in the gardens.

Car Parking: Pay & Display

Opening Times: Open all year

Telephone: 01872 861 914

Website: www.falriverlinks.co.uk

Geevor Tin Mine

Address: Pendeen. Penzance. TR19 7EW

Activities: The largest preserved mining site in the UK , now a museum, a guided underground tour through 18th / 19th century workings, also shop and a café

Restrictions: Dogs are welcome all over the site with the exception of the Underground Tour.

Car Parking: Free parking

Opening Times: Open all year except Saturdays

Telephone: 01736 788662

Website: www.geevor.com

Launceston Castle

Address: Launceston, PL15 7DR

Activities: Set on a large natural mound, Launceston Castle dominates the surrounding landscape. The Castle was the ultimate status symbol of Middle Age wealth and power.

Restrictions: Dogs are welcome on a lead

Car Parking: Pay & Display

Opening Times: 1st April - End Oct

Telephone: 01566 772365

Website: www.english-heritage.org.uk

Magnificent Music Machines

Address: St. Keyne Station, Near Liskeard,

Activities: Eccentric museum created on the back of one man's passion for music boxes, Wurlitzers, and organs of yesteryear. Tranquil setting by the old mill stream.

Restrictions: Dogs on leads are welcome.

Car Parking: Free parking

Opening Times: Open Good Friday - 7th Nov

Telephone: 01579 343108

Website: www.paulcorinmusic.co.uk

Minack Theatre

Address: Porthcurno, Penzance TR19 6JU

Activities: Outdoor theatre, surrounded by gardens. Sub-tropical rockeries have become a must for gardeners with a taste for the exotic.

Restrictions: Dogs are permitted.

on a lead for daytime visiting only. They will not be admitted to performances (Registered Guide Dogs excepted).

Car Parking: Free parking

Opening Times: Open all year

Telephone: 01736 810181

Website: www.minack.com

Mount Edgcumbe House

Address: Cremyll. Torpoint. PL10 1HZ

Activities: Former home of the Earls of Mount Edgcumbe. Set in Grade I Cornish Gardens within 865 acres Country Park on the Rame Peninsula, South East Cornwall

Restrictions: Dogs are to be kept under control in the Park. On a lead in the Formal Gardens, not allowed in the Earl's Garden. Scoop bag dispenser is located near the Lower Gate.

Car Parking: Pay and Display

Opening Times: Open April - Sept

Telephone: 01752 822236

Website:www.mountedgcumbe. gov.uk

Pencarrow House and Gardens

Address: Pencarrow Bodmin PL30 3AG

Activities: The home of the Molesworth-St Aubyn's - Winner of the Dog's Trust 2004 award for "We are Dog Friendly" Tourist Attraction/Day Out - super day with your pet.

Restrictions: Well behaved dogs very welcome

Opening Times: Open April/ End Sept

Telephone: 01208 841369

Website: www.pencarrow.co.uk

Pendennis Castle

Address: On Pendennis Headland, 1 mile SE of Falmouth. TR11 4LP

Activities: Constructed between 1540 and 1545, Pendennis and its sister St Mawes Castle form the Cornish end of the chain of coastal castles.

Restrictions: Dogs on leads are welcome.

Car Parking: Free parking

Opening Times: Open all year

Telephone: 01326 316594

Website: www.english-heritage.org.uk

Penhallam

Address: Week St Mary, HOLSWORTHY

Activities: The low and grass-covered but complete ground-plan of a moated 13th-century manor house, in a delightful woodland setting.

Restrictions: Dogs on leads are welcome

Car Parking: Parking is limited

Opening Times: Open all year

Telephone: 01326 212044

Website: www.english-heritage.org.uk

Restormel Castle

Address: Lostwithiel. PL22 0EE

Activities: English Heritage - great 13th-century circular shell-keep of Restormel still encloses the principal rooms of the castle in remarkably good condition.

Restrictions: Dogs welcomed every where on a lead.

Car Parking: Free parking

Opening Times: Open April - End Oct

Telephone: 01208 872687

Website: www.english-heritage.org.uk

St Breock Downs Monolith

Address: On St Breock Downs; 31/2 miles SW of Wadebridge off unclassified road to Rosenannon

Activities: This is Cornwall's largest and heaviest prehistoric monolith. It stands on the summit of the St Breock Downs, offering wonderful views.

Restrictions: Dogs on leads are welcome

Opening Times: Open all year

Telephone: 01208 813725

Website: www.english-heritage.org.uk

St Catherine's Castle

Address: St Catherine's Point, Fowey, Cornwall PL23 1JH

Activities: The castle remains overlook the estuary and can be accessed via a short path from the beach

Restrictions: Dogs allowed on a lead

Car Parking: Parking in Fowey 1/2 mile walk

Opening Times: Open all year

Telephone: 0870 3331181

Website: www.english-heritage.org.uk

St Mawes Castle

Address: St Mawes, TR2 3AA

Activities: The best preserved and most elaborately decorated of Henry VIII's coastal fortresses

Restrictions: Dogs on leads are welcome in the grounds, but not in the Castle

Car Parking: Free parking

Opening Times: Open all year

Telephone: 01326 270526

Website: www.cornwall-online.co.uk

The Seal Sanctuary

Address: Gweek. Nr Helston. TR12 6UG

Activities: The national seal sanctuary.

Restrictions: Dogs welcome as long as kept on leads, and any mess cleaned up after them.

Car Parking: Free parking

Opening Times: Open all year

Telephone: 01326 221361

Website: www.cornwall-online.co.uk

Tintagel Castle

Address: On Tintagel Head, 1/2 mile along uneven track from Tintagel, no vehicles (PL34 0HE)

Activities: With its spectacular location on one of England's most dramatic coastlines, Tintagel is an awe-inspiring and romantic spot, a place of legends.

Restrictions: Dogs are very welcome on leads

Car Parking: Pay & Display parking in village then foot path to castle

Opening Times: Open all year

Telephone: 01840 770328

Website: www.tintagelweb.co.uk

Trebah Garden

Address: Mawnan Smith, Falmouth. TR11 5JZ

Activities: Trebah Gardens - spectacular 26 acre Cornish ravine garden, rated among the 80 finest gardens in the world.

Restrictions: Dogs are welcome in the garden and on the beach - on a lead at all times.

Car Parking: Free parking

Opening Times: Open all year

Telephone: 01326 250448

Website: www.trebahgarden.co.uk

Tregiffian Burial Chamber

Address: Located 2 miles SE of St Buryan, on B3315

Activities: A Neolithic or early Bronze Age chambered tomb with an entrance passage, walled and roofed with stone slabs, leading into the central chamber

Restrictions:

Car Parking:

Opening Times: Open all year

Telephone: 0845 3010007

Website: www.english-heritage.org.uk

Trelissick Garden

Address: Feock, nr Truro. TR3 6QL

Activities: Beautifully positioned at the head of the Fal estuary the estate commands panoramic views over the area and has extensive park and woodland walks beside the river.

Restrictions: Dogs allowed in Park and Woodland Walks only (not gardens). There is an excellent dog walk of 2 or 3 miles around the outside of the estate.

Car Parking: Parking, 50 yds £3 (refunded on admission to garden)

Opening Times: Open all year

Telephone: 01872 862090

Website: www.nationaltrust.org.uk

Trengwainton Garden

Address: Madron, nr Penzance TR20 8RZ

Activities: National Trust - Splendid views of Mount Bay and the Lizard - Enormous tree ferns creating a 'Jurassic' feel

Restrictions: Dogs on leads welcome throughout the garden. Please clear up dog waste and dispose of it sensibly.

Car Parking: Free parking

Opening Times: Open Feb - Nov Sun to Thurs

Telephone: 01736 363148

Website: www.nationaltrust.org.uk

Trevarno Estate

Address: Trevarno, Crowntown, Nr Helston, TR13 0RU

Activities: You can explore the magnificent gardens, grounds and Woodland walks and enjoy the abundant wildlife.

Restrictions: Dogs are welcome on leads waste bins are provided throughout the gardens.

Car Parking: Free parking

Opening Times: Open all year

Telephone: 01326 574274

Website: www.trevarno.co.uk

Trewithen Gardens

Address: Grampound Road Near Truro. TR2 4DD

Activities: Trewithen is one of the most elegant eighteenth century houses in Cornwall. Set in a glorious landscaped parkland of ancient trees vistas and avenues.

Restrictions: Dogs on leads are welcome

Car Parking: Free parking

Opening Times: Open 1st March - End Sept Mon-Sat

Telephone: 01726 883647

Website: www.trewithengardens.co.uk

Brantwood - Historic House and Gardens

Address: The Brantwood Trust, Coniston, Cumbria, LA21 8AD

Activities:

Brantwood has unique and beautiful mountainside gardens, set in a 250 acre wood estate with spectacular views

Restrictions: Dogs allowed but must be kept on a lead

Car Parking: Free parking

Opening Times: All year daily except Novermber - March closed Monday's & Tuesday's

Telephone: 015394 41396

Website: www.brantwood.org.uk

Brougham Castle

Address: Brougham Castle, Penrith, Lake District, Cumbria, CA10 2AA

Activities: In what must be one of the most attractive settings for a castle in all of England, Brougham Castle rests on a low rise beside the River Eamont, a few miles east of Penrith.

Restrictions: Dogs allowed on a leads

Car Parking: Free parking

Opening Times: 1 Apr-30 Sep 10am-5pm Open daily

Telephone: 01768 862488

Website: www.english-heritage.org.uk

Carlisle Castle

Address: Cumbria - CA3 8UR (Carlisle City Centre)

Activities:

Impressive and forbidding, Carlisle Castle is a formidable fortress, amply repaying exploration of its absorbing 900-year history

Restrictions: Dogs allowed on a leads

Car Parking: City Car Parking: (pay and display)

Opening Times: Open All year daily

Telephone: 01228 591922

Website: www.english-heritage.org.uk

Furness Abbey

Address: Cumbria - LA13 0PJ, Located 11/2 miles North of Barrow-in-Furness, off A590

Activities: The impressive remains of an abbey include much of the east end and west tower of the church, the ornately decorated chapter house and the cloister buildings.

Restrictions: Dogs allowed on a leads

Car Parking: Free parking

Opening Times: 1 Apr - 30 Sep 10am-5pm Daily. 1-31 Oct Closed Tues & Wed. 1 Nov-20 Mar, Closed Mon-Wed.

Telephone: 01229 823420

Website: www.english-heritage.org.uk

Grizedale Forest

Address: Grizedale Forest, Grizedale, Ambleside, Cumbria, LA22 0QJ

Activities: Grizedale Forest has much to offer all ages and abilities: waymarked walking and cycling trails through beautiful oak woodland and conifer forest, orienteering courses, play area, café, bike hire etc.

Restrictions: Dogs allowed but must be kept under control

Car Parking: Pay & Display

Opening Times: Open all year - closed Christmas & New Year

Telephone: 01229 860010

Website: www.information-britain.co.uk

High Head Sculpture Valley

Address: High Head Farm, Ivegill, Carlisle, Cumbria CA4 0PJ

Activities: Art Gallery, Spa, Farmhouse Tea room and sculpture valley, country walks. Specially created trails enable visitors to experience the true pastoral beauty.

Restrictions: Dogs are welcome, but not in the gallery or tea room. Must be kept on a lead and pooper-scoopers are to be used at all times

Car Parking: Free parking

Opening Times: Open all year (closed Wednesdays)

Telephone: 016974 73552

Website: www.highheadsculpture valley.co.uk

Holker Hall & Gardens

Address: Cark-in-Cartmel, Grange-over-Sands, Cumbria, LA11 7PL

Activities: The gardens surrounding Holker Hall cover 25 acres of highly acclaimed woodland and formal garden areas, offering a richness and variety particular to this special micro-climate of the South Lakes.

Restrictions: Dogs on leads (park only)

Car Parking: Free parking

Opening Times: 1 Apr to 28 Oct Sun to Fri 10: 30-17: 30, Closed Sat.

Telephone: 015395 58328

Website: www.holker-hall.co.uk

Hutton-in-the-Forest

Address: Hutton-in-the-Forest, Penrith, Cumbria, CA11 9TH

Activities: Enjoy the rich history, architecture, art and gardens, while special events throughout the year include open-air Shakespeare theatre.

Restrictions: Dogs permitted on leads in the gardens, grounds and woodland walks.

Car Parking: Free parking

Opening Times: House 2nd May- 30th Sept, (Wed, Thur & Sun.) Gardens 11am - 5pm 1st April - 29th Oct except Sat.

Telephone: 017694 84449

Website: www.hutton-in-the-forest.co.uk

Lake Winemere

Address: Registered Office: Windermere Lake Cruises Ltd, Winander House, Glebe Road, Bowness-On-Windermere, Cumbria, LA23 3HE

Activities: A delightful 45 minute sightseeing tour from Bowness Bay to include the magnificent mountain scenery, lovely secluded bays and shore line and inevitably the many wooded islands around the central parts of the lake.

Restrictions: Dogs are allowed on the cruise but must be kept on a laed

Car Parking: Pay & Display

Opening Times: Open All year daily

Telephone: 015394 43360

Website: www.windermere-lakecruises.co.uk

Muncaster Castle

Address: Muncaster Castle, Ravenglass, Cumbria, CA18 1RQ

Activities: Muncaster Castle, home to the Pennington family for 800 years, is a genuine treasure trove of art and antiques.

Restrictions: Dogs on leads welcome in the gardens and Owl centre.

Car Parking: Free parking

Opening Times: Open February 10th - November 4th Gardens Open daily. Castle open Sunday - Friday 12 noon - 5pm

Telephone: 01229 717 614

Website: www.muncaster.co.uk

Piel Castle

Address: 37 Market Street, Ulverston, Cumbria LA12 7LR

Activities: The impressive ruins of a 14th century castle with a massive keep, inner and outer baileys, and towered curtain walls still standing.

Restrictions: Dogs allowed but must be kept on a lead

Car Parking: Free parking

Opening Times: Open daily throughout the year

Telephone: 0870 3331181

Website: www.english-heritage.org.uk

Ravenglass Roman Bath House

Address: Ravenglass, Cumbria CA18 1RW

Activities: Ravenglass was an important naval base for the Romans in the 2nd century. Little remains except for the remarkable bath house. One of the largest surviving Roman structures in England.

Restrictions: Dogs allowed but must be kept on a lead

Car Parking: Free parking

Opening Times: Open daily throughout the year

Telephone: 0870 3331181

Website: www.theravensworth.com

Rydal Mount & Gardens

Address: Rydal Mount & Gardens, Ambleside, Cumbria, LA22

Activities: Nestling between the beautiful fells, Lake Windermere and Rydal Water lies the 'most beloved' home of William Wordsworth from 1813 - 1850.

Restrictions: Dogs allowed but must be kept on a lead

Car Parking: Free parking

Opening Times: Open daily all year except November - February (Closed Tuesdays)

Telephone: 01539 433 002

Website: www.information-britain.co.uk

www.dogfriendly.co.uk

Sizergh Castle garden

Address: Kendal, Cumbria, LA8 8AE

Activities: Sizergh Castle's garden has two lakes and a superb rock garden. All this is set in a 1600 acre estate crossed by public footpaths, providing short walks from the castle to dramatic viewpoints.

Restrictions: Dogs on leads

Car Parking: Free parking

Opening Times: 1 Apr to 28 Oct, Sun-Thu 11:00-17:00.

Telephone: 0870 458 4000

Website: www.nationaltrust.org.uk

Wetheral Priory Gatehouse

Address: Wetheral, Carlisle

Activities: The 15th-century gatehouse of a Benedictine priory, where wrongdoers could claim pardon if they enlisted to fight the Scots.

Restrictions: Dogs allowed but must be kept on a lead

Car Parking: Free parking

Opening Times: Open daily throughout the year

Telephone: 0161 242 1400

Website: www.english-heritage.org.uk

Beehive Farm Lakes, Roliston

Address: Rosliston. near Burton upon Trent. Derbyshire. DE12 8HZ

Activities: Over 66 acres of emerging young woodland to explore with thriving wildlife, fishing lakes and a family-friendly animal farm. Wonderful walking trails and fishing lakes.

Restrictions: Dogs very very welcome

Car Parking: Pay & Display or Free parking in the farm

Opening Times: Open all year (weather permitting)

Telephone: 01283 763981

Website: www.beehivefarm-woodland lakes.co.uk

Carsington Water

Address: Visitor Centre. Ashbourne. Derbyshire. DE6 1ST

Activities: There are plenty of scenic walks in the immediate area around the reservoir but also pathways to other trails that stretch beyond Carsington.

Restrictions: Dogs allowed under control

Car Parking: Pay & Display

Opening Times: Open all year

Telephone: 01629 540696

Website: www.stwater.co.uk

Chatsworth Garden

Address: Bakewell. Derbys. DE45 1PP

Activities:

The 105 acre garden is a magical landscape, there are five miles of walks with rare trees, shrubs etc, and the famous waterworks falling 200 yards down the hill

Restrictions: Dogs very welcome on leads, but not in the house or farm yard

Car Parking: Pay & Display

Opening Times: Open March - December

Telephone: 01246 582204

Website: www.chatsworth.org

Crich Tramway Village

Address: Crich Tramway Village, nr Matlock, Derbyshire, DE4 5DP

Activities: A lovingly restored period village that is also home to the National Tramway Museum and its world renowned archives.

Restrictions: Dogs very welcome in village on a lead

Car Parking: Free parking

Opening Times: Open Feb - End Oct

Telephone: 01773 854321

Website: www.tramway.co.uk

Five Pits Trail

Address: Birkin Lane, Grassmoor, Chesterfield, Derbyshire, S42 5BW

www.dogfriendly.co.uk

243

Activities: It is a 5½ mile linear route from Grassmoor Country Park to Tibshelf Ponds, passing through a mainly agricultural and woodland landscape can be extended to 7½ miles.

Restrictions: Dogs very very welcome

Car Parking: Free parking

Opening Times: Open all year

Telephone: 01246 866960

Website:www.dms-visitpeakdistrict.com

Hardwick Old Hall

Address: 91/2 miles SE of Chesterfield, off A6175, from J29 of M1. Derbyshire S44 5QJ

Activities: The Old Hall is now roofless, visitors can still ascend four floors to view surviving decorative plasterwork, as well as the kitchen and service rooms

Restrictions: Dogs welcome on leads

Car Parking: Pay & Display

Opening Times: Open March - Sept

Telephone: 01246 850431

Website: www.english-heritage.org.uk

Ilam Park

Address: Ilam, Ashbourne, Derbyshire DE6 2AZ

Activities: Runs along both banks of the River Manifold, Spectacular views towards Dovedale. Small garden on site of old Italian garden

Restrictions: Dogs welcome on leads only

Car Parking: Pay & Display. 75yds away

Opening Times: Open all year

Telephone: 01335 350503

Website: www.nationaltrust.org.uk

Peveril Castle

Address: Market Place. Casleton. Hope Valley. Derbyshire S33 8WQ

Activities: High above the pretty village of Castleton, the castle offers breathtaking views of the Peak District. Most notable is the great square keep with its round-headed windows

Restrictions: Dogs are very welcome in the castle and visitors area on a lead.

Car Parking: Pay & Display

Opening Times: Open all year

Telephone: 01433 620613

Website: www.english-heritage.org.uk

Renishaw Hall Garden

Address: Renishaw Park. near Sheffield. Derbyshire S21 3WB

Activities: 300-acre park, eight acres of the most important Italianate gardens in England. An excellent day out for families, enjoy our children's trails and magic garden.

Restrictions: Dogs are very welcome in the gardens on leads

Car Parking: Pay & Display

Opening Times: Open End March - End Sept

Telephone: 01246 432310

Website: www.sitwell.co.uk

The Midland Railway, Butterley.

Address: Butterley Station. Ripley. Derbyshire DE5 3QZ

Activities: Take a stroll to the garden railway if you like. When you board your train, the guard will wave his flag, blow his whistle, the engine will reply and your journey will commence.

Restrictions: Dogs welcome on leads

Car Parking: Free parking

Opening Times: Open every day in summer, weekends in Winter. See website

Telephone: 01773 747674

Website: www.midlandrailwaycentre.co.uk

Arlington Court

Address: Arlington, nr Barnstaple, EX31 4LP

Activities: Hidden in a wooded valley the Arlington estate houses numerous extraordinary collections. 30 acres of grounds include the formal Victorian garden and walled garden.

Restrictions: Dogs on short leads in gardens, grounds and Carriage Collection. Please clear up dog waste and dispose of it sensibly.

Car Parking: Free parking 200 yds away

Opening Times: Open March - Oct

Telephone: 01271 850296

Website: www.nationaltrust.org.uk

Becky Falls Woodland Park

Address: Manaton. Newton Abbot. TQ13 9UG

Activities: Set within a stunning Dartmoor valley, our walks and scenery offer a fun-filled day out for both young and older visitors alike.

Restrictions: Dogs are very welcome but must be kept on a lead AT ALL TIMES. Dog waste bins are not provided on the walks. Please collect your dogs waste. Do not leave on path.

Car Parking: Parking in Park, not the moors.

Opening Times: Open 24th March - 4th Nov

Telephone: 01647 221259

Website: www.beckyfalls.com

Bicton Park Botanical Gardens

Address: East Budleigh, Budleigh Salterton,

Activities: The superbly landscaped park combines 18th century tranquillity with modern amenities to provide enjoyment for everyone, of all ages, through the four seasons.

Restrictions: All dogs must be on the lead. Entrance fee £1.00 for dogs

Car Parking: Yes

Opening Times: Open all year

Telephone: 01395 568465

Website: www.bictongardens.co.uk

Canonteign Falls

Address: Nr Chudleigh, Devon. EX6 7NT

Activities: The highest waterfall in England. Walks through woodland, wetlands, lakes and parkland.

Restrictions: Dogs welcome on leads.

Car Parking: Yes

Opening Times: March-Nov.

Telephone: 01647 252434

Website: www.canonteignfalls.com

Docton Mill Gardens

Address: Lymebridge. Hartland. N Devon. EX39 6EA

Activities: The Wild Flower Gardens theme is to make everything as natural as possible with the wildlife pond and vegetable garden and extensive herbaceous border of over 140m.

www.dogfriendly.co.uk

Restrictions: Dogs allowed on short leads

Car Parking: Free parking

Opening Times: Open 1st March - 31st Oct

Telephone: 01237 441369

Website: www.doctonmill.co.uk

Grimspound Dartmoor

Address: North west side of Hameldown tor, on Dartmoor.

Activities: The best known of many Dartmoor prehistoric settlements, dates from the late Bronze Age. The remains of 24 stone houses survive within a massive boundary wall.

Restrictions: Dogs on leads are welcome

Car Parking: Free parking & Pay and Display

Opening Times: Open all year

Telephone: 01822 890414

Website: www.prehistoric.org.uk

Hartland Abbey & Gardens

Address: Hartland, Bideford, EX39 6DT

Activities: Outstanding Natural Beauty. Wander around the beautiful gardens and grounds The Abbey contains collections of pictures, furniture etc accumulated over many generations.

Restrictions: We love dogs but on leads please.

Car Parking: Free parking Car Park adjacent to the house

Opening Times: Open April 1st - 30th Sept

Telephone: 01237 441264

Website: www.hartlandabbey.com

Heddon Hall Gardens

Address: Parracombe. Barnstaple. EX31 4QL

Activities: The garden is a feast of delights for both expert and amateur gardeners. This old-fashioned flower garden offers a warm welcome for every type of North Devon visitor.

Restrictions: Dogs on leads welcome

Car Parking: Free parking

Opening Times: 1st May-31st July Sundays and Wednesdays

Telephone: 01598 763541

Website: www.heddonhallgardens. eclipse.co.uk

Hound Tor Medieval Village. Dartmoor

Address: 11/2 miles South of Manaton, 1/2 mile from the Ashburton road

Activities: The remains of four 13th century stone farmsteads, on land originally farmed in the Bronze Age. This isolated Dartmoor hamlet was abandoned in the early 15th century

Restrictions: Dogs on leads are welcome, contact site for any Restrictions.

Car Parking: Park in Hound Tor car park - 0.5 mile walk

Opening Times: Open all year

Telephone: 01822 890414

Website: www.legendarydartmoor.co.uk

Lydford Castle and Saxon Town

Address: In Lydford off A386; 81/2 miles South of Okehampton

Activities: Beautifully sited on the fringe of Dartmoor, Lydford boasts three defensive features. Near the centre is a 13th-century tower keep on a mound.

Restrictions: Dogs on leads are welcome, contact site for any Restrictions.

Car Parking: Free parking & Pay and Display

Opening Times: Open all year

Telephone: 0870 3331181

Website: www.english-heritage.org.uk

Marwood Hill Gardens

Address: Marwood. Barnstable. EX31 4EB

Activities: 20 acres of beautiful gardens and three lakes in a valley setting with Plant Centre and Garden Tea Room.

Restrictions: Dogs on leads welcome

Car Parking: Free parking

Opening Times: Open all year

Telephone: 01271 342528

Website: www.marwoodhillgarden.co.uk

Milky Way Adventure Park

Address: Clovelly, EX39 5RY

Activities: A wide range of shows and facilities. Adventure play areas dodgems, roller coaster etc. pets corner where children can feed the baby goats and lambs.

Restrictions: Dogs allowed access to most areas of theme park including gift shop (only excluded from live animal shows.) Fresh water, shaded parking all available.

Car Parking: Free parking

Opening Times: Open March 24th to October 31st,

Telephone: 01237 431255

Website: www.themilkyway.co.uk

Okehampton Castle

Address: Located 1 mile SW of Okehampton town centre. EX20 1JA

Activities: The remains of the largest castle in Devon, in an outstandingly picturesque setting on a wooded spur above the rushing River Okement

Restrictions: Dogs on leads welcome

Car Parking: Free parking

Opening Times: Open 1st April - 1st Oct

Telephone: 01837 52844

Website: www.english-heritage.org.uk

Seaton Tramway

Address: Riverside Depot. Harbour Road. Seaton. EX12 2NQ

Activities: The three-mile route runs through East Devon's glorious Axe Valley, between the coastal resort of Seaton, the small village of Colyford and the ancient town of Colyton

Restrictions: All dogs travel at a flat fare of £1.00 each, but must ride on the lower deck

Car Parking: Pay and Display

Opening Times: Feb - Oct

Telephone: 01297 20375

Website: www.tram.co.uk

www.dogfriendly.co.uk

The Donkey Sanctuary

Address: Exmouth. EX10 0NU

Activities: The Donkey Sanctuary is home to around 500 donkeys. Set in unspoilt farmland and countryside, visitors return time and again.

Restrictions: Dogs on leads welcome

Car Parking: Free parking

Opening Times: Open all year

Telephone: 01395 578222

Website: www.thedonkeysanctuary.org.uk

The Gnome Reserve & Wild Flower Garden

Address: West Putford, Nr Bradworthy EX22 7XE

Activities: Reserve comprises woodland, stream, 30 yard pond, meadow and garden - home to 1000+ gnomes and pixies.

Restrictions: Dogs on leads and pooper scoops, just in case.

Car Parking: Yes

Opening Times: 21st March-31st Oct

Telephone: 01409 241435

Website: www.gnomereserve.co.uk

Totnes Castle

Address: Castle Street, Totnes, TQ9 5NN

Activities: This motte and bailey castle has one of the largest mottes and best preserved shell keeps in the country.

Restrictions: Dogs allowed on a lead

Car Parking: A council run car park 64 metres away. Pay & Display

Opening Times: Open April - October

Telephone: 01803 864406

Website: www.castlexplorer.co.uk

Tuckers Maltings

Address: Teign Road, Newton Abbot, TQ12 4AA

Activities: One of only a handful of floor Maltings that produces malt in the traditional way. The only traditional Maltings in England that is open to the public for guided tours.

Restrictions: Well behaved dogs on a lead are very welcome.

Car Parking: Pay & Display

Opening Times: Open Easter - 31 Oct

Telephone: 01626 334734

Website: www.tuckersmaltings.com

Winsford Walled Garden

Address: Winsford Lane, Halwill Junction, EX21 5XT

Activities: Offers something very different for the summer garden visitor. The site contains full details on the history, restoration, design and plantings of this amazing North Devon garden.

Restrictions: A Doggie Garden. All dogs who arrive with their owners on leads are assured of a warm welcome and a bowl of cool refreshing water.

Car Parking: Free parking

Opening Times: Open 1st May – 31st Oct

Telephone: 01409 221477

Website: www.winsfordwalledgarden.com

www.dogfriendly.co.uk

Dorset

Abbotsbury Sub-Tropical Gardens

Address: Bullers Way, Abbotsbury, Nr Weymouth, Dorset DT3 4LA

Activities: The Garden is a mixture of formal and informal, with charming walled garden walks and spectacular woodland valley views.

Restrictions: Dogs are very welcome on a lead

Car Parking: Free parking

Opening Times: Open all year

Telephone: 01305 871130

Website: www.abbotsbury-tourism.co.uk

Avon Heath Country Park

Address: Brocks Pine, St. Leonards, Nr. Ringwood, Dorset BH24 2DA

Activities: At Avon Heath Country Park you will find 580 acres of unspoilt heathland for you to explore, and discover some of the abundant wildlife in one of the walk trails.

Restrictions: Dogs are very welcome

Car Parking: Pay & Display

Opening Times: Open all year

Telephone: 01425 478470

Website: www.ruraldorset.com

Corfe Castle

Address: The Square, Corfe Castle, Wareham, Dorset BH20 5EZ

Activities: One of Britain's most majestic ruins. Guided tours of castle

often available, outdoor theatre and family treasure trails.

Restrictions: Dogs welcome all round the castle. Water bowl provided. No charge for dogs.

Car Parking: Pay & Display. Car park 10 mins from castle

Opening Times: Open all year

Telephone: 01929 481294

Website: www.nationaltrust.org.uk

Durlston Country Park

Address: Lighthouse Road, Swanage, Dorset, BH19 2JL

Activities: A fabulous 113 hectare (280 acre) countryside paradise, consisting of sea-cliffs, coastal limestone downland, haymeadows, hedgerows and woodland.

Restrictions: Dogs are welcome but please keep them on a lead or under close control and clear up after them.

Car Parking: Pay and Display

Opening Times: Open all year

Telephone: 01929 424443

Website: www.durlston.co.uk

Kingston Lacy Garden

Address: Wimborne Minster, Dorset BH21 4EA

Activities: Elegant country mansion with important collections, set in attractive formal gardens and extensive parkland.

Restrictions: Dogs are allowed on a lead in the grounds, but not in the House, Formal Gardens, Restaurant or shop.

Car Parking: Free parking

Opening Times: Open end March-end Oct

Telephone: 01202 883402

Website: www.nationaltrust.org.uk

Lulworth Castle

Address: East Lulworth. Wareham. BH20 5QS

Activities: Enjoy the woodland and park walks or the Adventure Playground with aerial runway and the fun of the friendly Animal Farm.

Restrictions: Dogs are welcome in the park on a lead, but not in the castle.

Car Parking: Free parking

Opening Times: Open March - Oct

Telephone: 01929 400352

Website: www.romancesouthwest.co.uk

Moors Valley Country Park & Forest

Address: Horton Road, Ashley Heath, Nr Ringwood. BH24 2ET

Activities: Moors Valley covers 750 acres in the Valley of the Moors River. Enjoy a variety of countryside activities including walking, cycling etc

Restrictions: Dogs are very welcome but must be kept on a lead and under control

Car Parking: Pay & Display

Opening Times: Open all year

Telephone: 01425 470721

Website: www.moors-valley.co.uk

Sherborne Castle

Address: New Road, Sherborne. DT9 5NR

Activities: Set in 40 acres of glorious Capability Brown landscaped gardens and grounds around his 50 acre lake.

Restrictions: Dogs welcomed on lead. Not allowed in castle, but welcome on grounds surrounding.

Car Parking: Free parking

Opening Times: Open 1st April - 31st October

Telephone: 01935 813182

Website: www.sherbornecastle.com

Swanage Railway

Address: Station House, Swanage, BH19 1HB

Activities: The award-winning Swanage Railway currently operates on the six miles of track between Swanage and Norden passing the magnificent ruins of Corfe Castle.

Restrictions: Dogs are very welcome and travel for free, but not allowed in the buffet car.

Car Parking: Pay & Display

Opening Times: Open April - Oct and Nov & Dec weekends

Telephone: 01929 425800

Website: www.swanagerailway.co.uk

www.dogfriendly.co.uk

The Blue Pool

Address: Furzebrook, Nr Wareham, Dorset BH20 5AR

Activities: Dorset's unique and tranquil beauty spots. The Pool is surrounded by twenty five acres of heathland, and is crossed by a network of sandy paths.

Restrictions: Dogs are very welcome, but must be kept on a lead. Neither dogs nor people should enter the water, it is not safe for bathing.

Car Parking: Free parking

Opening Times: Open Easter-end Oct

Telephone: 01929 551408

Website: blue.pool.users.btopenworld. com

Beamish the North of England Open Air Museum

Address: The North of England Open Air Museum, Beamish, County Durham, DH9 0RG

Activities: Britain's favourite open air museum, demonstrates the recent history of the region in a "living" way and provides entertainment and education for visitors of all ages and interests.

Restrictions: Dogs are very welcome but should be kept on a lead and accompanied at all times

Car Parking: Free parking

Opening Times: 31st March - 28th Oct, Open daily 10am to 5pm. Winter 29th October - 14th March Closed Mon & Fri.

Telephone: 0191 370 4000

Website: www.beamishmuseum.co.uk

Bowes Castle

Address: In the village of Bowes just off the A66, 4 miles W of Barnard Castle

Activities: Bowes Castle stands on the site of the Roman fort of Lavatrae. The Normans recognised the strategic importance of the fort, guarding the eastern approach to the Stainmore Pass over the Pennines

Restrictions: Dogs allowed on a leads

Car Parking: Pay & Display

Opening Times: Open access at any reasonable time, daily throughout the year

Telephone: 0870 333 1181

Website: www.castlexplorer.co.uk

Hamsterley Forest

Address: Forest Enterprise, Hamsterley Forest, Bishop Auckland, County Durham, DL13 3NL

Activities: Hamsterley Forest is County Durham's largest forest, covering over 2,000 hectares. It is centred around the steep valley of the Ayhope and Bedburn becks, and the varied topography has resulted in an extremely rich and diverse collection of habitats.

Restrictions: Dogs allowed off the lead

Car Parking: Pay & Display

Opening Times: Open access at any reasonable time, daily throughout the year

Telephone: Enquiries: 01388 488312

Website: www.durham.gov.uk

High Force Waterfall

Address: Forest-in-Teesdale, Middleton-in-Teesdale, Barnard Castle, County Durham, DL12 0QG

Activities: The woodland walk leads you to this spectacular sight. As you begin the descent down the gentle slope the well-maintained path twists and turns giving a different view every few yards.

Restrictions: Dogs allowed on a leads

www.dogfriendly.co.uk

253

Car Parking: Pay & Display

Opening Times: Open access at any reasonable time, daily throughout the year

Telephone: 01833 640209

Website: www.rabycastle.com

Hylton Castle

Address: Craigavon Road, Hylton Castle Estate, Sunderland, SR5 3PA

Activities: The distinctive and highly decorative gatehouse-tower of a castle built shortly before 1400.

Restrictions: Dogs allowed on a leads

Car Parking: Pay & Display

Opening Times: Open access at any reasonable time, daily throughout the year

Telephone: 0870 3331181

Website: www.english-heritage.org.uk

Raby Castle

Address: Staindrop, Darlington, Co. Durham, UK, DL2 3AH

Activities: Raby Castle is a large fortified mansion house that has gradually developed into an impressive stately home.

Restrictions: Dogs normally allowed on a lead within the gardens.

Car Parking: Free parking

Opening Times: Daily except Saturdays from May to end of September and Bank Holiday Weekends

Telephone: 01833 660 202

Website: www.rabycastle.com

Balvenie Castle

Address: At Dufftown on the A94.

Activities: Dating to the 1200s when Marjory, daughter of Fergus, the last Celtic Earl of Buchan, married William Comyn, one of the new breed of Scottish noblemen. Balvenie is a castle of enclosure with massive curtain wall

Restrictions: Dogs are permitted in the grounds if kept on a lead. They are not permitted in roofed buildings

Car Parking: Free parking

Opening Times: (1 April - 30 September), Monday to Sunday, 9.30 am to 5.30 pm

Telephone: 01340 820121

Website: www.historic-scotland.gov.uk

Deer Abbey

Address: 2m West of Mintlaw on the A95030 – NJ 968 481

Activities: Deer Abbey was founded in 1219 by William Comyn, the Earl of Buchan. It is now the remains of a Cistercian monastery

Restrictions: Dogs are permitted in the grounds if kept on a lead.

Car Parking: Free parking

Opening Times: Open daily all year round.

Telephone: 01667 460232

Website: www.undiscoveredscotland.co.uk

Doune Castle

Address: In Doune, 16km north west of Stirling off the A84. FK14 6EA

Activities: Built in the late 14th century Doune Castle is a place of pilgrimage for Monty Python fans from all over the world who come to see the place where they filmed parts of "Monty Python and the Holy Grail".

Restrictions: Dogs are permitted in the grounds if kept on a lead. They are not permitted in roofed buildings

Car Parking: Free parking

Opening Times: 1 April - 30 Sept, Daily. 1 October - 31 March, Sat to Wed

Telephone: 01786 841742

Website: www.undiscoveredscotland.co.uk

Duffus Castle

Address: Duffus, Elgin, Moray. 5 miles North West of Elgin on the B9012 to Burghead – NJ 189 672.

Activities: Built in the mid 12th century Duffus Castle is one of the finest examples of a motte and bailey castle in Scotland. The raised ground of the motte and baileystand out ike an island in a sea of very flat farmland.

Restrictions: Dogs are permitted in the grounds if kept on a lead.

Car Parking: Free parking

Opening Times: Open daily, however can also contact 'Key Holder' to book

Telephone: 01667 460232

Website: www.castlexplorer.co.uk

www.dogfriendly.co.uk

Edzell Castle and Garden

Address: Edzell, Nr Brechin, Angus, DD9 7UE

Activities: This is a remarkable and very beautiful complex, with a late-medieval tower house incorporated into a 16th century courtyard mansion, and a walled garden with a bathhouse and summer house laid out in 1604.

Restrictions: Dogs are permitted in the grounds if kept on a lead. They are not permitted in roofed buildings.

Car Parking: Free parking

Opening Times: 1 April - 30 Sept, daily. 1 Oct - 31 March, closed Thursday's and Friday's

Telephone: 01356 648 631

Website: www.aboutbritain.com

Fort George

Address: Fort George, Arderfier, Inverness, IV2 7TD 18 km north east of Inverness off the A96.

Activities: Fort George sits on an isolated spit of land, created as the ultimate defence against further Jacobite unrest. The result, Fort George, is the mightiest artillery fortification in Britain, if not Europe.

Restrictions: Dogs are permitted in the grounds if kept on a lead. They are not permitted in roofed buildings.

Car Parking: Free parking

Opening Times: April to Sept: 9.30-5.30pm daily. Oct to March: 9.30-4.30pm daily.

Telephone: 01667 460232

Website: www.historic-scotland.gov.uk

Huntingtower Castle

Address: Region - Perthshire, Kinross and Angus. Just west of Perth off the A85 to Crieff.

Activities: Huntingtower Castle comprises two fine and complete tower houses. The hall of the eastern tower has a fine painted ceiling.

Restrictions: Dogs are permitted in the grounds if kept on a lead. They are not permitted in roofed buildings.

Car Parking: Free parking

Opening Times: 1 April - 30 September Daily. 1 October - 31 March closed Thursday and Friday

Telephone: 01738 627231

Website: www.historic-scotland.gov.uk

Huntly Castle

Address: Huntly Castle is well signposted in parkland just north of the centre of Huntly. AB54 4SH

Activities: Remarkable for its splendid architecture, Huntly Castle served as a baronial residence for five centuries.

Restrictions: Dogs are permitted in the grounds if kept on a lead.

Car Parking: Free parking

Opening Times: 1 April - 30 Sept, daily. 1 Oct - 31 March, Sat to Wed (closed Thur and Fri)

Telephone: 01466 793191

Website: www.historic-scotland.gov.uk

ILPH Belwade Farm

Address: Aboyne, Aberdeen, AB34 5DL

Activities: It is a popular destination for educational visits and those who want to enjoy the tranquil nature walk or meeting our rescued horses and ponies.

Restrictions: Dogs have access to all areas of the farm

Car Parking: Free parking

Opening Times: Open all year round. Sat, Sun, Wed and Bank Holidays between 2pm and 4pm.

Telephone: 01953 498682

Website: www.ilph.org

Kildrummy Castle

Address: 16km south west of Alford on the A97. AB33 8RA

Activities: Although ruined it remains a fine example of a 13th century castle with its curtain wall, four round towers, hall and chapel.

Restrictions: Dogs are permitted inside walls of the castle if kept on a lead

Car Parking: Free parking

Opening Times: Summer (1 April - 30 September), Monday to Sunday, 9.30 am to 5.30 pm

Telephone: 01975 571331

Website: www.historic-scotland.gov.uk

Lochleven Castle

Address: On an island in Loch Leven reached by boat from Kinross off the M90. KY13 7AR

Activities: Securely located on Castle Island in Loch Leven, Lochleven Castle had an important role in Scotland's. Famous for Mary Queen of Scots' prison.

Restrictions: Dogs are permitted on boat trip and inside the grounds if kept on a lead

Car Parking: Free parking

Opening Times: The castle is open every day from April to Sept. 9.30am - 4.15pm.

Telephone: 07778 040483

Website: www.undiscoveredscotland.co.uk

Ruthven Barracks

Address: 1m from Kingussie. Signposted from the A9 and the A86 in the centre of Kingussie

Activities: The impressive mound on which Ruthven Barracks stands is said to be a natural leftover of the retreat of the glaciers at the end of the last ice age.

Restrictions: Dogs are permitted in the grounds if kept on a lead

Car Parking: Free parking

Opening Times: Open all year round

Telephone: 01667 460232.

Website: www.historic-scotland.gov.uk

Tolquhon Castle

Address: On a minor road off the B999, 1 mile north of the junction with the A920

Activities: Tolquhon is one of the most picturesque of the castles in the Grampian countryside. Tolquhon Castle is a comfortable 16th century mansion with an earlier 15th century tower in one corner.

Restrictions: Dogs are permitted in the grounds if kept on a lead. They are not permitted in roofed buildings. Please clear up after dogs.

Car Parking: Free parking

Opening Times: 1 April - 30 September, Daily. & 1 October - 31 March, Weekends only

Telephone: 01651 851286

Website: www.historic-scotland.gov.uk

www.dogfriendly.co.uk

East Sussex

1066 Battle of Hastings, Abbey and Battlefield

Address: East Sussex - TN33 0AD

Activities: Enjoy the new audio tour of the 100-acre battlefield, stand on the very spot where King Harold was slain, and explore the ruins of the atmospheric abbey.

Restrictions: Dogs on leads only in restricted areas.

Car Parking: Pay & Display, 75m from abbey entrance

Opening Times: Open all year

Telephone: 01424 775705

Website: www.english-heritage.org.uk

Bates Green Farm and Bluebell Walk

Address: Arlington. Tye Hill Road. Polegate. BN26 6SH

Activities: The Farm Trail has eight interesting walks over three working farms. One walk of 2/3 mile through Beatons Wood has been made suitable for wheelchair users.

Restrictions: Dogs are welcome, but must remain on leads at all times please.

Car Parking: Free parking in field opposite

Opening Times: Open Only Mid April - Mid May

Telephone: 01323 485151

Website: www.bluebellwalk.co.uk

Beachyhead Countryside Centre

Address: Beachy Head Road. Beachy Head. Eastbourne.East Sussex. BN20 7YA

Activities: The walking and cycling around Beachyhead are regarded as probably the best in England. Whether you are walking the South Downs way or taking a short circular walk

Restrictions: Dogs welcome under close control

Car Parking: Free parking

Opening Times: Open all year

Telephone: 01323 423906

Website: www.beachyhead.org.uk

Bluebell Railway

Address: Sheffield Park Station. East Sussex, TN22 3QL

Activities: Travel from the Victorian age at Sheffield Park, to the 1930s at Horsted Keynes, and to the 1950s at Kingscote.

Restrictions: Dogs are welcome, but must remain on leads at all times please.

Car Parking: Free parking

Opening Times: Open all year

Telephone: 01825 720800

Website: www.bluebell-railway.co.uk

Heaven Farm

Address: Furners Green. Uckfield. East Sussex TN22 3RG

Activities: The wood parkland and waterside walks offers much interest from an ancient Bloomery, an old

pack horse bridge, a 300 year old dam badger sets and foxes' earths,
Restrictions: Dogs very welcome on a lead
Car Parking: Free parking
Opening Times: Open all year
Telephone: 01825 790888
Website: www.heavenfarm.co.uk

Herstmonceux Castle and grounds

Address: Hailsham. BN27 1RN
Activities: A magnificent moated castle, set in beautiful parkland and superb Elizabethan gardens. Walk around our walled gardens and the many woodland trails.
Restrictions: Dogs very welcome on a short lead in the grounds.
Car Parking: Free parking
Opening Times: Open April - End Oct
Telephone: 01323 833816
Website: www.herstmonceux-castle.com

Horam Manor Farm and Nature Trail

Address: Horam Manor Farm, Heathfield, TN21 0JB
Activities: The Nature Trail gives an opportunity to wander a variety of planned paths, exploring unspoilt countryside beside streams through woodlands and along open fields.
Restrictions: Dogs welcome under control
Car Parking: Free parking
Opening Times: Easter to Oct, 10.00-17.00
Telephone: 01435 812597
Website: www.villagenet.co.uk

Pevensey Castle

Address: Pevensey. East Sussex. BN24 5LE
Activities: With a history stretching back over 16 centuries, Pevensey Castle chronicles more graphically than any other fortress the story of Britain's south coast defences.
Restrictions: Dogs very welcome on a lead in restricted areas
Car Parking: Pay & Display. 300m from entrance.
Opening Times: Open all year
Telephone: 01323 762604
Website: www.english-heritage.org.uk

Seven Sisters Country Park

Address: Exceat. Seaford. East Sussex. BN25 4AD
Activities: The Seven Sisters Country Park offers a range of excellent opportunities for walkers to enjoy this beautiful landscape. Trail maps can be found in the Visitor Centre.
Restrictions: Dogs welcome under control
Car Parking: Free parking
Opening Times: Open all year
Telephone: 01323 870280
Website: www.sevensisters.org.uk

Wilderness Wood

Address: Hadlow Down East Sussex TN22 4HJ
Activities: This is a unique, award-winning working woodland. Here you can have lots of fun, walk or find peace and quiet, learn about growing trees and using wood,
Restrictions: Dogs very welcome. Not allowed in the playground or café
Car Parking: Pay & Display
Opening Times: Open all year
Telephone: 01825 830509
Website: www.wildernesswood.co.uk

East Yorkshire

Burton Agnes Hall Gardens

Address: Burton Agnes, Driffield, East Riding, YO25 4NB

Activities: The old Elizabethan walled garden is accessed through a small gate and here you will find over 3000 different plants.

Restrictions: Dogs on leads are welcome

Car Parking: Free parking

Opening Times: Apr to 31 Oct, Daily, 11:00-17:00. 10-28 Feb Snowdrops, 17-23 Dec Xmas

Telephone: 01262 490324

Website: www.britainsfinest.co.uk

Burton Constable

Address: The Burton Constable Foundation, Burton Constable, Skirlaugh, East Yorkshire HU11 4LN

Activities: Burton Constable is a large Elizabethan mansion set in a 300 acre park with nearly 30 rooms open to the public.

Restrictions: Dogs welcome on leads and must be cleaned up after.

Car Parking: Free parking

Opening Times: Open every day except Friday from 31st March until the 28th October

Telephone: 01964-562400

Website: www.burtonconstable.com

Humber Bridge Country Park

Address: The junction of two major traffic routes, the A63 running east/west and the A15 running North & South

Activities: The nature trails wind their way through the woods and meadows. Each trail is distinctively signed with wildlife waymarkers to help you explore the nature reserve.

Restrictions: Dogs very welcome.

Car Parking: Free parking

Opening Times: Open all year

Telephone: 01482 395207

Website: www.humberbridgecountry park.co.uk

Pugneys Country Park

Address: Pugneys Country Park, Asdale Road off Denby Dale Road, Wakefield, WF2 7EQ

Activities: Pugneys Country Park is a 250 acre site, The Park has two lakes. The smaller lake is 24 acres and is a nature reserve overlooked by two bird hides. Also includes a new water sports centre which was opened in early 2005

Restrictions: Dogs are welcome

Car Parking: Pay & Display

Opening Times: Open daily throughout the year

Telephone: 01924 302360

Website: www.wakefield.gov.uk

Sewerby Hall Gardens

Address: Church Lane. Sewerby. YO15 1EA

Activities: Experience what this historic country house has to offer. Set in acres of beautiful countryside, with breathtaking views of the Yorkshire coast

Restrictions: Dogs are welcome but must be kept on a lead around gardens. Banned from the hall.

Car Parking: Free parking

Opening Times: Open Easter - end Sept

Telephone: 01262 673769

Website: www.eastriding.gov.uk

Essex

East Anglian Railway Museum

Address: Chappel Station, Near Colchester, CO6 2DS

Activities: The railway is a working museum dedicated to preserving over 150 years of railway heritage in the Eastern Counties. Trains run on most days for a fun day out.

Restrictions: Dogs welcome on leads

Car Parking: Free parking

Opening Times: Open all year

Telephone: 01206 242524

Website: www.earm.co.uk

Gosfield Lake Resort

Address: Church Road, Gosfield. Halstead, Essex, CO9 1UD

Activities: The 36 acre lake and surrounding countryside combine to create a natural beauty spot. There are lakeside picnic areas, with a variety of leisure activities all catered for.

Restrictions: Dogs welcome on leads

Car Parking: Pay & Display

Opening Times: Open April - End Sept

Telephone: 01787 475043

Website: www.gosfieldlake.co.uk

Hadleigh Castle country park

Address: Off Chapel Lane, Hadleigh, Benfleet, SS7 2PP

Activities: The park gets its from the nearby Hadleigh Castle: an impressive ruin of a fortress built over 700 years ago. A great place for a walk, picnic, fly a kite or discover wildlife

Restrictions: Dogs welcome under control

Car Parking: Pay & Display

Opening Times: Open all year

Telephone: 01702 551072

Website: www.essexcc.gov.uk

Hedingham Castle

Address: Halstead. CO9 3DJ

Activities: A visit to the castle and its beautiful grounds is ideal for a family outing, and during the summer there are a variety of special events which bring its colourful history alive

Restrictions: Visitors may bring their dogs into the grounds but they must be kept on leads at all times

Car Parking: Free parking

Opening Times: Open April - Sept. Sun - Thurs

Telephone: 01787 460261

Website: www.hedinghamcastle.co.uk

Hylands House

Address: London Road. Chelmsford. CM2 8WQ

Activities: Hylands Park - is set in 574 acres of historic landscaped parkland

Restrictions: Dogs are welcome in the park provided that they are kept under control at all times

Car Parking: Free parking

Opening Times: Open all year

Telephone: 01245 606227

Website: www.chelmsford.gov.uk

Langdon Visitor Centre

Address: 3rd Avenue, Lower Dunton Road, Basildon, Essex SS16 6EB

Activities: Follow the trail for a lovely 3.5k stroll through the nature reserve. Safari through the woods and meadows to discover the bugs and beetles that live there.

Restrictions: Friendly Dogs welcome on leads

Car Parking: Free parking

Opening Times: Open all year

Telephone: 01268 419103

Website: www.essexwt.org.uk

Fife

Cambo Victorian Walled Garden

Address: Cambo. Kingsbarns. St. Andrews. KY16 8QD

Activities: & Woodland Garden - absorb the beauty of the gardens, woodland walks and shoreline and unwind in the informal restful atmosphere

Restrictions: Dogs welcome on leads

Car Parking: Free parking

Opening Times: Open all year

Telephone: 01333 450054

Website: www.camboestate.com

Batsford Arboretum

Address: Batsford Arboretum, Admissions Centre, Batsford Park, Moreton-in-Marsh, Gloucestershire, GL56 9QB

Activities: One of the jewels of the Cotswolds and one of the largest private collections of trees and shrubs in the country

Restrictions: Dogs on leads are welcome

Car Parking: Pay and Display

Opening Times: Open daily throughout the year except December & January Closed Wednesdays

Telephone: 01386 701441

Website: www.batsarb.co.uk

Birdland Park and Gardens

Address: Rissington Rd, Bourton-on-the-Water, Glos, GL54 2BN

Activities: Birdland is a natural setting inhabited by over 500 birds from around the world, including the only King Penguins in England.

Restrictions: Dogs on leads are welcome

Car Parking: Free parking

Opening Times: Open daily all year except Christmas Day

Telephone: 01451 820480

Website: www.birdland.co.uk

Great Witcombe Roman Villa

Address: Located 5 miles SE of Gloucester off A46; 1/2 mile S of reservoir in Witcombe Park; 400 metres (440 yards) from Cotswold Way National Trail

Activities: Large villa built round three sides of a courtyard in a beautiful countryside setting overlooking an enchanting valley. The villa had a luxurious bath-house complex

Restrictions: Dogs on leads are welcome

Car Parking: Pay and Display

Opening Times: Open daily throughout the year

Telephone: 01451 862000

Website: www.gloucestershire.gov.uk

Misarden Park Gardens

Address: Miserden, Stroud, Glos, GL6 7JA

Activities: Miserden Park is an attractive garden of Edwardian detail by Lutyens, set upon 17th century bones. Spring flowers, shrubs, fine topiary, bold grass terraces and large herbaceous borders contained within a walled garden.

Restrictions: Dogs on leads are welcome

Car Parking: Free parking

Opening Times: 4 Apr to 28 Sep, Tue to Thu, 10:00-17:00.

Telephone: 01285 821303

Website: www.britainsfinest.co.uk

Painswick Rococo Garden

Address: The Stables, Painswick House, Painswick, Glos, GL6 6TH

Activities: The Painswick Rococo Garden, situated in a hidden 6 acre Cotswold valley, combines formality and informality in a flamboyant package and is famous for its display of snowdrops and anniversary maze.

Restrictions: Dogs on leads are welcome

Car Parking: Free parking

Opening Times: 10 Jan-Oct, Daily, 11:00-17:00

Telephone: 01452 813204

Website: www.britainsfinest.co.uk

Stanway House

Address: Stanway. Cheltenham. GL54 5PQ

Activities: The Stanway Watergarden is one of the finest in England, created in the 1720s and Stanway House is noted for its mellow, peaceful atmosphere.

Restrictions: Dogs on leads please.

Car Parking: Free parking

Opening Times: Open June July August

Telephone: 01386 584469

Website: www.stanwayfountain.co.uk

Temple Church

Address: Temple Church and Gardens, Church Lane, Bristol BS1

Activities: The 'leaning tower' and walls of this large late medieval church survived bombing during World War II. The graveyard is now a public garden.

Restrictions: Dogs on leads are welcome

Car Parking: Pay and Display

Opening Times: Open daily throughout the year

Telephone: 0870 333 1181

Website: www.ukattraction.com

The Shambles Victorian Village

Address: Newent Gloucestershire, GL18 1PP

Activities: The Shambles is a collection of Victorian buildings - cottages, houses, alleyways, streets, courtyards, shops and workshops, housing one of the largest collections of everyday Victoriana in the country!

Restrictions: Dogs on leads are welcome

Car Parking: Free parking

Opening Times: July and August & mid March to end October : Pen daily except Mondays.

Telephone: 01531 822144

Website: www.shamblesnewent.co.uk

Westonbirt The National Aboretum garden

Address: Westonbirt, Tetbury, Glos, GL8 8QS

Activities:

Set in 600 acres of glorious Cotswold countryside, it has seventeen miles of paths along which to stroll and over 18000 numbered trees, including 100 champions.

Restrictions: Dogs on leads are welcome

Car Parking: Free parking

Opening Times: Open daily throughout the year

Telephone: 01666 880220

Website: www.britainsfinest.co.uk

Woodchester Park - National Trust

Address: The Ebworth Centre, Ebworth Estate, The Camp, Stroud, Glos GL6 7ES.

Activities: Valley contains a 'lost garden.' Chain of five lakes thread through this delightful 18th and 19th-century landscape park. Waymarked trails through delightful scenery

Restrictions: Dogs on leads are welcome

Car Parking: Pay and Display

Opening Times: Open daily throughout the year

Telephone: 01452 814213

Website: www.nationaltrust.org.uk

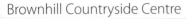
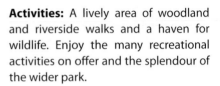

Greater Manchester

Brownhill Countryside Centre

Address: Wool Road, Dobcross, Oldham, OL3 5PB

Activities: Surrounded by dramatic Pennine scenery, Brownhill Countryside Centre is situated in the heart of Saddleworth between Dobcross and Uppermill.

Restrictions: Dogs welcome under control. Centre provides water

Car Parking: Free parking

Opening Times: Open all year

Telephone: 01457 872598

Website: www.visitoldham.co.uk

Daisy Nook Country Park

Address: Newmarket Road, Ashton-under-Lyne, OL7 9JY

Activities: It is built around a series of disused canal pools and canals. The river Medlock flows through the park, passing under a canal bridge.

Restrictions: Great place to walk the dog

Car Parking: Parking

Opening Times: Open all year

Telephone: 0161 308 3909

Website: www.ashton-under-lyne.com

Etherow Country Park

Address: Etherow Country Park, George Street, Compstall, Stockport, SK6 5JD

Activities: A lively area of woodland and riverside walks and a haven for wildlife. Enjoy the many recreational activities on offer and the splendour of the wider park.

Restrictions: Dogs welcome under control

Car Parking: Parking

Opening Times: Open all year

Telephone: 0161 427 6937

Website: www.stockport.gov.uk

Exbury Gardens and Steam Railay

Address: Exbury, Southampton, SO45 1AZ

Activities: The railway follows a one and a quarter mile circular route and is a wonderful way see the gardens. The railway follows a route through a myriad of colours and scents.

Restrictions: Dogs are very welcome on a lead, also welcome on the railway.

Car Parking: Free parking

Opening Times: March-Oct. (Special opening 8/9/15/16/21/22/23/Dec)

Telephone: 023 8089 1203

Website: www.exbury.co.uk

Houghton Lodge Gardens

Address: Stockbridge, Hampshire, SO20 6LQ

Activities: The gardens are glorious, with beautiful trees and swathes of lawn sweeping down to the River Test, with far reaching and untouched views across the valley.

Restrictions: Dogs are very welcome on a lead

Car Parking: Free parking

Opening Times: Open 1st March - 31st Oct

Telephone: 01264 810502

Website: www.houghtonlodge.co.uk

Hurst Castle

Address: Hampshire - SO41 0TP

Activities: One of the most advanced of the artillery fortresses built by Henry VIII: used as a prison for eminent 17th-century captives.

Restrictions: Dogs on leads only in restricted areas.

Car Parking: Pay & Display 1 and a half miles away in Key Haven

Opening Times: Open April - Oct

Telephone: 01590 642344

Website: www.english-heritage.org.uk

Northington Grange

Address: Northington, SO24 9TG

Activities: Set like a lakeside temple in a landscaped park, Northington Grange is the foremost example of the Greek Revival style in England.

Restrictions: Dogs allowed on and off leads in park

Car Parking: Free parking

Opening Times: Open all year but check in June & July closed in Opera season

Telephone: 01962 868600

Website: www.english-heritage.org.uk

Portchester Castle

Address: Castle Street. Portchester, Hampshire, PO16 9QW

Activities: The most impressive and best preserved of the Roman 'Saxon

www.dogfriendly.co.uk

Shore' forts, Portchester was originally built in the late 3rd century.

Restrictions: Dogs on leads (restricted areas only), allowed in the grounds but not in the inner bailey.

Car Parking: Free parking

Opening Times: Open all year

Telephone: 02392 378291

Website: www.english-heritage.org.uk

Wolvesey Castle

Address: Collage Street, Winchester, SO23 9NB

Activities: Begun as a 12th-century Norman keep and bailey castle, the palace was the chief residence of the Bishops of Winchester.

Restrictions: Dogs are very welcome on a lead

Car Parking: Restricted Free parking for 2 hours

Opening Times: 1st April -30th Sept

Telephone: 02392 378291

Website: www.english-heritage.org.uk

Herefordshire

Hergest Croft Gardens

Address: Kington, Herefordshire. HR5 3EG

Activities: Four distinct gardens extend over 50 acres, with over 4000 rear shrubs and trees. Also the Park Wood in a secluded valley hidden

Restrictions: Dogs on leads are welcome in the gardens

Car Parking: Free parking

Opening Times: Open all year

Telephone: 01544 230160

Website: www.hergest.co.uk

Kenchester Water Gardens

Address: Church Road. Lyde. Herefordshire. HR1 3AB

Activities: Beautiful Aquatic Centre, Water falls, ponds, and gardens.

Restrictions: Dogs are welcome on a lead. Not allowed in the restaurant car.

Car Parking: Free parking

Opening Times: Open all year

Telephone: 01432 270981

Website: www.kenchesterwatergardens. co.uk

Queenswood Country Park

Address: Dinmore Hill. Leominster. HR6 0PY

Activities: 67 acre tree collection (arboretum) with over 500 rare and exotic trees in an attractive parkland setting and 103 acres of semi natural ancient woodland .

Restrictions: Dogs welcome under control

Car Parking: Free parking

Opening Times: Open all year

Telephone: 01432 260848

Website: www.herefordshire.gov.uk

Shipley Gardens

Address: Holme Lacy. Herefordshire. HR2 6LS

Activities: The gardens are set within 30 acres of mixed environmental habitats as a magical structure of Garden Rooms, and a home for birds, insects; butterflies and small mammals

Restrictions: Dogs very welcome on a lead

Car Parking: Free parking

Opening Times: April - Oct

Telephone: 01432 870356

Website: www.shipleygardencentre. co.uk

View Point

Address: View website for all maps of the countryside.

Activities: Walks, Views, Woodland, Nature reserves, Towns, Villages and more. Look on the website to see more.

Restrictions: Dogs welcome under control

Car Parking: Free parking

Opening Times: Open all year

Telephone: 01600 713977

Website: www.wyevalleyaonb.org.uk

www.dogfriendly.co.uk

Fairlands Valley Park

Address: Six Hills Way, Stevenage, Hertfordshire, SG2 0BL

Activities: 120 acres of beautiful parkland situated within the heart of Stevenage. The park supports a varied selection of wildlife, and patrolled regularly by Park Wardens

Restrictions: Dogs welcome under control

Car Parking: Free parking

Opening Times: Open all year

Telephone: 01438 353241

Website: www.stevenage-leisure.co.uk

Hatfield Forest

Address: Takeley, nr Bishop's Stortford

Activities: Hatfield Forest - National Trust

Restrictions: On leads near livestock and around lake. Dog-free area near lake - please clear up dog waste and dispose of it sensibly.

Car Parking: Free parking: 60 yds

Opening Times: Open all year

Telephone: 01279 870678

Website: www.nationaltrust.org.uk

Knebworth House

Address: Knebworth, Hertfordshire. SG3 6PY

Activities: Home of the Lytton family since 1490. One of England's most beloved stately homes and gardens, and was the home of Victorian novelist Edward Bulwer Lytton. The gardens date back to 1600's

Restrictions: Dogs are welcome. Must be on a lead at all times. Dogs are not permitted in the Gardens, Dinosaur Trail or in Knebworth House, with the exception of guide dogs.

Car Parking: Free parking

Opening Times: Open 30th June - 5th September

Telephone: 01438 812661

Website: www.knebworthhouse.com

The Roman Theatre of Verulamium

Address: Bluehouse Hill, St Albans, Hertfordshire, AL3 6AE

Activities: The Roman Theatre was first discovered in 1847. The theatre was used for religious rites, ceremonies and entertainments. Wonderful walks near by.

Restrictions: Dogs welcome under control

Car Parking: Free parking for Theatre, Pay & Display for walk

Opening Times: Open all year

Telephone: 01727 835035

Website: www.romantheatre.co.uk

Douglas Steam Railway

Address: Banks Circus. Douglas. IM1 5PT

Activities: Sream Railway to Douglas - Santon - Ballasalla - Castletown - Colby - Port St Mary & Port Erin

Restrictions: Dogs allowed on trains.

Car Parking: Parking

Opening Times: Please look on website for timetable

Telephone: 01624 662525

Website: www.iombusandrail.info

Isle of Man Pleasure Cruises

Address: Villiers Steps (by the sea terminal) Douglas, IM4 6DS

Activities: Enjoy the relaxing atmosphere of another era by cruising the Manx coastline aboard the Island's largest coastal passenger vessel - the traditional M.V. Karina

Restrictions: Dogs welcome under control

Car Parking: Pay & Display

Opening Times: Open May - Sept

Telephone: 01624 861724

Website: www.iompleasurecruises.com

The Steam Packet Company

Address: Sea Terminal, Douglas, IM1 2RF.

Activities: Quality Ferry Services to the Isle of Man from Hetsham, Liverpool, Belfast, Dublin and Larne.

Restrictions: Both Ferries offer the facility for your dog to travel in your car on our well ventilated car decks (we do not charge for this service). You can also book a cabin if you wish.

Car Parking: Parking

Opening Times: Check timetable on website

Telephone: 0871 2221333

Website: www.steam-packet.com

Scarlett Point

Address: Scarlett Point, Castletown

Activities: Scarlett has spectacular geological formations with pavement-like limestone strata. A great variety of birds can be seen at Scarlett.

Restrictions: Dogs welcome under control

Car Parking: Free parking

Opening Times: Visitor Centre- April to September.

Telephone: 01624 801985

Website: www.gov.im/tourism

The National Folk Museum

Address: Cregneash, Port St Mary

Activities: A living, working illustration of life in a typical 19th century Manx upland crofting community, nestling under Meayll Hill and overlooking the Calf of Man.

Restrictions: Dogs allowed in village but not in the buildings

www.dogfriendly.co.uk

Car Parking: Ample Parking

Opening Times: Open April - Oct

Telephone: 01624 648000

Website: www.gov.im

Ayres Visitor Centre and Nature Trail

Address: On the Ballaghennie Road west of Bride. Grid Ref NX 435037

Activities: A nature reserve with a visitor centre and nature trail, internationaly important for its wildlife and excellent area for birdwatching.

Restrictions: Dogs welcome under control. Keep dogs on a lead during the breeding season.

Car Parking: Parking

Opening Times: Visitor Centre- April to September.

Telephone: 01624 801985

Website: www.wildlifetrust.org.uk

Appuldurcombe House

Address: Wroxall, PO38 3EW

Activities: Once the grandest and most striking house on the Isle of Wight and stroll peaceful through Capability Brown's idyllic orntal 11 acres of grounds.

Restrictions: Dogs are very welcome on a lead but not in the Falconry Centre.

Car Parking: Pay & Display

Opening Times: Open End March-end Sept

Telephone: 01983 852484

Website: www.english-heritage.org.uk

Carisbrooke Castle

Address: Castle Hill, Carisbrooke, PO30 1XY

Activities: Crowning a hilltop south of Newport, Carisbrooke Castle has held the dominant defensive position on the Isle of Wight for over 900 years.

Restrictions: Dogs are very welcome on a lead, but not in the museum or inside area of the tea room.

Car Parking: Free parking

Opening Times: Open all year

Telephone: 01983 522107

Website: www.english-heritage.org.uk

Blackgang Chine - Gardens, Maze

Address: Blackgang Chine, Nr Ventnor, Isle of Wight PO38 2HN

Activities: Set within rambling Victorian gardens, an eccentric mix of exciting rides, goblins and fairies, dinosaurs and nursery rhyme characters.

Restrictions: Dogs are allowed in both parks but not on rides.

Car Parking: Free parking

Opening Times: Open end March-end Oct

Telephone: 01983 730052

Website: www.blackgangchine.com

The Model Village.

Address: Godshill, Isle of Wight, PO38 3HH

Activities: Godshill's secret garden, hidden behind a high stonewall to keep it special and unique.

Restrictions: Dogs are very welcome in the model village

Car Parking: Parking 150 yds away, pay & display

Opening Times: Open March - End Nov

Telephone: 01983 840270

Website: www.iowight.com

www.dogfriendly.co.uk

275

Ventnor Botanic Garden

Address: Undercliff Drive, Ventnor, PO38 1UL

Activities: A place where the pleasure of plants can be enjoyed to the fullest.

Restrictions: Dogs are very welcome on a lead

Car Parking: Pay & Display

Opening Times: Open all year

Telephone: 01983 855397

Website: www.botanic.co.uk

Yarmouth Castle

Address: Yarmouth, PO41 0PB

Activities: A magnificent picnic spot, with views over the Solent, Yarmouth Castle is the last stone artillery fortress built for Henry VIII, in 1547.

Restrictions: Dogs are very welcome on a lead

Car Parking: Pay and Display parking in village 300 yds away

Opening Times: Open April - Sept

Telephone: 01983 760678

Website: www.english-heritage.org.uk

Bedgebury National Pinetum & Forest

Address: Bedgebury Road. Goudhurst. Cranbrook. Kent. TN17 2SJ

Activities: Bedgebury is the perfect place for walking, cycling, riding and playing in a spectacular world of trees. Wonderful walks in a beautiful setting.

Restrictions: Dogs welcome under control

Car Parking: Pay & Display

Opening Times: Open all year

Telephone: 01580 879820

Website: www.forestry.gov.uk

Capstone Farm Country Park

Address: Capstone Road. Gillingham. Kent. ME7 3JG

Activities: Covers 114 hectares of former farmland set on the North Downs. You will find ancient woodlands, old orchards, a freshwater lake, meadows and hedgerows.

Restrictions: Dogs allowed under control and on leads in restricted places

Car Parking: Free parking

Opening Times: Open all year

Telephone: 01634 812196

Website: www.medway.gov.uk

Dover Castle

Address: Dover Castle, Dover, Kent

Activities: If you are looking for a full day for all the family look no further than Dover Castle. Discover its labyrinth of secret wartime tunnels built deep in the White Cliffs of Dover.

Restrictions: Dogs on leads only in the grounds. Not allowed in buildings.

Car Parking: Within castle, 100m from keep

Opening Times: Open all year

Telephone: 01304 211067

Website: www.english-heritage.org.uk

Emmetts Garden

Address: Ide Hill, Sevenoaks, Kent TN14 6AY

Activities: This charming and informal 6-acre garden stands on one of the highest spots in Kent offering panoramic views over the Weald and towards the North Downs.

Restrictions: Dogs on short leads only

Car Parking: Free parking, 100 yds

Opening Times: Open March - End Oct

Telephone: 01732 868381

Website: www.nationaltrust.org.uk

Hever Castle

Address: Hever. Nr Edenbridge. Kent. TN8 7NG

Activities: A visit to Hever Castle and its idyllic gardens is an experience

www.dogfriendly.co.uk

277

to cherish and remember for years to come.

Restrictions: Dogs are permitted in the grounds on leads only.

Car Parking: Parking is plentiful and is free.

Opening Times: Open April - Oct

Telephone: 01732 865224

Website: www.hever-castle.co.uk

Kent & East Sussex Railway Company Ltd

Address: Tenterden Town Station. Station Road. Tenterton. Kent. TN30 6HE

Activities: Our all day hop-on, hop-off Rover fares allow unlimited travel along the full 10.5 miles (16.8 km) of the railway.

Restrictions: Dogs very welcome on a lead under close control

Car Parking: Free parking

Opening Times: Check on website for timetable

Telephone: 087060 06074

Website: www.kesr.org.uk

Mount Ephraim Gardens

Address: Mount Ephraim. Hernhill Nr Faversham. Kent. ME13 9TX

Activities: 9 acre gardens with lake, woodland area, rose terraces, Japanese rock garden and topiary. Wonderful views and trees with good walking paths for dogs.

Restrictions: Dogs are permitted in the gardens if kept on a lead.

Car Parking: Free parking

Opening Times: Easter Sunday to the end of September.

Telephone: 01227 751496

Website: www.mountephraimgardens. co.uk

Pines Garden

Address: Beach Road, St. Margaret's Bay. Nr Dover. Kent. CT15 6DZ

Activities: This six acre garden has many fine features including a cascade and adjoining lake, a specially created grass labyrinth and a roundhouse shelter for picnics.

Restrictions: Dogs very welcome on a lead

Car Parking: Free parking

Opening Times: Open all year

Telephone: 01304 851737

Website: www.baytrust.org.uk

Sandwich River Bus

Address: The Quay, Sandwich, Kent, CT13 9EN

Activities: Regular boat trips from Sandwich to the Roman Fort at Richbrough, short rides staying near the town. Mini cruises up river can go as far as Fordwich

Restrictions: Dogs allowed on boats on a lead

Car Parking: Pay & Display

Opening Times: Open for bookings all year

Telephone: 07958 376183

Website: www.sandwichriverbus.co.uk

Sissinghurst Castle Garden

Address: Sissinghurst, nr Cranbrook, Kent TN17 2AB

Activities: Intimate setting in the grounds of an Elizabethan mansion. lakeside, farmland and woodland walks Open all year, in the lovely unspoilt Wealden countryside

Restrictions: Dogs are very welcome in the surrounding woodland with wonderful walks. Dogs are not allowed in the formal gardens.

Car Parking: Pay & Display

Opening Times: Woodland walks Open all year.

Telephone: 01580 710700

Website: www.nationaltrust.org.uk

Squerryes Court Garden

Address: Squerryes Court, Westerham, Kent TN16 1SJ

Activities: A beautiful 17th century manor house which is surrounded by 20 acres of attractive and historic gardens which include a lake.

Restrictions: Dogs are alllowed in the grounds on a lead

Car Parking: Pay & Display

Opening Times: 1 April - 30 September: Wed, Sun and Bank Hol Mon

Telephone: 01959 562 345

Website: www.squerryes.co.uk

The Marsh Maize Maze

Address: St Mary's Road, Dymchurch, Romney Marsh, Kent TN29 0PW

Activities: The naturally grown maze reaches a height of over 6ft, creating pathways that will enthrall and disorientate you all in the fun!

Restrictions: Dogs very welcome on a lead

Car Parking: Free parking

Opening Times: Open Friday 20th July to Sunday 2nd September

Telephone: 01797 363254

Website: www.marsh-maize-maze. co.uk

Lancashire

Blackpool Model Village and Gardens

Address: East Park Drive, Stanley Park, Blackpool, Lancashire, FY3 9RB

Activities: Over 2 acres of beautiful landscaped gardens. The hand crafted, entertaining and amusing models are tactfully woven into the gardens. Our aim is to bring smiles to your faces and there is something for every member of the family

Restrictions: Dogs welcome but must be kept on the lead

Car Parking: Pay & Display

Opening Times: Mid March - 4th November

Telephone: 01253 763827

Website: www.information-britain.co.uk

Haigh Country Park

Address: Haigh Country Park, Haigh, Wigan, WN2 1PE

Activities: Lovely park with many displays and exhibitions featuring everything from pottery to paintings. There is also a model village and miniature railway for the kids to enjoy.

Restrictions: Dogs allowed in garden off the lead

Car Parking: Pay & Display

Opening Times: Open daily throughout the year during daylight hours

Telephone: 01942 832895

Website: www.haighhall.net

Jumbles Country Park

Address: Bradshaw Road, Bradshaw, Bolton, Lancashire, BL2 4JS

Activities: The valley and the surrounding area echo a long and interesting history of industrial activity based on textiles. The country park was opened in 1971

Restrictions: Dogs are welcome

Car Parking: Pay & Display

Opening Times: Open daily throughout the year during daylight hours

Telephone: 01204 853360

Website: www.unitedutilities.com

Moses Gate Country Park

Address: Rock Hall Visitor Centre, Hall Lane, Farnworth, Bolton

Activities: Moses Gate Country Park offers a diversity of habitats supporting many a varieties of wildlife. Activities here include- walking,, cycling, horse riding, model boating, orienteering and model aircraft flying.

Restrictions: Dogs are welcome

Car Parking: Free parking

Opening Times: Sun-Tues 9.00 am - 16.30 pm - Wed-Sat 13.00 pm - 16.30 pm Open daily throughout the year

Telephone: 01204 334343

Website: www.bolton4u.co.uk

Ashby de la Zouch Castle

Address: South Street. Ashby-De-La-Zouch. Leicestershire LE65 1BR

Activities: Ashby Castle forms the backdrop to the famous jousting scenes. See the mysterious castle garden famous for its elaborately shaped sunken features.

Restrictions: Dogs welcome on leads

Car Parking: Parking (restricted on site, park in town car park - charge applies).

Opening Times: Open all year

Telephone: 01530 413343

Website: www.english-heritage.org.uk

Bosworth Battlefield Visitor Centre and Country Park

Address: Sutton Cheney, Market Bosworth, Nuneaton, Warwickshire, CV13 0AD

Activities: With literally hundreds of things to see and do, you are genuinely spoilt for choice. Living history displays and Events.

Restrictions: Dogs welcome on leads only in outside area's, not shop or restaurant.

Car Parking: Pay & Display

Opening Times: Open all year. Closed January

Telephone: 01455 290 429

Website: www.leics.gov.uk

Great Central Railway

Address: Great Central Station, Great Central Road, Loughborough, LE11 1RW.

Activities: Mainline steam trains - every weekend throughout the year. Recreating the experience of famous expresses of the steam age.

Restrictions: Dogs are welcome on the trains, but not near the food cars.

Car Parking: Parking near some stations

Opening Times: End May - end Sept Mid week tours. Winter tours only weekends

Telephone: 01509 230726

Website: www.gcrailway.co.uk

Swannington Heritage

Address: St George's Hill, Swannington. LE67 8HH

Activities: An archive of village history and a number of important heritage sites. Walk through the village and surrounding delightful countryside.

Restrictions: Dogs welcome on leads

Car Parking: Free parking

Opening Times: Open all year

Telephone: 01530 222330

Website: www.swannington-heritage.co.uk

Watermead Country Park

Address: Alderton Close. LE4 7RN

Activities: A haven for wildlife and a peaceful stretch of countryside. It's an ideal spot for walking, cycling, picnics, birdwatching, fishing or more active watersports.

Restrictions: Dogs welcome under control

Car Parking: Pay & Display

Opening Times: Open all year

Telephone: 0116 267 1944

Website: www.leics.gov.uk

Lincolnshire

Bolingbroke Castle

Address: In Old Bolingbroke, 16 miles N of Boston off A16. Grid reference TF 349 650.

Activities: A walk around the village takes about half an hour, and there are wonderful longer circular walks up to the surrounding hills. Allow at least half an hour to visit the castle.

Restrictions: Dogs are very welcome on a lead

Car Parking: Parking Limited. Free

Opening Times: Open all year

Telephone: 01529 461499

Website: www.bolingbrokecastle.com

Burghley House - Park

Address: Burghley House, Stamford, PE9 3JY

Activities: Burghley is a real treasure house amongst beautiful gardens and wonderful walks, and lakeside walks.

Restrictions: Dogs are allowed in the park on leads, however they are not allowed in the South Gardens or the Sculpture Garden

Car Parking: Parking available

Opening Times: Open all year

Telephone: 01780 752451

Website: www.burghley.co.uk

Gainsthorpe Medieval Village

Address: Located on minor road W of A15; S of Hibaldstow; 5 miles SW of Brigg.

Activities: A deserted medieval village, one of the best-preserved examples in England, comprises earthworks of peasant houses, gardens and streets.

Restrictions: Dogs are very welcome on a lead

Car Parking: Parking limited on old road, and 3 miles from Kirton Lindsey

Opening Times: Open all year

Telephone: 0870 3331181

Website: www.english-heritage.org.uk

Grimsthorpe Castle Park and Gardens

Address: Grimsthorpe, Bourne, PE10 0LZ

Activities: Grimsthorpe Park was the southern edge of the great Lincolnshire forest. Oak trees had been recorded in the Doomsday Book of 1086.

Restrictions: Dogs are very welcome on a lead in the 3,000 acre historic park, but not in Garden or Adventure Play Ground.

Car Parking: Pay & Display

Opening Times: Open April - Sept

Telephone: 01778 591205

Website: www.grimsthorpe.co.uk

www.dogfriendly.co.uk

Hartsholme Country Park

Address: The Visitor Centre, Skellingthorpe Road, Lincoln, LN6 0EY

Activities: The site comprises Victorian landscaped gardens, a large reservoir, woodlands and grasslands. Over 200 acres to explore

Restrictions: Dogs are very welcome, but must be on a lead in the Swanholme.

Car Parking: Free parking

Opening Times: Open all year

Telephone: 01522 873577

Website: www.lincoln.gov.uk

Natureland Seal Sanctuary

Address: North Parade, Skegness, PE25 1DB

Activities: Whether feeding the pets in the children's corner or watching the beautiful Coral Fish or Tropical Butterflies, entertainment value is high at Natureland.

Restrictions: Dogs are admitted but must be kept on a lead (They are not allowed in the Floral Palace or restaurant).

Car Parking: Pay & Display

Opening Times: Open all year

Telephone: 01754 764345

Website: www.skegnessnatureland. co.uk

Thornton Abbey and Gatehouse

Address: North Lincolnshire, DN39 6TU

Activities: The enormous and ornate fortified gatehouse of Thornton Abbey is among the finest surviving in Britain. Within the grounds stand the remains of the monastic buildings.

Restrictions: Dogs on leads are welcome – contact site for any restrictions.

Car Parking: Parking available

Opening Times: End March - Beg Oct

Telephone: 0845 3010003

Website: www.english-heritage.org.uk

Chiswick House

Address: Burlington Lane, Chiswick - W4 2RP

Activities: One of the most glorious examples of 18th century British architecture. The Classical gardens are a perfect complement to the house.

Restrictions: Dogs on leads only in restricted areas.

Car Parking: Parking available off the westbound A4

Opening Times: Open 1st April - 31st October

Telephone: 0208 995 0508

Website: www.english-heritage.org.uk

Kenwood House

Address: Hampstead Lane NW3

Activities: A historic landscaped park with beautifully sloping lawns and lakes. The walled garden with its kidney shaped butterfly bed.

Restrictions: Dogs are allowed in the grounds which are part of Hampstead Heath.

Car Parking: Free parking

Opening Times: Apr-Oct 10am-6pm. Nov-Mar 10am-4pm

Telephone: 020 8348 1286

Website: www.english-heritage.org.uk

Capel Manor Gardens

Address: Bullsmoor Lane. Enfield. Middlesex. EN1 4RQ

Activities: A colourful inspiration and scented oasis surrounding a Georgian Manor House and Victorian Stables with 30 acres of richly planted themed gardens.

Restrictions: Dogs very welcome on a lead

Car Parking: Free parking

Opening Times: Open March - October

Telephone: 08456 122122

Website: www.capelmanorgardens. co.uk

Lee Valley Regional Park

Address: Information Service. Subbins Hall Lane. Crooked Mile. Waltham Abbey. EN9 9EG

Activities: The park stretches an incredible 26 miles along the leafy banks of the River Lee, from Ware in Hertfordshire, through Essex, to the Thames at East India Dock Basin.

Restrictions: Dogs welcome under control

Car Parking: Free parking

Opening Times: Open all year

Telephone: 01992 702 200

Website: www.leevalleypark.org.uk

www.dogfriendly.co.uk

Denham Country Park

Address: Denham Court Drive. Denham. Uxbridge. UB0 5PG

Activities: 69 acres to discover at this country park. Rivers and canals border it and you can have picnics, go fishing, fly kites or simply go for walks.

Restrictions: Dogs welcome under control

Car Parking: Free parking

Opening Times: Open all year

Telephone: 01753-511-060

Website: www.londonfreelist.com

Alby Craft

Address: Cromer Road, Erpingham, Norwich NR11 7QE

Activities: Surrounded by four acres of carefully tended gardens and ponds, The attractive brick and flint Norfolk farm buildings also accommodate a gallery and gift shop.

Restrictions: Dogs are allowed everywhere apart from the tea room

Car Parking: Free parking

Opening Times: Open all year

Telephone: 01263 761590

Website: www.albycrafts.co.uk

Bishop's Boat

Address: Westgate Street, Blakeney, NR25 7NQ

Activities: The trips vary, depending on the tides, seal trips are approximately one hour, seal trips and landing on Blakeney Point up to two hours.

Restrictions: Well behaved dogs are welcome if kept on leads. No charge for dogs.

Car Parking: Pay & Display

Opening Times: Open March -Oct

Telephone: 01263 740753

Website: www.norfolksealtrips.co.uk

Blickling Hall - Park and Woods

Address: Blickling Hall, Aylsham, Norwich, NR11 6NF

Activities: A spectacular and beautiful Jacobean house entices you to visit an equally spectacular and beautiful garden beyond.

Restrictions: Dogs on lead in park not the Garden.

Car Parking: Pay & Display

Opening Times: Open all year

Telephone: 01263 738030

Website: www.gardens-guide.com

Castle Acre Priory

Address: Stocks Green, Castle Acre, PE32 2AF

Activities: There is much more to see at the priory, including the substantial remains of many of the buildings, also a recreated herb garden and a a new display of artefacts.

Restrictions: Very, very dog friendly. Dogs must be on a lead. Doggy toilet available, and bowls of water available in summer months

Car Parking: Free parking

Opening Times: Open all year

Telephone: 01760 755394

Website: www.english-heritage.org.uk

www.dogfriendly.co.uk

287

Fairhaven Woodland & Water Garden

Address: School Road, South Walsham, Norwich, NR13 6DZ

Activities: The Fairhaven Woodland and Water Garden comprises of 131acres of beautiful ancient woodland and water gardens.

Restrictions: Dogs on lead welcome, admission 25p includes a poop scoop.

Car Parking: Free parking

Opening Times: Open all year

Telephone: 01603 270449/270683

Website: www.fairhavengarden.co.uk

Felbrigg Park & Estate

Address: Felbrigg, Norwich, NR11 8PR

Activities: The park, through which there are waymarked walks, is well known for its magnificent and aged trees, and one of the finest 17th-century country houses in East Anglia.

Restrictions: Dogs on leads in parkland when stock grazing. Under close control in woodland.

Car Parking: Parking, 100 yds Pay & Display

Opening Times: Open March - Dec

Telephone: 01263 837444

Website: www.nationaltrust.org.uk

Grime's Graves, Prehistoric flint mine

Address: Lynford, IP26 5DE

Activities: Set amid the distinctive Breckland heath landscape, a wide variety of plants and fauna. And over 400 shafts, pits, quarries and spoil dumps.

Restrictions: Dogs must be kept on a lead at all times. Not allowed into the mines which have a 30 ft ladder down.

Car Parking: Free parking

Opening Times: Open March - Oct

Telephone: 01842 810656

Website: www.english-heritage.org.uk

Holkham Hall Garden

Address: Wells-next-the-Sea, Norfolk, NR23 1AB

Activities: Designated walks allow visitors to explore the 3,000-acres grounds and a 3.7 mile walk circles around the Lake in Holkham Park.

Restrictions: Dogs must be kept on a lead at all times to avoid disturbing vulnerable wildlife.

Car Parking: Free parking

Opening Times: Open all year

Telephone: 01328 710227

Website: www.holkham.co.uk

Horsey Windpump

Address: Horsey, Great Yarmouth, NR29 4EF

Activities: Impressive drainage mill with striking views across Horsey Mere (one of the Norfolk Broads) to the coast. Waymarked circular walks, and access to the beach

Restrictions: Dogs on leads near livestock. Under close control elsewhere.

Car Parking: Separate parking, 50 yds

Opening Times: Open March - Oct

Telephone: 01284 747500

Website: www.nationaltrust.org.uk

Ilph Hall Farm

Address: Ada Cole Avenue, Snetterton, NR16 2LR

Activities: Recovery and Rehabilitation, Centre for Rescued Horses and Ponies. Free Guided Tours round the farm.

Restrictions: Dogs must be kept on the lead

Car Parking: Free parking

Opening Times: Open Wed/Sat/Sun and Bank Holidays

Telephone: 01953 497200

Website: www.ilph.org

Norfolk Shire Horse Centre

Address: West Runton Stables, West Runton, Cromer, NR27 9QH

Activities: The object of this centre is to bring together a collection of different breeds of draft horses. Old and young delight in enjoying the horses from the past up to modern times

Restrictions: Well behaved dogs are welcome if kept on a short lead.

Car Parking: Free parking

Opening Times: Open Easter - End Oct

Telephone: 01263 837339

Website: www.norfolk-shirehorse-centre.co.uk

Priory Maze & Garden

Address: Cromer Road, Beeston Regis, Sheringham, NR26 8SF

Activities: One of the most enchanting gardens in Norfolk, where you can experience peaceful relaxation in natural gardens of woodland, water and meadow.

Restrictions: Dogs are allowed provided they are kept on a lead. Entrance fee 50p per dog.

Car Parking: Free parking

Opening Times: Open March - Nov

Telephone: 01263 822986

Website: www.priorymazegardens.co.uk

Sheringham Park

Address: Visitor Centre, Wood Farm, Upper Sheringham, NR26 8TL

Activities: The large woodland garden is particularly famous for its spectacular show of rhododendrons and azaleas, also stunning views of the coast and countryside.

Restrictions: Dogs on leads only near livestock

Car Parking: Pay & Display 60 yds away

Opening Times: Open all year

Telephone: 01263 820550

Website: www.nationaltrust.org.uk

www.dogfriendly.co.uk

Antrim Castle Gardens

Address: Randalstown Road, Antrim, BT41 4LH

Activities: The 17th century water gardens are one of the earliest in the British Isles. Exceptional features include an ancient motte, spectacular and unique parterreround and paths

Restrictions: Dogs welcome on leads

Car Parking: Free parking

Opening Times: Open all year

Telephone: 028 9448 1338

Website: www.antrim.gov.uk

Giant's Causeway

Address: 44a Causeway Road, Bushmills, Co. Antrim BT57 8SU

Activities: Coast path with info panels extends 12 miles to the Carrick-a-Rede rope bridge. Geology, flora and fauna of international importance.

Restrictions: Dogs welcome under control

Car Parking: Pay & Display

Opening Times: Open all year

Telephone: 028 2073 1582

Website: www.nationaltrust.org.uk

Giant's Causeway Station

Address: Runkerry Road, Bushmills, Co Antrim, BT57 8RW.

Activities: The railway has been built to the Irish narrow gauge of three feet. The carefully planned design of the railway's station workshops, carriage sheds etc hark back in time.

Restrictions: Dogs welcome on leads

Car Parking: Free parking if you buy a ticket for the train.

Opening Times: See Website for time table

Telephone: 028 20732844

Website: www.freewebs.com

Glenariff Forest Park

Address: On A43 Ballymena/Waterfoot road

Activities: Walk on the many trails like the scenic trail (9.0 Km), waterfall trail (4.5 Km), garden trail (1.0 Km), and the glensway nature trail (2.5 Km).

Restrictions: Dogs welcome under control

Car Parking: Free parking

Opening Times: Open all year

Telephone: 028 217 58232

Website: www.ireland-holidays.net

Patterson's Spade Mill

Address: 751 Antrim Road, Templepatrick, Co. Antrim BT39 0AP

Activities: Vividly captures life during the Industrial Revolution. Discover the history and culture behind the humble spade. Handcrafted spades on sale and made to specification.

Restrictions: Dogs welcome on leads

Car Parking: Free parking

Opening Times: Open end March - End Oct

Telephone: 028 9443 3619

Website: www.nationaltrust.org.uk

Ardress House

Address: 64 Ardress Road, Annaghmore, Portadown, Co. Armagh, BT62 1SQ

Activities: Attractive garden with scenic woodland and riverside walks. Home to an important collection of farm machinery and tools.

Restrictions: Dogs welcome on leads on in the garden

Car Parking: Free parking

Opening Times: Open End March - End Sept

Telephone: 028 8778 4753

Website: www.nationaltrust.org.uk

Gosford Forest Park

Address: Markethill, Co. Armagh, BT60 1UG

Activities: Four way-marked trails of varying length wind through the forest leading into some of the park's most beautiful and tranquil areas.

Restrictions: Dogs welcome under control

Car Parking: A charge per car into the park applies.

Opening Times: Open all year

Telephone: 028 37552169

Website: www.gosford.co.uk

Derrymore House

Address: Bessbrook, Newry, Co. Armagh BT35 7EF

Activities: Walking trails with panoramic views of the local area and the ring of Gullion. An ideal stopping point on the drive between Belfast and Dublin.

Restrictions: Dogs welcome under control

Car Parking: Free parking, 30 yds

Opening Times: Open all year

Telephone: 028 8778 4753

Website: www.nationaltrust.org.uk

Lough Neagh Discovery Centre

Address: Oxford Island, Craigavon, Armagh, BT66 6NJ

Activities: View the area's varied birdlife from one of several hides or stroll the winding shoreline on a peaceful guided walk. Experience the wonders of Oxford Island for yourself.

Restrictions: Dogs welcome under control

Car Parking: Free parking

Opening Times: Open all year

Telephone: 028 38322205

Website: armagh.goireland.com

www.dogfriendly.co.uk

Peatlands Park

Address: 33 Derryhubbert Road, Dungannon, BT71 6NW

Activities: The narrow gauge railway is a big attraction for the young and old alike within the Park, and explore the 680 acre site on foot along its many paths and wooden walkways

Restrictions: Dogs welcome under control, and are welcome on the trains on a lead.

Car Parking: Free parking is available for 200 cars

Opening Times: Train available March - Oct. Park Open all year

Telephone: 028 3885 1102

Website: www.ehsni.gov.uk

The Argory

Address: 144 Derrycaw Road, Moy, Dungannon, Co. Armagh, BT71 6NA

Activities: Garden, woodland and riverside walks with wonderful sweeping views. Neo-classical Irish gentry house: virtually unchanged since 1900.

Restrictions: Dogs on leads and only in grounds and garden

Car Parking: Parking, 100 yds

Opening Times: Open all year

Telephone: 028 8778 4753

Website: www.nationaltrust.org.uk

Castle Ward

Address: Strangford, Downpatrick, Co. Down BT30 7LS

Activities: A 332-hectare (820-acre) walled demesne is in a stunning location overlooking Strangford Lough Free trail maps from leaflet dispensers in car park area & visitor reception.

Restrictions: On leads and only in grounds

Car Parking: Free parking, 250 yds

Opening Times: Grounds Open all year. House open March - Sept

Telephone: 028 4488 1204

Website: www.nationaltrust.org.uk

Downpatrick & Co. Down Railway

Address: Market Street, Downpatrick, Co Down, BT30 6LZ

Activities: The Downpatrick & County Down Railway offers a number of exciting events for your enjoyment, or just to keep the kids (and big kids busy).

Restrictions: Dogs on leads welcome

Car Parking: Free parking

Opening Times: Every weekend Mid June-Mid Sept, and special holiday events.

Telephone: 028 4461 5779

Website: www.downrail.co.uk

Mount Stewart House

Address: Portaferry Road, Newtownards, Co. Down BT22 2AD

Activities:

One of Northern Ireland's most popular National Trust properties. Celebrated landscaped park: European Garden of Inspiration 2003. Dramatic views across Strangford Lough

Restrictions: On leads only in grounds and garden. Please clear up dog waste and dispose of it sensibly.

Car Parking: Free parking

Opening Times: Open all year

Telephone: 02842 788387

Website: www.nationaltrust.org.uk

Murlough National Nature Reserve

Address: Dundrum, Co Down, BT33 0NQ

Activities: The best and most extensive example of dune heath within Ireland. Network of paths and boardwalks through the dunes. Self-guided nature walk, additional guided walks

Restrictions: Dogs allowed under control. Some resrictions apply.

Car Parking: Pay & Display

Opening Times: Open all year

Telephone: 028 4375 1467

Website:

www.dogfriendly.co.uk

293

Quoile Countryside Centre

Address: 5 Quay Road, Downpatrick, Co Down, BT30 7JB

Activities: The Quoile Pondage National Nature Reserve provides Castle Island Hide, Pond-dipping stands, Wildlife gardens and a Picnic area.

Restrictions: Dogs on leads welcome

Car Parking: Free parking

Opening Times: Open all year

Telephone: 028 4461 5520

Website: www.ehsni.gov.uk/quoile

Rowallane Garden

Address: Saintfield, Ballynahinch, Co. Down BT24 7LH

Activities: Much of the garden reflects the natural landscape of the surrounding area, into which many exotic species have been introduced.

Restrictions: Dogs allowed on a leads

Car Parking: Free parking

Opening Times: Open all year

Telephone: 028 9751 0131

Website: www.nationaltrust.org.uk

Scrabo Country Park

Address: 203A Scrabo Road, Newtownards, Co Down, BT23 4SJ

Activities: The Park includes the woodlands of Killynether, the disused quarries where Scrabo stone was once quarried a pond and a prehistoric hill fort.

Restrictions: Dogs welcome under control

Car Parking: Free parking

Opening Times: Open all year

Telephone: 028 91811491

Website: www.ehsni.gov.uk

Castle Archdale Country Park

Address: Irvinestown, Co. Fermanagh, BT94 1PP

Activities: Features within the Park include a red deer enclosure, wildfowl ponds, nature trail, butterfly garden and wildflower meadow.

Restrictions: Dogs welcome under control

Car Parking: Free parking

Opening Times: Open all year

Telephone: 028 6862 1588

Website: www.ehsni.gov.uk

Castle Coole

Address: Enniskillen, Co. Fermanagh, BT74 6JY

Activities: Magnificent 18th-century mansion and landscape park. The surrounding historic wooded landscape park sloping down to Lough Coole is ideal for long walks.

Restrictions: Dogs on leads and only in grounds and garden

Car Parking: Parking, 150 yds. Pay & Display

Opening Times: House open March - Sept. Grounds Open all year

Telephone: 028 6632 2690

Website: www.nationaltrust.org.uk

Crom

Address: Upper Lough Erne, Newtownbutler, Co. Fermanagh, BT92 8AP

Activities: Romantic and tranquil landscape of islands, woodland and historical ruins. There are nature trails a programme of guided walks and boats for hire.

Restrictions: Dogs welcome on leads

Car Parking: Parking, 100 yds Pay & Display

Opening Times: Open March - Sept

Telephone: 028 6773 8118

Website: www.nationaltrust.org.uk

Florence Court

Address: Enniskillen, Co. Fermanagh BT92 1DB

Activities: One of Ulster's most important 18th-century houses. There are extensive walks in the grounds, a sawmill, holiday cottage and walled garden.

Restrictions: Dogs on leads and only in grounds and garden

Car Parking: Parking, 200 yds

Opening Times: Grounds Open all year. House open March - Sept

Telephone: 028 6634 8249

Website: www.nationaltrust.org.uk

www.dogfriendly.co.uk

Northern Ireland
Londonderry

Mussenden Temple and Downhill Demesne

Address: Mussenden Road, Castlerock, Co. Londonderry, BT51 4RP

Activities: Landscaped demesne and historic monuments in a dramatic coastal setting. Cliff top and garden walks with breathtaking views. Striking 18th-century ruins to explore.

Restrictions: Dogs on leads

Car Parking: Parking (Pay & Display) at Lion's Gate.

Opening Times: Open all year

Telephone: 028 2073 1582

Website: www.nationaltrust.org.uk

Roe Valley Country Park

Address: 41 Dogleap Rd, Limavady, Co Londonderry, BT49 9NN

Activities: The river plunges through spectacular gorges and its banks are clothed with mature mixed woodland. It is a beautiful tranquil location.

Restrictions: Ensure all dogs are kept under control and not allowed to foul paths and mown grass or the beaches.

Car Parking: Free parking

Opening Times: Open all year

Telephone: 028 7772 2074

Website: www.ehsni.gov.uk

Wellbrook Beetling Mill

Address: 20 Wellbrook Road, Corkhill, Cookstown, Co. Tyrone

Activities: Last working beetling mill in Northern Ireland. Situated in an attractive glen, with many good walks. Picnic opportunities by the Ballinderry River.

Restrictions: Dogs on leads and only in grounds.

Car Parking: Free parking, 10 yds

Opening Times: House open March - Sept

Telephone: 028 8674 8210

Website: www.nationaltrust.org.uk

North Yorkshire

Bolton Abbey

Address: General Enquiries: Estate Office, Bolton Abbey, Skipton, North Yorkshire, BD23 6EX

Activities: There are over eighty miles of footpaths across some of the most spectacular countryside in England.

Restrictions: Dogs are welcome on leads in the countryside surrounding the abbey

Car Parking: Free parking

Opening Times:

Telephone: 01756 718009

Website: www.boltonabbey.com

Castle Howard Gardens

Address: York, YO60 7DA

Activities: The Castle Howard gardens and park are breathtaking throughout the seasons and, with many diverse areas to explore, you can find peace and tranquillity whichever path they choose.

Restrictions: Dogs welcome on leads

Car Parking: Free parking

Opening Times: All year, Daily, 10:00-18:30 or dusk.

Telephone: 01653 648 444

Website: www.britainsfinest.co.uk

Constable Burton Hall Gardens

Address: Constable Burton, Leyburn, North Yorkshire, DL8 5LJ

Activities: In April there is a fine show of daffodils and in May there are over 6000 tulips on display.

Restrictions: Dogs on leads are welcome

Car Parking: Free parking

Opening Times: 24th March - 14th Oct, daily 9am - 6pm

Telephone: 01677 450 428

Website: www.information-britain.co.uk

Easby Abbey

Address: North Yorkshire, 1 mile South East of Richmond off B6271

Activities: After winding down a very narrow country lane in the heart of North Yorkshire, having passed a 14th century gatehouse that is essentially intact, and the delightful parish church of St Agatha, the substantial ruins of Easby Abbey are an imposing sight.

Restrictions: Dogs on leads are welcome

Car Parking: Free parking

Opening Times: Open daily throughout the year

Telephone: 0870 3331181

Website:
www.english-heritage.org.uk

Embsay & Bolton Abbey Steam Railway

Address: Bolton Abbey Station, Skipton, North Yorkshire, BD23 6AF

Activities: Travel between Embsay station, and the new award-winning station at Bolton Abbey. Your journey takes you through picturesque Yorkshire Dales scenery. Bolton Abbey station is the ideal stopping off point for a pleasant one and a half mile walk to the ruins

Restrictions: Dogs are welcome on the trains but please keep them off the carriage seats

Car Parking: Pay & Display

Opening Times: Steam trains run every Sunday throughout the year, with Summer services up to 7 days a week.

Telephone: 01756 710614

Website: www.embsayboltonabbey railway.org.uk

Fountains Abbey & Studley Royal Water Garden

Address: Ripon Nr Harrogate, North Yorkshire, HG4 3DY

Activities: One of the most remarkable places in Europe and a World Heritage Site, comprising the spectacular ruin of a 12th-century Cistercian abbey, an Elizabethan mansion and one of the best surviving examples of a Georgian water garden.

Restrictions: Dogs on leads are welcome

Car Parking: Visitor centre: free. Studley Royal lakeside: £3 per car.

Opening Times: Open daily throughout the year

Telephone: 01765 608888

Website: www.fountainsabbey.org.uk

Helmsley Castle

Address: Castlegate, Helmsley, North Yorkshire, YO62 5AB

Activities: The most impressive features of Helmsley castle are its large earthworks with two deep ditches that are cut down through the outcrop of rock on which the castle stands.

Restrictions: Dogs on leads are welcome

Car Parking: Free parking

Opening Times: Open daily throughout the year except between (1 Nov-29 Feb) - Closed on Tues & Wed

Telephone: 01439 770442

Website: www.english-heritage.org.uk

Ingleton Waterfalls Trail

Address: Broadwood Enterance. Ingleton, Carnforth, LA6 3ET

Activities: The famous Waterfalls Trail has some of the most spectacular waterfall and woodland scenery in the North of England.

Restrictions: Dogs are allowed on the trail although they must be kept on leads in certain sections

Car Parking: Free parking

Opening Times: The trail is open seven days a week, all year round,

Telephone: 015242 41930

Website: www.ingletonwaterfallswalk. co.uk

Middleham Castle

Address: North Yorkshire - DL8 4QR

Activities: Though roofless, many of these buildings survive, making Middleham a fascinating castle to explore.

www.dogfriendly.co.uk

Restrictions: Dogs on leads are welcome

Car Parking: Pay & Display

Opening Times: Daily throughout the year

Telephone: 01969 623899

Website: www.english-heritage.org.uk

Monk Bretton Priory

Address: Located 1 mile E of Barnsley town centre, off A633

Activities: The open space of the priory grounds and the views across the wooded countryside still convey the feeling of peace and tranquility as benefited monastery life. But this belies the turbulent and often violent past of this sleeping ruin.

Restrictions: Dogs on leads are welcome

Car Parking: Free parking

Opening Times: Daily throughout the year

Telephone: 0870 3331181

Website: www.english-heritage.org.uk

Parcevall Hall Gardens

Address: Skyreholme, Skipton, N Yorks, BD23 6DE

Activities: Parcevall Hall Gardens is a hidden gem. Located on a steep hillside and the only large garden to be open to the public within the Yorkshire Dales National Park.

Restrictions: Dogs welcome on Leads

Car Parking: Free parking

Opening Times: 1 Apr-30 Sep Daily, 10:00-18:00.

Telephone: (01756) 720311

Website: www.parcevallhallgardens.co.uk

Richmond Castle

Address: North Yorkshire - DL10 4QW. In Richmond

Activities: Richmond Castle, founded in 1071, is a gray stone fortress standing proudly atop a rocky spur overlooking the turbulent River Swale. The great castle of Richmond is among the oldest Norman stone fortresses in Britain

Restrictions: Dogs on leads are welcome

Car Parking: Pay & Display

Opening Times: Daily throughout the year

Telephone: 01748 822493

Website: www.english-heritage.org.uk

Rievaulx Abbey

Address: North Yorkshire - YO62 5LB. In Rievaulx; 21/4 miles N of Helmsley, on minor road off B1257

Activities: The majestic, almost regal, appearance of Rievaulx Abbey looming from the depths of a narrow river valley symbolises the power and importance of monasticism in medieval England. Escape the crowds and experience the serene beauty of this impressive monasti.

Restrictions: Dogs on leads are welcome

Car Parking: Free parking

Opening Times: 1 Apr-30 Sep Daily. 1-31 Oct Closed Tues & Wed. 1 Nov-20 Mar 10am-4pm Closed Tues & Wed

Telephone: 01439 798228

Website: www.english-heritage.org.uk

www.dogfriendly.co.uk

Scarborough Castle

Address: Castle Road, Scarborough, North Yorkshire, YO11 1HY

Activities: With over 2,500 years of turbulent history behind it, Scarborough Castle defends a prominent headland between two bays, there is evidence of Iron Age settlements and the remains of a Roman signal station on the site.

Restrictions: Dogs on leads are welcome

Car Parking: (Pay & Display.) There is a public car park at the start of Castle Road, about a ten minute walk fro

Opening Times: Open all year round

Telephone: 01723 372451

Website: www.castlexplorer.co.uk

Studley Royal Water Garden

Address: Fountains, Ripon, N Yorks, HG4 3DY

Activities: Studley Royal Water Garden is a serenely beautiful landscape garden. Featuring one of the best water gardens in England.

Restrictions: Dogs welcome on leads

Car Parking: Free parking

Opening Times: Open daily throughout the year

Telephone: 01765 608888

Website: www.britainsfinest.co.uk

Sutton Park Garden

Address: Sutton-on-the-Forest, York, YO61 1DP

Activities: The gardens featuring herbaceous rose borders are full of rare and interesting plants laid out with great care over the past thirty five years. In the grounds are a Georgian Icehouse and woodland walks.

Restrictions: Dogs welcome on leads

Car Parking: Free parking

Opening Times: Open daily, April - September

Telephone: 01347 810249

Website: www.statelyhome.co.uk

Thorp Perrow Arboretum garden

Address: Bedale, N Yorks, DL8 2PR

Activities: one of the largest and rarest collections of trees and shrubs in the north of England and holds five National Collections. An onsite captive breeding and conservation centre that gives you the opportunity to learn more about birds of prey.

Restrictions: Dogs welcome on leads

Car Parking: Free parking

Opening Times: Open daily from dawn - dusk throughout the year

Telephone: 01677 425323

Website: www.britainsfinest.co.uk

www.dogfriendly.co.uk

301

Northampton

Brampton Valley Way Linear Park

Address: c/o Brixworth Country Park, Northampton Road, Brixworth, Northampton, NN6 9DG

Activities: A 14-mile former railway line which is now a linear park with a cycle track for walking and cycling from the outskirts of Northampton to Market Harborough. There are car parks, picnic areas, tunnels, wildlife and countryside fields, streams and woods.

Restrictions: Dogs welcome

Car Parking: Pay & Display

Opening Times: Open daily throughout the year

Telephone: 01604 883920

Website: www.enjoyengland.com

Canons Ashby House garden

Address: Daventry, Northants, NN11 3SD

Activities: Mixed rose and herbaceous borders; old fruit varieties including plums, pears and apples; early 18th century timber gates and seat in the Green Court make the gardens at Canons Ashby complete.

Restrictions: Dogs on leads are welcome

Car Parking: Free parking

Opening Times: Open every weekend throughout the year as well as 17 Mar-30 Sep Mon-Wed, Sat-Sun.

Telephone: 01327 861900

Website: www.britainsfinest.co.uk

Daventry Country Park

Address: Daventry Country Park, Northern Way, Daventry, Northamptonshire, NN11 5JB

Activities: The Country Park is an Ideal place to come and enjoy the countryside with beautiful lakeside scenery, flowery grassland and shady woodland.

Restrictions: Dogs welcome

Car Parking: Pay & Display

Opening Times: Open daily throughout the year

Telephone: 01327 877193

Website: www.daventrydc.gov.uk

Irchester Country Park

Address: On B570, off A509, 2 miles south of Wellingborough

Activities: Irchester Country Park contains a mixture of mature woodland and grassy open meadows. The park began life as an ironstone quarry and the old quarry face, with its layers of rock and fossils, is a Regionally Important Geological Site.

Restrictions: Dogs welcome

Car Parking: Pay & Display

Opening Times: Open daily throughout the year

Telephone: 01933 276866

Website: www.east-northantsonline.co.uk

Kelmarsh Hall

Address: Kelmarsh Hall, Kelmarsh, Northampton, NN6 9LY

Activities: Kelmarsh Hall is a graceful 18 th century historic house, set in beautiful romantic gardens and surrounded by its own working estate in the rolling Northamptonshire and Leicestershire countryside.

Restrictions: Dogs on leads are welcome

Car Parking: Free parking

Opening Times: Open Tuesday, Wednesday, Thursday and Sundays from Easter until the end of September

Telephone: 01604 686543

Website: www.kelmarsh.com/

Kirby Hall

Address: English Heritage, Kirby Hall, Near Corby, Northamptonshire

Activities: Kirby Hall is an outstanding example of a large, stone-built Elizabethan mansion, begun in 1570 with 17th Century alterations.

Restrictions: Dogs on leads are welcome

Car Parking: Free parking

Opening Times: Throughout the year open on, Thu, Fri, Sat, & Sun. Except 1 Jul-31 Aug Open every day

Telephone: 01536 203230

Website: www.ukattraction.com

Rockingham Castle & Gardens

Address: Rockingham Castle, Rockingham, Market Harborough, Leicestershire, LE16 8TH

Activities: The castle overlooks the picturesque village of Rockingham, whose main street, lined with thatched and slated cottages, leads into the Welland valley. The castle was built on the orders of William the Conqueror, on a commanding hill site previously occupy

Restrictions: Dogs welcome in the gardens but must be kept under control. Not allowed in the house

Car Parking: Free parking

Opening Times: 8th April to the end of May only open Sundays & Bank holidays. June to September open Tuesdays, Sund

Telephone: 01536 770240

Website: www.rockinghamcastle.com

Wicksteed Park

Address: Wicksteed Park, Kettering, Northamptonshire. NN15 6NJ

Activities: Wicksteed Park has one of the biggest and best free playgrounds in Europe! In recent years over £250,000 has been invested on a huge variety of themed play areas - swings, see-saws, climbing frames, adventure modules and activities - all designed to kee

Restrictions: Dogs on leads are welcome

Car Parking: Free parking

OpeningTimes: Open daily throughout the year

Telephone: 08700 621 193

Website: www.wicksteedpark.co.uk

www.dogfriendly.co.uk

Northern Scotland

Attadale Gardens

Address: Strathcarron, Highland, IV54 8YX

Activities: Attadale House was built in 1755. Gardens and woodlands were started in 1890 by Baron Schroder and planted with rhododendrons, azaleas and specimen trees. The garden has been given 4 stars by the tourist board.

Restrictions: Dogs on lead please

Car Parking: Free parking

Opening Times: Apr to Oct, Mon-Sat, 10:00-17:30

Telephone: 01520 722603

Website: www.britainsfinest.co.uk

Beauly Priory

Address: In Beauly on the A862

Activities: An outdoor ancient monument. The ruined church of a Valliscaulian priory, one of three founded in 1230

Restrictions:

Car Parking: Free parking

Opening Times: Open all year. Between 1st Oct-31st March, Closed on Sun

Telephone: 01463 783 444.

Website: www.historic-scotland.gov.uk

Castle of Old Wick

Address: 1 mile South of Wick on Shore Road

Activities: Ruin of the best-preserved Norse castle in Scotland. This spectacular site is on a spine of rock projecting into the sea.

Restrictions:

Car Parking: Free parking

Opening Times: Open all year round

Telephone: 01667 460232

Website: www.castlexplorer.co.uk

Culloden Battlefield

Address: Culloden Moor, Inverness IV2 5EU

Activities: Culloden Battlefield is the moor where Bonnie Prince Charlie was defeated in a heroic battle. The exhibition explores the famous battle and the weaponry used.

Restrictions: Dogs allowed on a lead on the battlefield. Allowed off the lead in surrounding fields. Not allowed inside roofed houses.

Car Parking: Free parking

Opening Times: 10am - 4pm (November - March) 9am - 6pm (April - October)

Telephone: 01463 790607

Website: www.nts.org.uk/culloden

Dun Carloway

Address: Carloway, Isle of Lewis HS2 9DY.

Activities: An ancient dwelling - One of the best preserved broch towers in Scotland. Great scenery and views. Fantastic for hill walkers

Car Parking: Free parking

Opening Times:
Visitor Centre- April to September, Mon to Sat, 10.00- 17.00

Telephone:
01851 643338

Website: www.undiscoveredscotland.co.uk

Hackness Martello Tower and Battery

Address: At the south east end of Hoy. KW16 3PQ.

Activities: Towers built between 1813 and 1815 to provide defence for British convoys. Evidence of life e.g barrack room furniture & other military memorabilia

Restrictions: Dogs allowed in grounds on a lead - but not permitted in roofed houses. Please clear up after your dog.

Car Parking: Free parking

Opening Times: April to September every day from 9.30am to 5.30pm

Telephone: 0131 668 8800

Website: www.undiscoveredscotland.co.uk

Jarlshof Prehistoric and Norse Settlement

Address: At Sumburgh Head, 35 km south of Lerwick on the A97

Activities: Prehistorics settlement provides insight into the way of life of the inhabitants during the periods of Bronze, Iron and Pictish ages.

Restrictions: Dogs allowed in grounds on a lead - but not permitted in roofed houses. Please clear up after your dog.

Car Parking: Free parking

Telephone: 0131 668 8800

Website: www.historic-scotland.gov.uk

Pitmuies Gardens

Address: House of Pitmuies, Guthrie, By Forfar, Angus, DD8 2SN

Activities: Two semi-formal wall gardens adjoin 18th century house and shelter long border of herbaceous perennials.

Restrictions: Dogs on lead please

Car Parking: Free parking

Opening Times: Open 1 April - 31 October 10am - 5 pm

Telephone: 01241 828 245

Website: www.pitmuies.com

Ring of Brodgar Stone Circle and Henge

Address: About 5 miles North East of Stromness on the B9055. Near Stromness, Orkney, KW16

Activities: Magnificent and unique view. A beautiful circle of upright stones, dating back to the late Neolithic period

Restrictions: Dogs allowed in grounds on a lead. Please clear up after your dog.

Car Parking: Free parking

Opening Times: Open all year

Telephone: 0131 668 8800

Website: www.historic-scotland.gov.uk

www.dogfriendly.co.uk

The Bishop's Palace and Earl's Palace

Address: In Kirkwall on the A960.

Activities: Great sight with great views. The earliest visible parts of the Bishop's Palace date to the 12th century.

Restrictions: Dogs allowed in grounds on lead -not permitted in roofed houses. Please clear up after your dog. Warning - combination of a large number of steps and a gravel path

Car Parking: Free parking

Opening Times: April to September every day from 9.30am to 5.30pm.

Telephone: 01856 871918

Website: www.undiscoveredscotland. co.uk

The Black House, Arnol

Address: Arnol village, Isle of Lewis, 18km norh west of Stornoway on the A858. The Western Isles. Postcode HS2 9DB.

Activities: Taking walkers back through time, with fully furnished historic sites.

Restrictions: Dogs allowed in grounds on a lead - but not permitted in roofed houses.

Car Parking: Free parking

Opening Times: 1 April - 30 September and 1 October - 31 March

Telephone: 01851 710395

Website: www.historic-scotland.gov.uk

The Castle & Gardens of Mey

Address: Thurso, Highland, KW14 8XH

Activities: The Castle & Gardens of Mey was owned by the Queen Mother who bought the Castle of Mey in 1952. Her Majesty created a traditional Scottish walled garden with vegetables, fruit and herbaceous plants.

Restrictions: Dogs allowed in grounds on lead - not permitted in roofed houses.

Car Parking: Free parking

Opening Times: 1st May - 30th September. Open daily

Telephone: 01847 851473

Website: www.britainsfinest.co.uk

Allen Banks & Staward Gorge

Address: Bardon Mill, Hexham, Northumberland NE47 7BU

Activities: Site of Special Scientific Interest for its rich plant and animal life. Beauty and tranquillity with miles of footpath to explore.

Restrictions: Dogs allowed

Car Parking: Free parking

Opening Times: All year, daily, dawn-dusk

Telephone: 01434 344218

Website: www.nationaltrust.org.uk

Aydon Castle

Address: Aydon Castle, Corbridge, Northumberland, NE45 5PJ

Activities: One of the finest and most unaltered examples of a 13th-century English manor house, Aydon Castle stands in a secluded woodland setting.

Restrictions: Dogs allowed on the grounds and inside the castle if kept under close control/lead

Car Parking: Free parking

Opening Times: 1 Apr-30 Sep 10am-5pm Mon, Thu, Fri, Sat, & Sun

Telephone: 01434 632450

Website: www.english-heritage.org.uk

Bedlington Country Park

Address: Bedlington Country Park, Humford Mill, Church Lane, Bedlington, Northumberland, NE22 5RT

Activities: Bedlington Country Park has over 5 miles of pathways and nature trails along the banks of the river Blyth, giving access to some stunning riverside views

Restrictions: Dogs allowed off leads

Car Parking: Free parking

Opening Times: Open all year round

Telephone: 01670 843444

Website: www.wansbeck.gov.uk

Belsay Hall, Castle and Gardens

Address: Belsay, Tyne and Wear, NE20 0DX

Activities: There's something for everyone at Belsay. Explore a spectacular medieval castle, a Grecian-revival-style 19th-century mansion and thirty acres of stunning Grade I gardens linking the two

Restrictions: Dogs allowed on a lead in the gardens

Car Parking: Free parking

Opening Times: Open all year round except for winter (November-March) closed on Tuesday & Wednesday

Telephone: 01670 528080

Website: www.english-heritage.org.uk

Dunstanburgh Castle

Address: Northumberland - NE66 3TT

Activities: Dunstanburgh Castle is now ruinous, rated at one time among the largest and grandest castles in the north of England. The castle was protected on two sides by the sheer cliff face and the sea.

Restrictions: Dogs on leads are welcome

Car Parking: Pay & Display

Opening Times: 1 Apr - 31 Oct Daily. 1 Nov-20 Mar Closed on Tuesdays & Wednesday's

Telephone: 01665 576231

Website: www.english-heritage.org.uk

Edlingham Castle

Address: Edlingham Castle, Edlingham, Alnwick

Activities: The riverside ruins, principally the solar tower, of a manor house progressively fortified against the Scots during the 14th century stand next to Edlingham Burn in a rugged but attractive valley.

Restrictions:

Car Parking: Pay & Display

Opening Times: All year daily

Telephone: 0870 3331181

Website: www.english-heritage.org.uk

Etal Castle

Address: Etal Castle, Etal Village, Cornhill-on-Tweed, Northumberland, TD12 4TN

Activities: Etal was built in the mid-14th century by Robert Manners as a defence against Scots raiders, in a strategic position by a ford over the River Till.

Restrictions: Dogs allowed on the grounds and inside the castle if kept under close control/lead

Car Parking: Free parking

Opening Times:
1 Apr-30 Sep 11am-4pm Mon, Tue, Wed, Thu, Fri, Sat, & Sun.

Telephone: 01890 820332

Website: www.english-heritage.org.uk

Hadrian's Wall

Address: Hadrian's Wall Heritage Ltd, East Peterel Field, Dipton Mill Road, Hexham, Northumberland, NE46 2JT

Activities: Hadrian's Wall is perhaps the most important structure remaining from the Roman's occupation, with numerous centres and activities along the wall.

Restrictions: Dogs welcome in the grounds and round the outdoor monuments. Not allowed inside of roofed buildings

Car Parking: Pay & Display

Opening Times: Open daily 9:30 - 1pm & 2pm -5:30. Closed on sundays as of 1st October

Telephone: 01434 322002

Website: www.hadrians-wall.org

Hauxley Nature Reserve and Visitor Centre

Address: Low Hauxley, Amble-by-the-Sea, Northumberland, NE65 0JR

Activities: A picturesque lake sprinkled with islands is home to a wide variety of breeding birds, especially terns and is a popular spot for migrating waders

Restrictions: Dogs allowed on a lead

Car Parking: Free parking

Opening Times: All year daily 10.00 - dusk

Telephone: 01665 711578

Website: www.britinfo.net

www.dogfriendly.co.uk

Lindisfarne Priory

Address: On Holy Island, only reached at low tide across causeway. TD15 2RX

Activities: When you cross the dramatic causeway to Holy Island, you journey into our spiritual heritage. Few places are as beautiful or have such special significance.

Restrictions: Dogs on leads are welcome in the priory, but not in the museum

Car Parking: Pay & Display

Opening Times: 1 Apr --31 Oct 2007 (daily) 1 Nov - 31 Jan 10am-2pm (Sat-Mon)

Telephone: 01289 389200

Website: www.holy-island.info

National Park Centre, Ingram

Address: Ingram Visitor Centre, Ingram, Powburn, Alnwick, NE66 4LT

Activities: Ingram is ideal base for starting out on a number of hill walks that take in a number of ancient hill fort settlements.

Restrictions: Dogs only allowed in the Bremish Valley and must be kept under close control.

Car Parking: Free parking

Opening Times: Open daily throughout the year

Telephone: 01665 578890

Website: www.northumberlandnational park.org.uk

Paxton House

Address: Paxton House, Berwick upon Tweed, TD15 1SZ

Activities: Paxton lies at the heart of eighty acres of woodland, parkland and gardens. There are footpaths, adjacent to the breathtaking Tweed where you may see salmon, cormorants, seals, herons etc.

Restrictions: Dogs on leads welcome in the grounds and gardens.

Car Parking: Free parking

Opening Times: Open daily, 1st April to 31st October. Garden: 10.00am to sunset

Telephone: 01289 386291

Website: www.paxtonhouse.co.uk

Queen Elizabeth II Jubilee Country Park, Local Nature Reserve

Address: Woodhorn Road, Ashington, NE63 9AS

Activities: The country park, once the site of a colliery spoil heap, features a wide variety of wildlife in its new woodland, grassed bank, and a 40-acre lake.

Restrictions: Dogs allowed in country park, but not allowed past gates to the museum

Car Parking: £2 for parking

Opening Times: Open daily throughout the year

Telephone: 01670 528080

Website: www.enjoyengland.com

Tynemouth Priory and Castle

Address: Tynemouth, Newcastle, NE30 4BZ

Activities: Set in an almost impregnable position on a steep headland between the river and the North Sea, Tynemouth has always been as much a fortress as a religious site.

www.dogfriendly.co.uk

Restrictions: Dogs on leads are welcome

Car Parking: Free parking

Opening Times: 1 Apr-30 Sep 10am-5pm Daily. 1-31 Oct 10am-4pm Daily

Telephone: 0191 257 1090

Website: www.english-heritage.org.uk

Wallington Garden

Address: Cambo, Morpeth, Northumberland, NE61 4AR

Activities: Inside the egg-shaped walled garden are fine glasshouses, a sculpture terrace, a system of pools and some first-class colourful cottage gardening.

Restrictions: Dogs on leads welcome in the grounds and gardens.

Car Parking: Free parking

Opening Times: All year daily

Telephone: 01670 773600

Website: www.britainsfinest.co.uk

Warkworth Castle and Hermitage

Address: Warkworth, Alnwick, NE65 0UJ

Activities: One of the largest, strongest and most impressive fortresses in northern England.

Restrictions: Dogs on leads are welcome

Car Parking: Free parking

Opening Times: 1 Apr-30 Sep 10am-5pm Daily. 1-31 Oct 10am-4pm Daily. 1 Nov-20 Mar 10am-4pm Mon, Sat, & Sun.

Telephone: 01665 711423

Website: www.english-heritage.org.uk

Attenborough Nature Centre

Address: Barton Lane Attenborough, Nottingham, Nottinghamshire, NG9 6DY

Activities: Eco-friendly visitor & education centre with beautiful views overlooking the lakes of attenborough nature reserve.

Restrictions: Dogs are allowed on a lead only and under control.

Car Parking: £1.00 charge for parking

Opening Times: Open all year

Telephone: 0115 9721777

Website: www.attenboroughnature centre.co.uk

Clumber Park

Address: Clumber Park, Worksop, Nottinghamshire S80 3AZ

Activities: Idyllic lakeside walks in the pleasure ground. The longest avenue of lime trees in Europe. Bring your own, or hire a cycle and explore the woodland trails

Restrictions: Dogs welcome in the park

Car Parking: Pay & Display

Opening Times: Open all year

Telephone: 01909 476592

Website: www.nationaltrust.org.uk

Newstead Abbey Park & Gardens

Address: Ravenshead. Notts. NG15 8NA

Activities: The park and gardens cover more than 300 acres with paths that meander past lakes, ponds and waterfalls.

Restrictions: Dogs are welcome on leads

Car Parking: Free parking

Opening Times: Open all year

Telephone: 01623 455900

Website: www.newsteadabbey.org.uk

The Blue Line Trail

Address: Mansfield Road. Eastwood. NG16 3DZ

Activities: A one and a half mile walk round Eastwood, with lots to see.

Restrictions: Dogs very welcome on leads

Car Parking: Free parking

Opening Times: Open all year

Telephone: 0115 972 1777

Website: www.broxtowe.gov.uk

Vernon Park

Address: Vernon Park. Turncroft Lane. Stockport. SK1 4AR

Activities: The park boasts a mature woodland along the river terraces, water cascades, fountain, lily pond, walkways etc.

Restrictions: You must clean up after your dog. Dog restrictions exist in some areas of the park

Car Parking: Free parking

Opening Times: Open all year

Wollaton Park Garden

Address: Wollaton. Nottingham. NG8 2AE

Activities: Set in over 500 acres of historic deer park with a rich diversity of habitats and species. Visitors can stroll around the historic lake or relax in the formal flower gardens.

Restrictions: Dogs are welcome on leads

Car Parking: Pay & Display

Opening Times: Open all year

Telephone: 0115 9153900

Website: www.wollatonhall.org.uk

Blenheim Palace Gardens

Address: Woodstock, Oxford, OX20 1PP

Activities: Blenheim Palace gardens are one of the great 18th century parks. The Secret Garden is one of Blenheim´s most popular attractions for plant lovers as it is a garden for all seasons, combining mature trees with new plantings.

Restrictions: Dogs on leads are welcome

Car Parking: Free parking

Opening Times: 5th May -28th October. 31st October - 9th December

Telephone: 08700 60 20 80

Website: www.britainsfinest.co.uk

Chiltern Sculpture Trail

Address: Forest Enterprise, Upper Icknield Way, Aston Clinton, Aylesbury HP22 5NF

Activities: Boasting over twenty specially commissioned sculptures, the Chiltern Sculpture Trail offers the visitor a unique environment in which to experience contemporary art

Restrictions: Dogs are welcome round the trail

Car Parking: Free parking

Opening Times: Open daily throughout the year

Telephone: 01296 625825

Website: www.aylesburyvale.net

Cotswold Wildlife Park & Gardens

Address: Burford, Oxfordshire, United Kingdom, OX18 4JP

Activities: The Park is home to a fascinating and varied collection of mammals, birds, reptiles and invertebrates from all over the world and aspires to show animals to people

Restrictions: Dogs welcome, but must be kept on leads at all times. There are some areas where dogs are prohibited

Car Parking: Free parking

Opening Times: Open daily throughout the year

Telephone: 01993 823006

Website: www.cotswoldwildlifepark.co.uk

Didcot Railway Centre

Address: Didcot Railway Centre, Didcot, Oxfordshire, England, OX11 7NJ

Activities: Welcome to Didcot Railway Centre, home of the Great Western Society and its unique collection of Great Western Railway steam engines, coaches, wagons, buildings and small relics and a recreation of Brunel's broad gauge railway.

Restrictions: Well-behaved dogs are welcome at the Centre but they should be kept on a lead.

Car Parking: Pay & Display

Opening Times: 27 - 1 January. 10 to 18 February. 31 March to 15 April. 26 May to 3 June. 23 June to 2 September. 2

Telephone: 01235 817200

Website: www.didcotrailwaycentre.org.uk

Uffington Castle, White Horse and Dragon Hill

Address: Uffington Castle, White Horse and Dragon Hill, Oxfordshire, England

Activities: The White Horse is cut out of the turf on the chalky upper slopes of Uffington Castle near to the Ridgeway. It is 374 feet long. The Uffington white horse is Britain's oldest and most famous hill figure at 2,000 to 3000 years old.

Restrictions: Dogs on leads are welcome

Car Parking: Free parking

Opening Times: Open daily through out the year

Telephone: 0870 3331181

Website: www.english-heritage.org.uk

Wallingford Castle Gardens

Address: Castle Street, Wallingford, Oxfordshire, OX10 0AL

Activities: These gardens are situated on part of the site of Wallingford Castle, which was built by William the Conqueror and demolished by Oliver Cromwell in 1652.

Restrictions: Dogs not allowed in castle gardens, but are allowed in caslte meadows.

Car Parking: Free parking

Opening Times: Apr - Oct, 6pm. Nov-Mar 10, 3pm

Telephone: 01491 826 972

Website: www.johansens.com

Waterperry Gardens

Address: Waterperry Gardens, Nr. Wheatley, Oxfordshire, England. OX33 1JZ

Activities: Whether you're looking for a stroll around magnificent gardens, excellent home-baked teas and lunches, a look back in time in our Museum of Rural Life or Saxon Church or a spot of retail therapy, you can be sure Waterperry will meet your every needs.

Restrictions: Dogs on leads are welcome in the main part of the gardens.

Car Parking: Free parking

Opening Times: Open daily throughout the year except MONDAYS

Telephone: 01844 339254

Website: www.waterperrygardens.co.uk

Acton Burnell Castle

Address: Acton Burnell, Shrewsbury SY5 7PF

Activities: The red sandstone shell of a semi-fortified tower house, built in 1284-93.

Restrictions: Dogs welcome on leads

Car Parking: Free parking

Opening Times: Open all year

Telephone: 0870 3331181

Website: www.english-heritage.org.uk

Attingham Park Garden

Address: Shrewsbury. Shropshire. SY4 4TP

Activities: The Park is mainly shrubs and large trees with a grove of Lebanon cedars. Attractive walks along the River Tern are particularly colourful in spring.

Restrictions: Dogs welcome in grounds on leads

Car Parking: Free parking

Opening Times: Open all year

Telephone: 01743 708162

Website: www.britainsfinest.co.uk

Blists Hill Victorian Town

Address: Legges Way. Madeley. Telford. TF7 5DU

Activities: Meet the Victorians in this recreated Victorian town. Costumed staff give a warm welcome and a fascinating insight into how life was lived in Victorian times

Restrictions: Dogs welcome on leads. Restrictions apply in the museums.

Car Parking: Pay & Diplay

Opening Times: Open all year

Telephone: 01952 435900

Website: www.ironbridge.org.uk

Dudmaston Garden

Address: Quatt, Bridgnorth, Shropshire WV15 6QN

Activities: Enjoy a walk in the Dingle, a wooded valley, the restored rock garden of local red sandstone or the popular `Big Pool´ surrounded by attractive plantings.

Restrictions: Dogs welcome in grounds on leads. Some restrictions apply

Car Parking: Free parking

Opening Times: Open April - Sept

Telephone: 01746 780866

Website: www.nationaltrust.org.uk

Ludlow Castle

Address: Castle Square, Ludlow SY8 1AY

Activities: Walk through the Castle grounds and see the ancient houses of kings, queens princes, judges and the nobility - a glimpse into the lifestyle of medieval society.

Restrictions: Well behaved dogs are allowed in the Castle grounds. And on leads at all times.

Car Parking: Parking pay & display.

Opening Times: Open all year

Telephone: 01584 873355

Website: www.ludlowcastle.com

www.dogfriendly.co.uk

The Dorothy Clive Garden

Address: Willoughbridge, Market Drayton, Shropshire TF9 4EU

Activities: The Dorothy Clive Garden is intimate and informal. Visitors discover the great variety of form and colour and the fine views of the surrounding hilly countryside.

Restrictions: Dogs welcome in grounds on leads

Car Parking: Free parking

Opening Times: Open End March - End Oct

Telephone: 01630 647237

Website: www.dorothyclivegarden.co.uk

Wroxeter Roman City

Address: Shropshire SY5 6PH

Activities: Wroxeter (or 'Viroconium') was the fourth largest city in Roman Britain. Most impressive features are the 2nd century municipal baths and the remains of the huge wall.

Restrictions: Dogs welcome on leads

Car Parking: 8m from entrance, with uneven surface.

Opening Times: Open all year

Telephone: 01743 761330

Website: www.english-heritage.org.uk

Barle Valley Safaris

Address: Pick Up in Dunster, Dulverton & Minehead Car Parks

Activities: The perfect way to explore Exmoor, one of England's most beautiful National Parks. Spacious 110 Land Rover takes leisurely trails of discovery

Restrictions: Dogs are welcome on the Safari with prior notice at a nominal charge of £2 for a Half day and £4 for a Full day Safari.

Car Parking: Car Parking on Pick up sites

Opening Times: Open all year

Telephone: 01643 851386

Website: www.exmoorwildlifesafaris.co.uk

Cheddar Caves & Gorge

Address: Cheddar, Somerset, BS27 3QF

Activities: A major tourist attraction for over 200 years. Outstanding Natural Beauty, where you'll find many rare species.

Restrictions: Dogs are very welcome on leads.

Car Parking: Pay & Display

Opening Times: Open all year

Telephone: 01934 742343

Website: www.cheddarcaves.co.uk

Cleeve Abbey

Address: Located in Washford, 1/4 mile S of A39. TA23 0PS

Activities: The picturesque Cistercian abbey of Cleeve boasts the most impressively complete and unaltered set of monastic cloister buildings in England.

Restrictions: Dogs on leads only in the grounds not in the Abbey

Car Parking: 70m from entrance, then 150m to admission point, via tarmac.

Opening Times: Open April - Oct

Telephone: 01984 640377

Website: www.english-heritage.org.uk

Forde Abbey & Gardens

Address: Forde Abbey, Chard, Somerset. TA20 4LU

Activities: Forde Abbey is a treasure in an area already known for its outstanding beauty. 30 acres of exquisite award winning gardens.

Restrictions: Dogs are welcome on a short lead and the gardens make a favourite walking spot. Dogs are allowed to accompany their owners into the tearoom, but not in the house.

Car Parking: Free parking

Opening Times: House open April - Oct. Gardens Open all year

Telephone: 01460 220231

Website: www.fordeabbey.co.uk

www.dogfriendly.co.uk

Gallox Bridge

Address: Dunster, West Somerset TA24

Activities: Lies at the southern end of the mediaeval village of Dunster and was used to help pack animals to cross the River Avill. The starting point for a number of walks.

Restrictions: Dogs allowed on a lead

Car Parking:

Opening Times: Open all year

Telephone: 0117 975 0700

Website: www.english-heritage.org.uk

Glastonbury Abbey

Address: Magdalene Street, Glastonbury, BA6 9EL

Activities: As well as the original Abbey buildings the site has a wealth of other attractions. Glastonbury Abbey is set in 36 beautifully peaceful acres of parkland.

Restrictions: Dogs are welcomed provided they are kept on leads at all times. Two 'dog loos' can be found within the grounds and plastic bags can be obtained from the ticket office.

Car Parking: Pay & Display

Opening Times: Open all year

Telephone: 01458 832267

Website: www.glastonburyabbey.com

Hestercombe Gardens

Address: Cheddon Fitzpaine, Taunton, TA2 8LG

Activities: A unique collection of three gardens spanning three centuries of garden history and design. Walk the gardens, visit the Courtyard to enjoy delicious refreshments

Restrictions: Dogs are welcome are welcome in all areas of the gardens on a lead, also welcome in the outside seating area in the Courtyard Cafe.

Car Parking: Free parking

Opening Times: Open all year

Telephone: 01823 413923

Website: www.hestercombe.com

Montacute House

Address: Montacute, Somerset TA15 6XP

Activities: Magnificent Elizabethan stone-built house, garden and park.

Restrictions: Dogs not allowed in the gardens, but are allowed in the Parkland around the property.

Car Parking: Free parking

Opening Times: House open April - Oct. Gardens Open all year

Telephone: 01935 823289

Website: www.nationaltrust.org.uk

Nunney Castle

Address: Nunney, Frome, Somerset BA11

Activities: Striking and picturesque moated castle of Nunney was built in the 1370s. It was designed in the latest French style, resembling a miniature version of the Paris Bastille

Restrictions: Dogs on leads. Pretty Village location

Car Parking: Parking in Village

Opening Times: Open all year

Telephone: 0117 975 0700

Website: www.english-heritage.org.uk

Pot House Hamlet

Address: Silkstone, Barnsley, South Yorkshire, S75 4JU

Activities: A great day out. Walk down the ancient wagon way, bring a picnic, wander around the quaint village and visit the village shops. Enjoy the lovely walk ways and relax.

Restrictions: Dogs welcome on leads

Car Parking: Free parking

Opening Times: Open all year

Telephone: 01226 790441

Website: www.pothousehamlet.co.uk

Rother Valley Country Park

Address: Mansfield Road, Wales Bar, Rotherham, South Yorkshire, S26 5PQ

Activities: With an area currently of 300 hectares the park offers extensive scope for many types of recreation. Walkers will enjoy the use of a network of public footpaths.

Restrictions: Dogs welcome under control

Car Parking: Pay & Display

Opening Times: Open all year

Telephone: 0114 247 1452

Website: www.rothervalley.f9.co.uk

Worsbrough Mill & Country Park

Address: Park Road, Worsbrough Bridge, Barnsley, South Yorkshire, S70 5LJ

Activities: Worsbrough Mill is a 17th century working corn mill set in over 200 acres of country park located in a nature Reserve with fishing, walking and cycling.

Restrictions: Dogs welcome under control

Car Parking: Pay & Display

Opening Times: Closed January and February

Telephone: 01226 774527

Website: www.barnsley.gov.uk

Wortley Top Forge Industrial Museum

Address: Forge Lane, Thurgoland, South Yorkshire. S35 7DN

Activities: Exhibits include the original water wheels and water powered drop hammers within the original Forge building. Adjoining buildings house a 1920s Machine Shop.

Restrictions: Dogs welcome on leads with no Restrictions

Car Parking: Free parking

Opening Times: Open Easter - Beg Nov. Open Sundays & Bank Hol Monday

Telephone: 0114 2887576

Website: www.topforge.co.uk

www.dogfriendly.co.uk

Castle Kennedy and Gardens

Address: Stair Estates, Rephad, Stranraer, DG9 8BX

Activities: At Castle Kennedy, spring finds snowdrops and daffodils throughout the gardens together with magnolias. There is a charming tea room, a gift shop, plant centre and seasonal children's activities

Restrictions: Dogs on leads

Car Parking: Free parking

Opening Times: Apr-Sep, Daily 10:00-17:00.

Telephone: 01776 702024

Website: www.britainsfinest.co.uk

Crichton Castle

Address: 4km south west of Pathhead off the A68. Post code EH37 5QH

Activities: Nothing built by man in the past 500 years can be seen in this extensive landscape: and this is within 15 miles of the centre of Edinburgh. Crichton Castle's unexpected sense of isolation is itself enough reason to visit

Restrictions: Dogs are permitted in the grounds if kept on a lead. They are not permitted in roofed buildings

Car Parking: Free parking

Opening Times: Open summer only (1 April - 31 March), Monday to Sunday 9.30 am to 5.30pm.

Telephone: 01875 320017

Website: www.historic-scotland.gov.uk

Dirleton Castle and Gardens

Address: Edinburgh and the Lothians. Post code EH39 5ER. In Dirleton village 5km west of North Berwick on the A198

Activities: Today, there is a colourful blend of traditional formal gardens and more contemporary plantings including 'as the Guinness Book of Records testifies' the world's longest herbaceous border.

Restrictions: Dogs are permitted in the grounds if kept on a lead. They are not permitted in roofed buildings.

Car Parking: Free parking

Opening Times: 1 April - 30 Sept Daily, 9.30 - 5.30 pm. 1 Oct - 31 March Daily, 9.30 - 4.30 pm

Telephone: 01620 850330

Website: www.historic-scotland.gov.uk

Drumlanrig Castle, Gardens & Country Park

Address: Thornhill, D & G, DG3 4AQ

Activities: Drumlanrig Castle, Gardens & Country Park date back to the time of William Douglas the 1st Duke of Queensbury. The garden today has undergone major restoration

Restrictions: Dogs on leads (park only)

Car Parking: Free parking

Opening Times: 31 Mar to 30 Sept, Daily, 11:00-17:00.

Telephone: 01848 331555

Website: www.britainsfinest.co.uk

www.dogfriendly.co.uk

Dundonald Castle

Address: In the village of Dundonald on the A71, Leave A77 onto B730 follow signs for Dundonald. KA2 9HD.

Activities: There is nothing subtle about Dundonald Castle. The structure whose remains are on view today can be traced back to the accession of Robert II to the Scottish throne in 1371

Restrictions: Dogs are permitted off the lead around the grounds. But must be kept on a lead inside the grounds.

Car Parking: Free parking

Opening Times: Summer (1 April - 31 October), Monday to Sunday, 10.00 am to 5.00 pm

Telephone: 01563 851489

Website: www.historic-scotland.gov.uk

Floors' Castle

Address: Floors Castle, Kelso, Roxburghshire, TD5 7SF

Activities: Floor's Castle houses excellent works of art. Offering several outdoor pursuits including golf and shooting. In the parkland are areas of native trees, while the woodlands contain many magnificent mature oak, lime trees

Restrictions: Dogs are permitted in the grounds if kept on a lead. They are not permitted in roofed buildings

Car Parking: Free parking

Opening Times: Daily from 1st May until 28th October 2007. 11am to 5pm

Telephone: 01573 223333

Website: www.floorscastle.com

Glenwhan Garden

Address: Dunragit, by Stranraer, D & G, DG9 8PH

Activities: Glenwhan is a plantswomans garden for all seasons; in spring and early summer rhododendrons and azaleas by mid-summer, Roses, Rockroses, primulas & iris carry on through to the magnificent array of hydrangeas.

Restrictions: Dogs on leads,

Car Parking: Free parking

Opening Times: 26 Mar-Oct, Daily 10:00-17:00.

Telephone: 01581 400222

Website: www.britainsfinest.co.uk

Hermitage Castle

Address: 10km north east of Newcastleton. TD9 0LU

Activities: Hermitage Castle is a forbidding and oppressive place. Seen from the east or west the architecture seems utterly brutal: Hermitage Castle has a history filled with intrigue, murders, trysts, torture, and treason.

Restrictions: Dogs are permitted off the lead around the grounds. But must be kept on a lead inside the grounds.

Car Parking: Free parking

Opening Times: 1 April - 30 September, Monday to Sunday, 9.30 am to 5.30 pm

Telephone: 01387 376222

Website: www.undiscoveredscotland.co.uk

Linlithgow Palace

Address: In Linlithgow off the M9. Post code EH49 7AL.

Activities: The magnificent, roofless remains of Linlithgow Palace occupy the top of a slight hill. Immediately to its south is St Michael's Parish Church, with whose history its own is closely entwined.

Restrictions: Dogs are permitted in the grounds if kept on a lead

Car Parking: Free parking

Opening Times: April to Sept: 9.30am to 5.30pm daily. Oct to March: 9.30am to 4.30pm daily.

Telephone: 01506 842896

Website: www.undiscoveredscotland. co.uk

Loch Doon Castle

Address: Turn right 2m South of Dalmellington on the A713 on to an unclassified road signed for Loch Doon.

Activities: The castle takes the form of an irregular polygon, having eleven sides. This came about as it was built to fit the shape of the island.

Restrictions: Dogs are permitted in the grounds if kept on a lead. They are not permitted in roofed buildings.

Car Parking: Free parking

Opening Times: Open All year daily

Telephone: 0131 6688800

Website: www.highlandtraveller.com

Manderston garden

Address: Duns, Scottish Borders, TD11 3PP

Activities: Overlooking the serpentine lake and a Chinoiserie bridging dam, Manderston with its four formal terraced gardens planted in Edwardian style is an impressive example of gardening on a grand scale.

Restrictions: Dogs permitted within the grounds on a lead

Car Parking: Free parking

Opening Times: 10 May-30 Sep, Sun,

Telephone: 01361 883450

Website: www.manderston.co.uk

Newark Castle

Address: In Port Glasgow between the A8 and the Clyde. PA14 5NH.

Activities: Newark Castle is a fine and well-preserved building sitting on the south shore of the Firth of Clyde and enjoying wonderful views across the river.

Restrictions: Dogs off the lead are permitted on Linlithgow Peel. Dogs are permitted in the grounds if kept on a lead. They are not permitted in roofed buildings.

Car Parking: Free parking

Opening Times: April to September only, 9.30am to 5.30pm every day.

Telephone: 01475 741858

Website: www.undiscoveredscotland. co.uk

Rothesay Castle

Address: Rothesay Castle is located in the town of Rothesay on the Isle of Bute. PA20 0DA

Activities: In Scottish terms it is an unusual castle, being largely circular. It is also remarkably well preserved for such an early castle, with much of what you see today dating directly back to its original construction in the early 1200s

Restrictions: Dogs are permitted in the grounds if kept on a lead. They are not permitted in roofed buildings.

Car Parking: Free parking

Opening Times: April to September: Daily. October to March: (closed Thursdays and Fridays).

Telephone: 01700 502691

Website: www.historic-scotland.gov.uk

St. Ninian's Cave

Address: Physgill, on the coast 4 miles South West of Whithorn on the A747

Activities: on the Solway shore south of Whithorn, St. Ninian's Cave is said to have been St. Ninian's retreat and although no evidence has been found there is no reason to doubt the connection

Restrictions: No dog restrictions

Car Parking: Free parking

Opening Times: Open all year

Telephone: 01988 500 508

Website: www.whithorn.com

Tantallon Castle

Address: Edinburgh and the Lothians. EH39 5PN. 5km east of North Berwick off the A198.

Activities: The Castle stunning views north to the sea-bird colony on Bass Rock. Anywhere else, Bass Rock would dominate the attention, but here it takes second place to the remarkable curtain wall of Tantallon Castle.

Restrictions: Dogs are permitted in the grounds if kept on a lead. They are permitted within the walls of the castle but not permitted in roofed buildings

Car Parking: Free parking

Opening Times: April to Sept: Daily. Oct to March: Saturday to Wednesday

Telephone: 01620 892727

Website: www.historic-scotland.gov.uk

The Outdoor Centre Glenluce

Address:
Carscreugh, Glenluce, Newton Stewart, Scotland, DG8 ONU

Activities: An Outdoor Centre based in South West Scotland offering a range of activities for all ages. E.e. Paintballing, Clay pigeon shooting, team building activities, as well as other events.

Restrictions: Dogs allowed on site, but must be kept under control. Not allowed on all activity sites, but most.

Car Parking: Free parking

Opening Times: Open 24/7 all year round

Telephone: 01581 300 237

Website: www.scotlandsoutdoorcentre. co.uk

St Marys

Carreg Dhu Garden

Address: Near Longstone Terrace in the centre of St. Mary's.

Activities: The perfect spot to relax and enjoy the tranquil atmosphere and to appreciate the variety of sub-tropical plants, shrubs and trees.

Restrictions:

Car Parking: No Cars on the islands

Opening Times: Open all year

Telephone: 01720 422404

Website: www.scillyonline.co.uk

Garrison Walls

Address: Around the headland W of Hugh Town

Activities: You can enjoy a two-hour walk alongside the ramparts of these defensive walls and earthworks, dating from the 16th to 18th centuries.

Restrictions: Dogs welcome on leads

Car Parking: No Cars on the islands

Opening Times: Open all year

Telephone: 0871 716 1939

Website: www.english-heritage.org.uk

Amerton Farm

Address: Stowe by Chartley. Stafford. ST18 0LA

Activities: A great day out for the whole family. Lots to do and see. Arts & Crafts, Farm Shop, Workshops, Wildlife rescue centre, Garden centre etc.

Restrictions: Dogs allowed on a leads, but not in the house.

Car Parking: Free parking

Opening Times: Open all year

Telephone: 01889 270294

Website: www.amertonfarm.co.uk

Churnet Valley Railway

Address: Cheddleton Station, Station Road, Cheddleton, Nr Leek, ST13 7EE

Activities: Cheddleton station, home of the Churnet Valley Railway. The whole site is seen as a "living museum" preserving part of Britain's heritage.

Restrictions: Dogs allowed on a leads. Small charge applies

Car Parking: Pay & Display

Opening Times: Check on Web site for time table

Telephone: 01538 360522

Website: www.churnetvalleyrailway. co.uk

Consall Hall Landscape Gardens

Address: Wetley Rocks. Stoke on Trent. ST9 0AG

Activities: The exceptional landscape set amidst the beautiful scenery consists of four intersecting valleys which have been skilfully developed to create a series of vistas

Restrictions: Dogs welcome on leads

Car Parking: Free parking

Opening Times: Open Easter - End Oct. Wed, Sun and Bank hol Mon only

Telephone: 01782 551947

Website: www.consallgardens.co.uk

Greenway Bank Country Park

Address: Bemmersley Road, Knypersley, Biddulph, Stoke-on-Trent, ST8

Activities: A variety of attractive scenery within its 114 acres. Extensive areas of quiet woodland around the Serpentine Pool provide the perfect setting for a longer walk.

Restrictions: Dogs allowed

Car Parking: Free parking

Opening Times: Open all year

Telephone: 01782 518200

Website: www.enjoyengland.com

Moseley Old Hall garden

Address: Moseley Old Hall Lane, Fordhouses, Staffs, WV10 7HY

Activities: Moseley Old Hall´s garden has been re-created in the 17th century style. A formal knot garden, a wooden arbour covered with clematis, vines and fruits.

Restrictions: Dogs welcome on leads

Car Parking: Free parking

www.dogfriendly.co.uk

Opening Times: 3 Mar-31 Oct, Sat, Sun & Wed 12:00-17:00.

Telephone: 01902 782808

Website: www.britainsfinest.co.uk

Shugborough Hall garden

Address: Milford, Stafford, ST17 0XB

Activities: Between the house and the river are terraces and a grand 19th century parterre with clipped yews and many vases. Also growing pineapples, lemons, melons and vines.

Restrictions: Dogs welcome on leads

Car Parking: Pay & Display

Opening Times: 16 Mar to 26 Oct, Daily, 11:00-17:00.

Telephone: 01889 881388

Website: www.shugborough.org.uk

The Trentham Estate

Address: Trentham Leisure Limited, Stone Road, Trentham, Stoke on Trent ST4 8AX

Activities: There is something for everyone – Formal Gardens and Fountains, Wild and Colourful Prairies, 12 Show Gardens, Woodland Walks, Tree Trails, Bird Hid etc

Restrictions: Dogs very welcome but not in the formal gardens

Car Parking: Free parking

Opening Times: Open all year

Telephone: 01782 646646

Website: www.trenthamleisure.co.uk

Uttoxeter Racecourse

Address: Wood Lane. Uttoxeter. ST14 8BD

Activities: From Irish Night to Medieval Day – there is truly something for everyone.You are guaranteed a day of fun and excitement in beautiful surroundings.

Restrictions: Dogs are only allowed in the Centre Course, and MUST be kept on leads at all times.

Car Parking: Free parking

Opening Times: Open all year. Closed August

Telephone: 01889 562561

Website: www.uttoxeter-racecourse. co.uk

Framlingham Castle

Address: Suffolk, IP13 9BP

Activities: Take a walk around the magnificent Framlingham Mere and the castle's outer courts and moats? Or perhaps negotiate the impressive wall-walk and take in the veiws.

Restrictions: Dogs on leads allowed

Car Parking: Free parking

Opening Times: Open all year

Telephone: 01728 724189

Website: www.english-heritage.org.uk

Helmingham Hall Gardens

Address: Helmingham, Stowmarket, IP14 6EF

Activities: A visit to the gardens makes a perfect day out for everyone. A relaxed atmosphere for visitors to enjoy the serenity and tranquillity of the gardens.

Restrictions: Dogs are allowed but must be kept on a lead at all times.

Car Parking: Free parking

Opening Times: Open May – Sept. Sunday and Wednesday afternoons

Telephone: 01473 890799

Website: www.helmingham.com

Ickworth Garden

Address: Horringer, Bury St Edmunds, IP29 5QE

Activities: Heavily wooded garden with yews, evergreen oak and box and paths

giving vistas of the house's central rotunda from various points. Parkland/Woodland Acreage: 1800

Restrictions: Dogs must be kept on the lead near livestock. 1850 acres of land

Car Parking: Free parking

Opening Times: Open all year

Telephone: 01284 735270

Website: www.britainsfinest.co.uk

Orford Castle, English Heritage Property

Address: Orford, Woodbridge, Suffolk, IP12 2ND

Activities: Come and visit the great keep of Henry II, explore the maze of rooms and passageways with our free audio tour and hear all about the Orford Merman.

Restrictions: Small dogs only that can be held inside castle. Large dogs allowed in grounds.

Car Parking: No parking on site – please use the car park in the Quay

Opening Times: Open all year

Telephone: 01394 450472

Website: www.english-heritage.org.uk

Sutton Hoo, Anglo-Saxon Ship Burial

Address: Tranmer House, Sutton Hoo, Woodbridge, Suffolk, IP12 3DJ

Activities: Burial ground of Anglo-Saxon Kings, 'page one of English

www.dogfriendly.co.uk

history'. Exhibition hall with video & full-size reconstruction of the ship's burial chamber.

Restrictions: Dogs allowed on a leads.

Car Parking: Pay & Display

Opening Times: Open all year

Telephone: 01394 389700

Website: www.visit-suffolk.org.uk

Restrictions: Dogs are allowed in park but not in Saxon Village. There are tie up posts and water bowls.;

Car Parking: Free parking

Opening Times: Open all year

Telephone: 01284 728718

Website: www.visit-suffolk.org.uk

West Stow Country Park

Address: The Visitor Centre, Icklingham Road, West Stow, Bury St Edmunds, Suffolk, IP28 6HG

Activities: Beyond the West Stow Anglo-Saxon Village car park, play area, visitor centre, shop and cafe is a 52 hectare Country Park bursting with life.

Basingstoke Canal

Address: Mytchett Place Road. Mytchett. Surrey. GU16 6DD

Activities: One of Britain's most beautiful waterway. The canal is a SSSI nature reserve, teeming with wildlife. From the North Hampshire hills to the dramatic flights of locks in Surrey

Restrictions: Dogs on leads in the visitor centre. Dogs welcome under control on the canel

Car Parking: Free parking at Visitor centre

Opening Times: Open all year

Telephone: 01252 370073

Website: www.basingstoke-canal.org.uk

Box Hill

Address: The Old Fort, Box Hill Road, Box Hill, Tadworth, Surrey. KT20 7LB

Activities: An outstanding area of woodland and chalk downland. Rare truly natural open-space so close to London. Nature trails with spectacular views towards the South Downs.

Restrictions: Dogs welcome under close control (where sheep grazing)

Car Parking: Parking pay & display.

Opening Times: Open all year

Telephone: 01306 885502

Website: www.nationaltrust.org.uk

Farnham Castle Keep

Address: Castle Street, Farnham, GU9 0AG

Activities: The impressive motte, shellkeep, bailey wall and other defences of a castle founded in 1138 and redeveloped by Henry II after 1155.

Restrictions: Dogs only allowed on a leads.

Car Parking: 10m from entrance.

Opening Times: Open April - Sept

Telephone: 01252 713393

Website: www.english-heritage.org.uk

Leith Hill

Address: Leith Hill Lane, Holmbury St Mary. Dorking, Surrey RH5 6LY

Activities: The highest summit in south-east England. Rare variety of heath and woodland wildlife – stonechats, woodlarks and barn owls. Mature hazel and oak woodlands

Restrictions: Dogs welcome under control

Car Parking: Free parking

Opening Times: Open all year

Telephone: 01306 711777

Website: www.nationaltrust.org.uk

Painshill Park garden

Address: Portsmouth Road. Cobham. KT11 1JE

Activities: Within its 160 acres include

www.dogfriendly.co.uk

329

authentic 18th century plantings, working vineyard, Gothic Temple, Chinese Bridge, Crystal Grotto, and Turkish Tent.

Restrictions: Dogs very welcome on a short lead

Car Parking: Free parking

Opening Times: Open all year

Telephone: 01932 868 113

Website: www.painshill.co.uk

The Witley Centre

Address: Witley, Godalming, Surrey GU8 5QA

Activities: At the heart of Witley Common, a fascinating mix of woodland and heath, the purpose-built centre houses a countryside exhibition. Walks leaflets are available at shop

Restrictions: Dogs welcome under close control

Car Parking: Free parking 100 yds

Opening Times: Common Open all year. Centre open End March - End Oct

Telephone: 01428 683207

Website: www.nationaltrust.org.uk

Cromwell's Castle

Address: Tresco, Isles of Scilly. (On the shoreline, approach with care, 3/4 mile NW of New Grimsby)

Activities: Standing on a rocky promontory guarding the lovely anchorage between Bryher and Tresco, this round tower is one of the few surviving Cromwellian fortifications in Britain

Restrictions: Dogs welcome on leads

Car Parking:

Opening Times: Open all year

Telephone: 0871 716 1939

Website: www.english-heritage.org.uk

Tresco Abbey Garden

Address: Tresco Estate, Tresco, TR24 0QQ

Activities: The garden is home to species from 80 countries, ranging from Brazil to New Zealand and Burma to South Africa.

Restrictions: Dogs welcome on leads

Car Parking: No Cars on the islands

Opening Times: Open all year

Telephone: 01720-424108

Website: www.gardens-guide.com

www.dogfriendly.co.uk

Foel Farm Park

Address: Brynsiencyn, Anglesey, LL61 6TQ

Activities: Experience the sights, sounds and smells of a real working farm. We invite all visitors to meet, touch and feed the animals.

Restrictions: Dogs are very welcome on a lead in open area's

Car Parking: Free parking

Opening Times: Open Easter - End Oct

Telephone: 01248 430646

Website: www.foelfarm.co.uk

Henblas Park

Address: In the heart of Anglesey. Henblas is on the B4422 Aberffraw Road

Activities: Entertainment for the whole family - whatever the weather! From Sheepdog Shows to Adventureland Shearing Shows and Duck Shows .

Restrictions: Dogs are very welcome on a lead

Car Parking: Parking available

Opening Times: Open 1st April - 2nd November

Telephone: 01407 840440

Website: www.parc-henblas-park.co.uk

Model Village and Gardens

Address: Anglesey Model Village Parc. Newbourgh, LL61 6RS

Activities: An acre of landscaped gardens with water features and a range of plants and trees, and the gardens are dotted with models of Anglesey landmarks

Restrictions: Dogs are very welcome on a lead

Car Parking: Free parking

Opening Times: Open Easter - end Sept

Telephone: 01248 440477

Website: www.bbc.co.uk

Penrhos Nature Reserve

Address: On the A5 from Bally into Holyhead.

Activities: There are walks through the forest, around ponds and along the coast.

Restrictions: Dogs are very welcome on a lead

Car Parking: Free parking

Opening Times: Open all year

Telephone: 01407 762622

Website: www.bbc.co.uk

Porth Amlwch Heritage Trail

Address: The Old Sail Loft, Amlwch Port, Amlwch, LL68 9DB

Activities: Industrial copper site from the 1800's. 2 trails to go on. Both about an hour's walk. Guides available, and private guides can be booked in advance.

Restrictions: Dogs are allowed on the trail but not in the café

Car Parking: Free parking

Opening Times: Open Easter- End Sept

Telephone: 01407 832255

Website: www.copperkingdom.co.uk

Cardiff Castle

Address: Castle Street, CF10 3RB

Activities: The Castle's enchanting fairytale towers conceal an elaborate and splendid interior. As well as visiting the spectacular interiors, visitors can enjoy the Castle grounds.

Restrictions: Dogs are very welcome on a lead, but only in the grounds not the interiors.

Car Parking: Parking in town Pay & Display 5 min walk

Opening Times: Open all year

Telephone: 029 2087 8100

Website: www.cardiffcastle.com

Dyffryn Botanic Garden

Address: St.Nicholas, Vale of Glamorgan, CF5 6SU

Activities: Outstanding Grade I listed Edwardian gardens. This garden has everything - formal lawns, fountains and pools, seasonal beds, trees and Theatre gardens.

Restrictions: Dogs are very welcome on a lead

Car Parking: Parking available

Opening Times: Open all year

Telephone: 029 2059 3328

Website: www.dyffryngardens.org.uk

St Fagans National Museum

Address: Cardiff, CF5 6XB

Activities: One of Europe's foremost open air museums and Wales's most popular heritage attraction.

Restrictions: Dogs are very welcome on a lead everywhere but not in the cottages.

Car Parking: Pay & Display

Opening Times: Open all year

Telephone: 029 20573500

Website: www.museumwales.ac.uk

www.dogfriendly.co.uk

Pembrey Country Park

Address: Pembrey Country Park, Pembrey, SA16 0EJ

Activities: Enjoy the freedom to wander around 202 hectares of glorious parkland, some to take advantage of one of the best beaches in the UK.

Restrictions: Dogs can roam freely under control

Car Parking: Free parking

Opening Times: Open April - Oct

Telephone: 01554 833913

Website: www.carmarthenshire.gov.uk

Cae Hir Gardens

Address: Cribyn, Lampeter, Ceredigion, SA48 7NG

Activities: Gerddi Cae Hir Gardens are probably West Wales' best kept secret. One of the best private gardens in Wales, and one that is well worth a visit.

Restrictions: Dogs are very welcome on a lead

Car Parking: Parking available

Opening Times: Open all year

Telephone: 01570 470839

Website: www.caehirgardens.ws

www.dogfriendly.co.uk

Ffestiniog Railway

Address: Harbour Station. Porthmadog, Gwynedd. LL49 9NF

Activities: Trains currently run on a 12-mile journey from the main station in Caernarfon, overlooked by the magnificent castle, to the village of Rhyd.

Restrictions: Dogs and Bicycles are welcome. We regret, however, that dogs cannot be accommodated in the first-class portions of our trains

Car Parking: Small car park £2.00 all day

Opening Times: Open all year

Telephone: 01766 516000

Website: www.stayinwales.co.uk

Greenwood Forest Park

Address: Y Felinheli, Gwynedd, LL56 4QN

Activities: There's a day packed with adventure and fun for you and all your family, exceptional award-winning family attraction with so much to enjoy, whatever the weather.

Restrictions: Dogs are very welcome on a lead

Car Parking: Free parking

Opening Times: Open Mid March - End Nov

Telephone: 01248 671493

Website: www.greenwoodforestpark. co.uk

Penrhyn Castle Garden

Address: Bangor, Gwynedd, LL57 4HN

Activities: A fascinating walled garden with formal terrace, below is a sloping lawn planted with old flowering trees

Restrictions: Dogs are very welcome on a lead but not in the walled Garden and Picnic area

Car Parking: Free parking

Opening Times: Open 31 Mar to 4 Nov

Telephone: 01248 353084

Website: www.britainsfinest.co.uk

Caldicot Castle & Country park

Address: Church Road, Caldicot, Monmouthshire, NP26 4HU

Activities: Caldicot Castle is set in fifty five acres of beautiful settings and tranquil gardens in a wooded country park.

Restrictions: Dogs are welcome, must be kept on a lead and supervised in the castle

Car Parking: Free parking

Opening Times: Open Easter - 30th Sept

Telephone: 01291 420241

Website: www.caldicotcastle.co.uk

www.dogfriendly.co.uk

Wales
Pembrokeshire

Upton Castle Gardens

Address: Upton Castle, Cosheston SA72 4SE

Activities: 37 acre Gardens surround a fine medieval castle

Restrictions: Dogs on lead are allowed in the gardens

Car Parking: Free parking:

Opening Times: April to October. Tues-Sunday

Telephone: 01646 689996

Website: www.uptoncastle.com

Begelly Countryside Gardens

Address: Begelly, Kilgetty, SA68 0YH

Activities: Oriental Gardens, Walk ways, Lakes, Monkey Sanctuary. Also has a six berth caravan to rent on site which takes dogs.

Restrictions: Dogs on lead are welcomed at the gardens.

Car Parking: Free parking

Opening Times: Open all year. Not Jan

Telephone: 01834 811320

Website: www.onebiggarden.com

Carew Castle and Mill

Address: Carew, Nr Tenby, SA70 8SL

Activities: Set in a stunning location, overlooking a 23 acre millpond.

Restrictions: Dogs on leads are welcome. Also in castle

Car Parking: Free parking

Opening Times: April- late October

Telephone: 01646 651782

Website: www.carewcastle.com

Castell Henllys

Address: Meline, Nr Crymych, SA41 3UT

Activities: Castell Henllys is a Scheduled Ancient Monument and one of many prehistoric promontory forts in the National Park dating to around 600BC

Restrictions: Dogs on lead are welcome

Car Parking: Free parking

Opening Times: April to end Oct

Telephone: 01239 891319

Website: www.castellhenllys.com

Clerkenhill Adventure Farm

Address: Slebech, Haverfordwest, SA62 4PE

Activities: Adventure trail, observing the farm animals and working farmland. Picnic areas available

Restrictions: Dogs are welcome but we ask that you keep them under control near the animals and other people

Car Parking:

Opening Times: April - End Oct

Telephone: 01437 751227

Website: www.clerkenhill.co.uk

Colby Gardens

Address: Amroth, Narberth, SA67 8PP

Activities: Open and wooded pathways through the valley offer lovely walks.

Restrictions: Dogs on lead. But can run in the open space. No dogs allowed in the walled garden or Tea room.

Car Parking: Free parking

Opening Times: Mid March - End Oct

Telephone: 01834 811885

Website: www.nationaltrust.org.uk

Dale Sailing

Address: Brunel Quay. Neyland Milford Haven. SA73 1PY

Activities: Round Island Cruises

Restrictions: Dogs only allowed on round island trips. Not allowed on islands. Dogs on lead welcome.

Car Parking: NCP Car Park

Opening Times: April - End Oct

Telephone: 01646 603110

Website: www.dale-sailing.co.uk

Heatherton Activity Park

Address: Heatherton. St Florence. Teby. SA70 8RJ

Activities: Provide a range of sporting activities, for all ages

Restrictions: Dogs are welcomed - must be on a lead.

Car Parking: Free parking:

Opening Times: Open all year

Telephone: 01646 652000

Website: www.heatherton.co.uk

Llys Y Fran Country Park

Address: Nr Clarbeston Road, Haverfordwest. SA63 4RR

Activities: Country park - 187 acre reserve. Wonderful woodland walks which can be a 71/2 mile hike or shorter strolls

Restrictions: Dogs on lead are welcome.

Car Parking: Car Park £1.00

Opening Times: Open all year

Telephone: 01437 532694

Website: www.thewoofguide.com

Oakwood Theme Park

Address: Canaston Bridge, Narberth. SA67 8DE

Activities: Theme and adventure park

Restrictions: Dogs not allowed in the park, but there are kennels available at a £5.00 returnable deposit.

Car Parking: Free parking

Opening Times: April - End Sept

Telephone: 01834 861889

Website: www.oakwoodthemepark. co.uk

Pembroke Castle

Address: Pembroke. SA71 4LA

Activities: Idyllically set on the banks of the River Estuary. Birth place of Henry VII

Restrictions: Dogs on lead are welcome. Also in Castle

Car Parking: Few mins walk. Down on common

Opening Times: Open all year

Telephone: 01646 681510

Website: www.pembrokecastle.co.uk

www.dogfriendly.co.uk

339

Picton Castle

Address: Haverfordwest. S62 4AS

Activities: The Castle is still a home retaining its medieval features. Comprises 40 acres of some of the most beautiful woodland gardens and grounds in West Wales

Restrictions: Dogs welcome on lead in the grounds only

Car Parking: Free parking

Opening Times: April -Sept

Telephone: 01437 751326

Website: www.pictoncastle.co.uk

Scolton Manor & Country Park

Address: Spittal. Haverfordwest. SA62 5QL

Activities: County museum, exhibition museum, wildlife parks. Nature Trails through the surrounding woodland.

Restrictions: Dogs welcome but not in the Manor. Must be under control and please pick up waste

Car Parking: Pay and Display

Opening Times: Manor 1st April - 31st Oct. park Open all year

Telephone: 01437 731457 (Park)

Website: www.inspirationalwales.com

Silent World

Address: Slippery Back, Mayfield Drive. Narberth Road, Tenby SA70 8HR

Activities: Silent World Aquarium is housed in an attractive 19th century chapel .The Aquarium and Reptile Collection offers a fascinating view of all sorts of aquatic creatures

Restrictions: Dogs on lead are welcome

Car Parking: Parking at North Beach.

100 yds away. Pay & Display

Opening Times: Open all year

Telephone: 01834 844498

Website: www.silentworld.org.uk

Solva Woollen Mill

Address: Middle Solva, Haverfordwest. SA62 6XD

Activities: Woollen Mill - specialises in the production of flat woven floor coverings

Restrictions: Dogs on lead are welcome everywhere apart from tea room, drinking water available for dogs.

Car Parking: Free parking. Mon-Fri

Opening Times: Open all year

Telephone: 01437 721112

Website: www.solvawoollenmill.co.uk

Stackpole Estate

Address: Old Home Farm Yard, Stackpole, nr Pembroke,

Activities: National trust site -National Nature Reserve. Beautiful and varied stretch of the Pembrokeshire coast.

Restrictions: All dog friendly, as long as well behaved.

Car Parking: Free parking Sept - Easter

Opening Times: Open all year

Telephone: 01646 661359

Website: www.nationaltrust.org.uk

Thousand Islands Expeditions

Address: Cross Square, St. Davids, SA62 6SL.

Activities: Boat Trips - home to UK's largest Grey Seal colonies

Restrictions: Dogs on leads allowed on boat trips, but not advised on the 3 hours trips.

Car Parking: Pay and Display

Opening Times: April 1st - Oct 1st

Telephone: 01437 721721

Website: www.thousandislands.co.uk

Voyages Of Discovery

Address: 1 High Street. St Davids. CA62 6SA

Activities: Dog Friendly Boat Trips - offshore whale and dolphin watching. Dogs allowed on trips no longer that 1and half hours

Restrictions: Dogs on lead are allowed on the boats. Some trips are three hours long and may not be suitable for all dogs.

Car Parking: 10 yards away. Pay & Display

Opening Times: Open all year

Telephone: 01437 721911

Website: www.ramseyisland.co.uk

Wide Life Centre at Cilgerran

Address: Teifi Marshes Nature Reserve, Cilgerren, SA43 2TB

Activities: Wildlife Centre - chance to view rare species. No Entrance Fee

Restrictions: Dogs must be kept on lead. Extension café where you can eat with your dog

Car Parking: Charge for parking.

Opening Times: Open all year

Telephone: 01239 621600

Website: www.welshwildlife.org

www.dogfriendly.co.uk

Ashford Garden

Address: Ashford House, Talybont-on-Usk, Brecon, Powys, LD3 7YR

Activities: A walled garden surrounded by a woodland and water garden.

Restrictions: Dogs are very welcome on a lead

Car Parking: Parking available

Opening Times: Open 3 Apr to 25 Sep

Telephone: 01874 676271

Website: www.britainsfinest.co.uk

Brecon Beacons National Park

Address: Brecon Beacons

Activities: Fantastic open countryside for walking your dog.

Restrictions: Dog Friendly

Car Parking: Free parking

Opening Times: Open all year

Telephone: 01874 623366

Website: www.breconbeacons.org

Craig-y-Nos Castle

Address: Brecon Road, Pen-y-cae, Powys, SA9 1GL

Activities: Primarily a hotel, but due to it's historic past you can also view the hotel and guided tours.

Restrictions: Dogs are very welcome on a lead everywhere in Castle and grounds but not in the Restaurant. Enjoy the splendour of the lovely Brecon Beacons.

Car Parking: Free parking

Opening Times: Open all year

Telephone: 01639 730205

Website: www.craigynoscastle.com

Elan Valley

Address: Elan Valley, Rhayader, LD6 5HP

Activities: The Estate consists of rounded hills dissected by steep valleys, many of which are covered in deciduous woodland dominated by Sessile Oak. Wonderful walks.

Restrictions: Dogs can roam freely, but please put on a lead if near the animals

Car Parking: Pay & Display £1.00 for the day

Opening Times: Open Mid March - Beg Nov

Telephone: 01597 810898

Website: www.elanvalley.org.uk

The National Cycle Collection

Address: Temple Street, Llandrindod Wells, Powys, LD1 5DL,

Activities: Their are approximately 250 machines on display within the 6,000 square feet of floor space at any one time, also walk along our historic street.

Restrictions: Very Very Dog Friendly. Dogs are allowed everywhere.

Car Parking: Free parking

Opening Times: Open March - Oct

Telephone: 01597 825531

Website: www.cyclemuseum.org.uk

www.dogfriendly.co.uk

Chirk Castle garden

Address: Chirk, Wrexham, LL14 5AF

Activities: In the formal garden of Chirk Castle are substantial clipped yews, rose garden and climbers on the castle wall.

Restrictions: Dogs are allowed on only woodland walk, 2 klm

Car Parking: Free parking

Opening Times: Open Mid March - End Oct

Telephone: 01691 777701

Website: www.britainsfinest.co.uk

Erddig Garden

Address: Wrexham, LL13 0YT

Activities:

Restrictions: Dogs are not allowed in the Gardens, but allowed in the 1000 acre parkland estate

Car Parking: Free parking

Opening Times: Open March - Dec

Telephone: 01978 355314

Website: www.britainsfinest.co.uk

www.dogfriendly.co.uk

343

Avon Boating Limited

Address: The Boathouse. Swan's Nest Lane. Stratford-upon-Avon. CV37 7LS

Activities: The river naturally draws people down to its grassy banks, and what better way to enjoy its tranquil waters than by boat. Come and relax and enjoy it with us.

Restrictions: Dogs very welcome on a lead

Car Parking: Pay & Display

Opening Times: April - End Oct

Telephone: 01789 267073

Website: www.avon-boating.co.uk

Burton Dassett Hills Country Park

Address: Burton Dassett. Southam. Warks. CV47 2AB

Activities: The 100 acres park contain a wealth of historical interest such as the prominent beacon, quarry remains and the nearby 12th Century All Saints Church.

Restrictions: Dogs must be kept on a lead in Visitor Centre courtyards, in car parks and in designated picnic areas . Please see web site for more information

Car Parking: Pay & Display

Opening Times: Open all year

Telephone: 01827 872660

Website: www.warwickshire.gov.uk

Hartshill Country Park

Address: Oldbury Road, Hartshill, Nr Nuneaton, Warwickshire, CV10 0TE

Activities: This country park, covering 137 acres of woodland and open hilltop has magnificent views across the Anker Valley, with self guided walks, and an adventure play area.

Restrictions: Dogs welcome under control

Car Parking: Pay & Display

Opening Times: Open all year

Telephone: 01827 872660

Website: www.visitcoventry.co.uk

Hatton Country World

Address: Dark Lane. Hatton. Warwick. CV35 7LD

Activities: The Shopping Village shops are housed in old Victorian farm buildings, some of them are not accessible due to narrow doorways and steps to the entrance

Restrictions: Dogs very welcome on a lead in the shopping village, but not allowed in the Farm village.

Car Parking: Free parking

Opening Times: Open all year

Telephone: 01926 843411

Website: www.hattonworld.com

Kenilworth Castle

Address: Kenilworth. Warwickshire - CV8 1NE

Activities: Take your family to one of England's most spectacular castle ruins in Warwickshire. Take in the breathtaking views from the castle grounds.

Restrictions: Dogs only allowed on a leads.

Car Parking: 300m from entrance; uneven surface

Opening Times: Open all year

Telephone: 01926 852078

Website: www.english-heritage.org.uk

The Battlefield Railway

Address: Shackerstone Station CV13 0BS

Activities: The Steam train runs from Shackerstone via Market Bosworth to Shenton in Leicestershire.

Restrictions: Dogs are welcome but can only travel in an assigned carriage with owner. Dogs are not allowed on seats and there is a charge for travel.

Car Parking: Free parking

Opening Times: Open April - End Oct

Telephone: 01827 880754

Website: ourworld.compuserve.com

Ufton Fields Nature Reserve

Address: Ufton. Leamington Spa. Warks. CV33 9PU

Activities: This 100 acre site is a wildlife haven with all weather footpaths providing access to varied habitats in every season, and noted for its abundance of butterflies and dragonflies

Restrictions: Dogs only allowed on a leads.

Car Parking: Free parking

Opening Times: Open all year

Telephone: 01827 872660

Website: www.warwickshire.gov.uk

Warwickshire

www.dogfriendly.co.uk

345

Baggeridge Country Park

Address: Gospel End, Sedgley, Dudley, DY3 4HB

Activities: There are many activities available at Baggeridge Country Park, and the Ranger Service conducts various guided walks around Baggeridge Country Park.

Restrictions: Dogs welcome under control

Car Parking: Pay & Display

Opening Times: Open all year

Telephone: 01902 882605

Website: www.sstaffs.gov.uk

Castle Bromwich Hall Gardens

Address: Chester Road, Bromwich, Birmingham, B36 9BT

Activities: Restored 17th and 18th century formal gardens set within a 10 acre walled area, offering an oasis of tranquillity.

Restrictions: Dogs in the garden if under control on a short lead. There is plenty of room to exercise your dog in the Parkland adjacent to the Car Park.

Car Parking: Free parking Car Park

Opening Times: Open April - Sept

Telephone: 0121 749 4100

Website: www.cbhgt.org.uk

Coombe Country Park

Address: Brinklow Road, Binley, Coventry, CV3 2AB

Activities: The Park's gardens, parkland, surrounding woodlands and a magnificent 90 acre lake cover an area of 372 acres.

Restrictions: Dogs welcome under control

Car Parking: Pay & Display

Opening Times: Open all year

Telephone: 024 76453720

Website: www.coventry-walks.org.uk

Copt Heath Wharf

Address: Barston Lane near Catherine de Barnes, Solihull, West Midlands B91 2SX

Activities: For a different day out, why not hire an easy to drive 24 foot narrowboat for a day or half day self drive cruise along the Grand Union Canal near Catherine de Barnes?

Restrictions: Dogs are welcome on board only on day trips.

Car Parking: Free parking

Opening Times: Open Easter - End Oct

Telephone: 0121 704 4464

Website: www.coptheathwharf.co.uk

Edgbaston Reservoir

Address: The Rangers Lodge. 115 Reservoir Road. Ladywood. Birmingham. B16 9EE

Activities: Edgbaston Reservoir is a Site of Importance for Nature Conservation. The 70 acres site is mainly open water and supports a variety of birdlife; it is also a site for newts and bats.

Restrictions: Dogs welcome under control

Car Parking: The Free car park is at the end of Reservoir Road.

Opening Times: Open all year

Telephone: 0121 454 1908

Website: www.birmingham.gov.uK

Kings Heath Park

Address: Off Vicarage Road. Kings Heath. Birmingham, B14 7TQ

Activities: Kings Heath Park has a green flag status, covers 35 acres. This is where the BBC's Gardener's World has been filmed for many years.

Restrictions: Dogs welcome under control

Car Parking: Free parking

Opening Times: Open all year

Telephone: 0121 444 2848

Website: www.birmingham.gov.uk

Kingsbury Water Park

Address: Bodymoor Heath Lane, Bodymoor Heath, Sutton Coldfield, West Midlands, B76 0DY

Activities: The Park has 15 lakes situated in over 600 acres of country park. Explore hidden corners, spot birds and wildlife, and stroll along the surfaced paths.

Restrictions: Dogs must be kept on a lead in Visitor Centre courtyards. In other areas please keep your dog on a short lead or under very close control.

Car Parking: Pay & Display

Opening Times: Open all year

Telephone: 01827 872660

Website: www.warwickshire.gov.uk

Lickey Hills Country Park

Address: Warren Lane. Rednal. Birmingham. B45 8ER

Activities: The Park covers an area of 524 acres. The hills are covered by a mosaic of mixed deciduous woodland, conifer plantations and heathland, all are rich in a variety of wildlife.

Restrictions: Dogs welcome under control

Car Parking: Free parking

Opening Times: Open all year

Telephone: 0121 445 6036

Website: www.birmingham.gov.uk

Sandwell Valley

Address: Salter's Lane, West Bromwich, B71 4BG

Activities: Sandwell Valley has 2000 acres of woodland, parkland and there are two local nature reserves, wildfowl lakes and the remains of an old Benedictine Priory.

Restrictions: Dogs welcome under control

Car Parking: Free parking

Opening Times: Open all year

Telephone: 0121 553 0220

Website: www.laws.sandwell.gov.uk

Second City Canal Cruises

Address: Gas Street Basin. Birmingham. B1 2JU

Activities: Scenic and heritage-based waterborne tours of Birmingham city

www.dogfriendly.co.uk

centre; day trips to Cadbury World and Black Country Museum, Great live commentaries

Restrictions: Dogs welcome on boats under control and on a lead.

Car Parking: Free parking

Opening Times: Open all year

Telephone: 0121 236 9811

Website: www.birminghamheritage.org.uk

Sutton Park

Address: Sutton Park Visitor Centre, Sutton Park, Park Road, Sutton Coldfield, B74 2YT

Activities: Birmingham's largest park, covering 2,400 acres consisting of woodlands, heathlands and wetlands. Home for a wide variety of wildlife, and prehistoric mounds and ruins.

Restrictions: Dogs must be kept under control at all times and must be kept on a lead during bird nesting season in sensitive areas of the Park.

Car Parking: Pay & Display

Opening Times: Open all year

Telephone: 0121 355 6370

Website: www.birmingham.gov.uk

Wightwick Manor and Gardens

Address: Wightwick Bank, Wolverhampton, West Midlands. WV6 8EE

Activities: Superb Arts and Crafts survival, a rich feast of colour inside and out. Victorian gardens, with terraces, water pools and woodland.

Restrictions: Dogs are not allowed in the house. Dogs allowed in the gardens on a lead.

Car Parking: Parking charge for the gardens

Opening Times: Gardens open 1st March - Christmas Eve

Telephone: 01902 761400

Website: www.nationaltrust.org.uk

Amberley Working Museum

Address: Amberley Working Museum, Amberley, West Sussex, BN18 9LT

Activities: 36 acres of crafts, vintage transport, exhibitions and nature trails. Amberley Working Museum is a 36 acre open-air museum containing a wide range of exhibits.

Restrictions: Dogs very welcome on a lead

Car Parking: Free parking

Opening Times: Open Feb - End Oct

Telephone: 01798 831370

Website: www.amberleymuseum.co.uk

Borde Hill Garden & Country Park.

Address: Haywards Heath. West Sussex. RH16 1XP

Activities: Stunningly beautiful and botanically rich heritage Garden. Over 150 acres of traditional parkland. Fine woodland, lakes and outstanding views across the Sussex High Weald

Restrictions: Dogs very welcome on a lead. Not allowed in the playground.

Car Parking: Free parking

Opening Times: 1st April-31st Oct

Telephone: 01444 450326

Website: www.bordehill.co.uk

Weald & Downland Open Air Museum.

Address: Town Lane. Singleton. Chichester. PO18 0EU

Activities: A very special place to wander amongst a fascinating collection of nearly 50 historic buildings, with period gardens, together with farm animals, woodland walks and lake.

Restrictions: Dogs very welcome on a lead

Car Parking: Free parking

Opening Times: Open all year

Telephone: 01243 811363

Website: www.wealddown.co.uk

West Yorkshire

Bramham Park garden

Address: Wetherby, West Yorks, LS23 6ND

Activities: The gardens extend to some 66 acres and with the Pleasure Grounds extend to over 100 acres. This is a garden of walks and views, architectural features and reflecting water, rolling parkland and formal rose gardens.

Restrictions: Dogs on leads are welcome

Car Parking: Free parking

Opening Times: 1 Apr-30 Sep, Daily. Closed 4-10 Jun & 13 -31 Aug.

Telephone: 01937 846000

Website: www.britainsfinest.co.uk

Chevin Forest Park

Address: Visitor Centre. The White House. Chevin Forest Park. Johnny Lane. Otley. LS21 3JL

Activities: Over 180 hectares of mixed woodland, moorland, grassland and rocky crags with an extensive network of paths. A place of outstanding beauty with panoramic views.

Restrictions: Dogs very welcome.

Car Parking: Free parking

Opening Times: Open all year

Telephone: 01943 465023

Website: www.chevinforest.co.uk

Hardcastle Crags

Address: Hollin Hall, Crimsworth Dean, Hebden, Bridge, West Yorkshire HX7 7AP

Activities: Beautiful wooded valley with 19th century Gibson Mill at its heart. Guided-walks and orienteering courses available. A rich habitat for flora and fauna.

Restrictions: Dogs very welcome.

Car Parking: Pay & Display

Opening Times: Open all year

Telephone: 01422 844518

Website: www.nationaltrust.org.uk

Harewood House Gardens

Address: Harewood, Leeds, W Yorks, LS17 9LG

Activities: Stroll through the mature woodland and rhododendrons to view the lake with its abundant wildlife.

Restrictions: Dogs on leads are welcome

Car Parking: Free parking

Opening Times: 16 Mar to 28 Oct, Daily

Telephone: 0113 218 1010

Website: www.britainsfinest.co.uk

Keighley & Worth Valley Railway

Address: Keighley Train Station, Station Bridge, Keighley, BD21 4HP

Activities: Step back in time and enjoy

a train ride through the heart of Brontë country. Most services are operated by steam trains.

Restrictions: Dogs are welcome on the trains but please keep them off the carriage seats

Car Parking: Pay & Display

Opening Times: Open on weekends throughout the year

Telephone: 01535 645214

Website: www.kwvr.co.uk/index.htm

Kirklees Light Railway

Address: Park Mill Way, Clayton West, Nr Huddersfield, West Yorkshire, HD8 9XJ

Activities: More than just a train ride. We have full range of amenities to entertain you and your family while you wait for the train or after you return.

Restrictions: Dogs very welcome on trains on a lead

Car Parking: Free parking

Opening Times: Every day from End May-End Aug. Only weekends Sept-April

Telephone: 01484 865727

Website: www.kirkleeslightrailway.com

Lotherton Hall

Address: Selby Road. Leeds LS15 0AD

Activities: So much to see and do in the Formal Gardens, Stable Courtyard, Captain Wood Walk, Boundary Trail, Coburnhill Wood Walk, The Bird Garden and more.

Restrictions: Dogs very welcome on leads. Not in the Farm or House.

Car Parking: Pay & Display

Opening Times: Open all year

Telephone: 0113 281 3259

Website: www.leeds.gov.uk

Marsden Moor Estate

Address: The Old Goods Yard, Station Road, Marsden, Huddersfield, West Yorkshire HD7 6DH

Activities: A vast swathe of unspoilt valleys, reservoirs, peaks and crags. Extensive events and guided walks programme. Memorable location for Last of the Summer Wine.

Restrictions: Dogs very welcome.

Car Parking: Free parking

Opening Times: Open all year

Telephone: 01484 847016

Website: www.nationaltrust.org.uk

Oakwell Hall Country Park

Address: Nutter Lane, Birstall, Batley, West Yorkshire, WF17 9LG

Activities: A wonderfully authentic 16th Century Manor House in Yorkshire - and for its surrounding 110 acres of country park and enjoy the waymarked nature trails.

Restrictions: Dogs very welcome on leads

Car Parking: Free parking

Opening Times: Open all year

Telephone: 01924 326240

Website: www.friendsofoakwellhall.org.uk

www.dogfriendly.co.uk

Ogden Water Country Park

Address: Ogden Lane, Keighley Road, Ogden, Halifax, West Yorkshire, HX2 8YA

Activities: There are numerous woodland trails and waterside paths to explore, with stunning views extending across Calderdale. A range of walks, from easy to strenuous.

Restrictions: Dogs very welcome.

Car Parking: Pay & Display

Opening Times: Open all year

Telephone: 01422 249136

Website: www.ogdenwater.org.uk

Piece Hall

Address: The Piece Hall, Halifax, HX1 1RE

Activities: Come down to the Piece Hall and experience the feel of yester year. The Open air Courtyard houses a flee market and there are over 50 small retail shops to visit.

Restrictions: Dogs on leads are welcome, and allowed into the shops at the owners discretion.

Car Parking: Pay & Display

Opening Times: Open all year

Telephone: 01422 321002

Website: www.piecehall.info

Temple Newsam

Address: Temple Newsam, Temple Newsam Road, off Selby Road, Leeds, LS15 0AE

Activities: The estate encompasses 600 hectares (1500 acres) of parkland, farmland, woodland, and gardens.

Restrictions: Dogs are welcome but we request they be kept on a lead. They are not allowed into roofed buildings

Car Parking: Pay & Display

Opening Times: Open Tuesday to Sunday and bank holidays all year round

Telephone: 0113 264 5535

Website: www.leeds.gov.uk

Yorkshire Sculpture Park

Address: Yorkshire Sculpture Park West Bretton Wakefield WF4 4LG

Activities: Yorkshire Sculpture Park is an extraordinary place that sets out to challenge, inspire, inform and delight. Within 500 acres of 18th century parkland, it is an international centre for modern and contemporary art, experienced by thousands of visitors each

Restrictions: Dogs must be kept on leads at all times and are not allowed in the buildings

Car Parking: £4 Car Parking for the day

Opening Times: Open daily throughout the year

Telephone: 01924 832631

Website: www.ysp.co.uk

Western Scotland

Achamore Gardens

Address: Isla of Gigha, Argyll, PA41 7AD

Activities: Achamore Gardens are a magnificent tapestry of camellias, primulas, daffodils, azaleas and various sub-tropical shrubs as well as rhododendron.

Restrictions: Dogs on lead please

Car Parking: Free parking

Opening Times: All year, Daily, dawn to dusk

Telephone: 01583 505390

Website: www.gigha.org.uk

Achnacloich garden

Address: Connel, Oban, Argyll, PA37 1PR

Activities: The 19th century walled garden, terraces and three small ponds are a fine setting for late 1820s Scots pine.

Restrictions: Dogs on lead please

Car Parking: Free parking

Opening Times: 31 Mar to 31 Oct, Daily, 10:00-18:00.

Telephone: 01631 710796

Website: www.britainsfinest.co.uk

Ardchattan Priory

Address: Ardchattan Priory By Oban, Argyll, PA37 1RQ

Activities: The ruins of a Valliscaulian priory founded in 1230 and later converted to secular use.

Restrictions: Dogs on lead please. Please clear up after dog

Car Parking: Free parking

Opening Times: 1st April - 31st October, 9am to 5pm

Telephone: 01796 481355

Website: www.gardens-of-argyll.co.uk

Ardkinglas Woodland Garden

Address: Cairndow, Argyll, PA26 8BH

Activities: Ardkinglas Woodland Garden is set on a hillside in a peaceful location overlooking Loch Fyne. It is home to many of Britain´s Champion Trees

Restrictions:

Car Parking: Free parking

Opening Times: All year, Daily, dawn to dusk.

Telephone: 01499 600261

Website: www.ardkinglas.com

Benmore Botanic Garden

Address: Dunoon, Argyll, PA23 8QU

Activities: Boasting a world-famous collection of magnificent conifers, flowering trees and shrubs, its 150 acres feature some of the tallest trees in Britain,

Restrictions:

Car Parking: Free parking

Opening Times: 1 Mar-31 Oct, 10:00-18:00. Mar & Oct closes 17:00.

Telephone: 01369 706261

Website: www.britainsfinest.co.uk

Western Scotland

www.dogfriendly.co.uk

Blair Castle Garden

Address: Blair Atholl, Pitlochry, Perth & Kinross, PH18 5TL

Activities: Blair Castle garden with its highly unusual formal landscape from the 1730s, has a central line of ponds and islands with banks of fruit trees and herbaceous borders against the walls

Restrictions: Dogs allowed in gardens on leads. Dogs not allowed in the castle

Car Parking: Free parking

Opening Times: Gardens open 21st March - 24th Oct.

Telephone: 01796 481207

Website: www.britainsfinest.co.uk

Bonawe Historic Iron Furnace

Address: Argyll, PA35 1JQ

Activities: The most complete charcoal-fuelled ironworks in Britain, Bonawe was founded in 1753.

Restrictions: Dogs on lead please. Please clear up after dog

Car Parking:

Opening Times: April to September only, 9.30am to 5.30pm

Telephone: 01866 822432

Website: www.undiscoveredscotland.co.uk

Carnasserie Castle

Address: 2 miles North of Kilmartin off the A816

Activities: This is a good example of a French Renaissance-influenced tower-house with hall-house.

Restrictions:

Car Parking:

Opening Times: Open all year

Telephone: 0131 668 800

Website: www.highlandtraveller.com/

Drummond Gardens

Address: Muthill, Crieff, Perth & Kinross, PH7 4HZ

Activities: At Drummond Gardens, pass into the inner courtyard and reach the top of the terracing and the full extent and majesty of this garden is suddenly revealed.

Restrictions: Dogs on leads are allowed in the gardens. The castle is not open to the public

Car Parking: Free parking

Opening Times: Gardens open from May - October

Telephone: 01764 681433

Website: www.britainsfinest.co.uk

Dunstaffnage Castle & Chapel

Address: Lochetive, Dundeg, PA37 1PZ

Activities: Standing atop a rock, Dunstaffnage Castle is an impressive fortification overlooking what was once the most important junction of the sea-lanes on the west coast of Scotland

Restrictions: Dogs allowed inside the castle on a lead

Car Parking: Free parking

Opening Times: 1 April - 30 Sept Mon to Sun. 1 Oct - 31 March Sat - Wed

Telephone: 01631 562465

Website: www.historic-scotland.gov.uk

www.dogfriendly.co.uk

Inverlochy Castle

Address: Old Inverlochy Castle, Inverlochy, Fort William, Invernessshire

Activities: One of the most important castles in Scottish history and was the backdrop for two major historical events, the 1st & 2nd battles of Inverlochy

Restrictions: dogs allowed inside the castle

Car Parking: Free parking

Opening Times: Open all year

Telephone: 01397 701801

Website: www.inverlochycastle.co.uk

Kilchurn Castle

Address: 2.5m West of Dalmally off the A85. Access by boat from Kilchrenan hotel PA35 1HE: park by railway station

Activities: Kilchurn has a four-storey tower built in 1450. The ruins are some of the most picturesque in the country with spectacular views

Restrictions: Dogs allowed on a lead inside castle and on boat trip

Car Parking: Railway station parking is pay and display

Opening Times: April - Sept, every day from 9.30am to 5.30pm,

Telephone: 01866 833333

Website: www.undiscoveredscotland.co.uk

Kisimul Castle

Address: Castlebay Street HS9 5XA. In Castlebay, Isle of Barra, reached by small boat from Castlebay.

Activities:"The rock in the bay" and the origin is obvious from the castle's location. The only significant surviving medieval castle in the Western Isles

Restrictions: Dogs allowed on a lead inside castle and on boat trip

Car Parking: Free parking

Opening Times: April - Sept, every day from 9.30am to 5.30pm,

Telephone: 01871 810313

Website: www.undiscoveredscotland.co.uk

Scone Palace Gardens

Address: Perth, PH2 6BD

Activities: Lawns are home to free-roaming peacocks, and the unique Murray Star Maze shouldn't be missed. Overlooking the relics of the abbey is a special Douglas Fir raised from the original seed.

Restrictions: Dogs on leads are allowed in the gardens

Car Parking: Free parking

Opening Times: Gardens open from 21st March - 31st October

Telephone: 0845 126 1060

Website: www.britainsfinest.co.uk

Torosay Castle & Gardens

Address: Craignure, Isle of Mull, Argyll, PA65 6AY

Activities: 12 acres of spectacular gardens surround Torosay Castle, including formal terraces covered in roses, other climbers and perennials

Restrictions:

Car Parking:

Opening Times: Easter-Oct, Daily, 09:00 - 19:00. Winter daylight

Telephone: 01680 812421

Website: www.britainsfinest.co.uk

www.dogfriendly.co.uk

Wiltshire

Barbury Castle

Address: Swindon. Wiltshire, SN4 0QH

Activities: Noted as an ancient monument the hill fort stands exposed atop the Ridgeway and gives commanding views over the Downs, covering approximately 11 acres.

Restrictions: Dogs welcome under control

Car Parking: Free parking at the Eastern End Car Park, Opp Restaurant.

Opening Times: Open all year

Telephone: 01793 771419

Website: www.leisure-barbury castlenaturereserve

Bratton Camp and White Horse

Address: 2 miles E of Westbury off B3098, I mile SW of Bratton

Activities: Below an Iron Age hillfort, enclosing a much earlier long barrow, stands the Westbury White Horse which was cut into the hillside in 1778.

Restrictions: Dogs welcome under control

Car Parking: Parking available

Opening Times: Open all year

Telephone:

Website: www.english-heritage.org.uk

Broadleas Gardens

Address: Broadleas, Devizes, Wiltshire, SN10 5JQ

Activities: It is a garden of tireless perfectionism at its most stunning in spring when sheets of bulbs stretch out beneath the flowering trees.

Restrictions: Dogs are welcome on leads but not in the house.

Car Parking: Free parking

Opening Times: April- October: Sunday, Wednesday and Thursday

Telephone: 01380 722035

Website: www.statelyhomes.com

Brokerswood Country Park

Address: Brokerswood, Westbury, Wiltshire. BA13 4EH

Activities: Visitors can spend a day and experience the Woodland railway, Heritage Centre, and the tranquillity of a woodland with the sights and sounds of nature all around them.

Restrictions: Dogs are always welcome.

Car Parking: Free parking

Opening Times: Open all year

Telephone: 01373 822238

Website: www.brokerswood.co.uk

Lackham Country Park

Address: Wiltshire College Lackham. Lacock. Chippenham. SN15 2NY

Activities: You will discover a fascinating Museum of Agriculture and Rural Life, delightful display gardens, a meandering woodland walk and an animal trail.

Restrictions: Dogs welcome on leads

Car Parking: Free parking

Opening Times: March-October. Open weekends but all week in August.

Telephone: 01249 466800

Website: www.lackhamcountrypark.co.uk

Longleat

Address: Warminster, BA12 7NW

Activities: Set within 900 acres of Capability Brown landscaped parkland, wonderful walks and Safari Park.

Restrictions: Dogs are welcome in the grounds and free Kennelling when on the Safari.

Car Parking: Free parking

Opening Times: Open all year

Telephone: 01985 844400

Website: www.longleat.co.uk

M. V. Barbara McLellan

Address: Wharf Cottage, Frome Road, Bradford on Avon, BA15 1LE

Activities: We run a number of Special Trips throughout the year unless stated. Cream Tea's, Ploughman's Lunch, Mulled wine at Christmas, look at the web page for details.

Restrictions: Well behaved dogs allowed on board at the discretion of the Captain.

Car Parking: Free parking

Opening Times: Easter-October

Telephone: 01225 868683

Website: www.katrust.org

Old Sarum

Address: Castle Road. Salsbury. Wiltshire, SP1 3SD

Activities: The remains of the prehistoric fortress and of the Norman palace, castle and cathedral evoke memories of thousands of years of history.

Restrictions: Dogs welcome on leads

Car Parking: Parking 50m from entrance, via loose gravel surface

Opening Times: Open all year

Telephone: 01722 335398

Website: www.english-heritage.org.uk

Old Wardour Castle

Address: Wiltshire - SP3 6RR

Activities: Beautifully sited beside a lake, Old Wardour Castle was built in the late 14th century, its romantic setting, situated as it is in a secluded wooded valley.

Restrictions: Dogs are very welcome on leads everywhere

Car Parking: Free parking

Opening Times: Open all year

Telephone: 01747 870487

Website: www.english-heritage.org.uk

Stourhead Garden

Address: Stourton, Warminster, BA12 6QD

Activities: Stourhead is a fine example of English landscape gardens from the 18th century, re-planted in the 19th century with Conifers, flowering trees and shrubs.

Restrictions: Dogs are allowed on a leads in gardens Nov - End Feb. From March - Oct dogs are only allowed in the surrounding fields, but they are wonderful walks.

Car Parking: Free parking

Opening Times: Open all year

Telephone: 01747 841152

Website: www.britainsfinest.co.uk

The Swindon & Cricklade Railway

Address: Blunsdon Station, Tadpole Lane, Blunsdon, SN25 2DA

Activities: Based on the site of Blunsdon Station between Swindon and Cirencester, the line uses part of the trackbed of the former Midland & South Western Junction Railway

Restrictions: Dogs welcome on leads

Car Parking: Free parking

Opening Times: Trains run Saturdays, Sundays and Special days. See Link

Telephone: 01793 7716159 (weekends)

Website: www.swindon-cricklade-railway.org

Avoncroft Museum of Historic Buildings

Address: Stoke Heath, Bromsgrove, Worcestershire, B60 4JR

Activities: One of Britain's best known open-air museums. The museum seeks to bring the past more vividly into focus for the visiting public alike.

Restrictions: Dogs are very welcome everywhere in grounds and buildings on a lead, apart from food hall.

Car Parking: Free parking

Opening Times: Open March till end Nov. Check on web site

Telephone: 01527 831886

Website: www.avoncroft.org.uk

Bodenham Arboretum

Address: Wolverley, Kidderminster, Worcestershire DY11 5SY

Activities: A collection of over 2700 trees set in 156 acres of countryside with 11 pools, four miles of footpaths and a working farm.

Restrictions: Dogs are welcome but must be kept on a lead.

Car Parking: Free parking

Opening Times: Open all year. Check on web site

Telephone: 01562 852444

Website: www.bodenham-arboretum. co.uk

Croome Park

Address: Croome Park, Severn Stoke, WR8 9DW

Activities: The gardens consist of winding shrubberies leading to ornate buildings, with an artificial lake, over a mile long. The wider parkland offers views of 'eye-catcher' follies

Restrictions: Dogs welcome under control and on a lead near wildlife.

Car Parking: Free parking

Opening Times: 1st Nov- 30h De Weekends only. Re open 1st March

Telephone: 01905 371006

Website: www.information-britain.co.uk

Hanbury Hall garden

Address: School Road, Droitwich Spa, WR9 7EA

Activities: A formal 18th century garden with fruit trees, wilderness and sunken geometric parterre of clipped box. The orangery is well stocked with fruit trees.

Restrictions: Dogs not allowed in the house, but allowed in the gardens where there is a dog walk.

Car Parking: Pay & Display

Opening Times: March-Oct Open Sat-Wed. Nov-Dec Weekends only

Telephone: 01527 821214

Website: www.britainsfinest.co.uk

www.dogfriendly.co.uk

Hartlebury Common

Address: B1495 Stourport to Hartlebury road.

Activities: Tracks lead you all around the site, some wide, open and sandy, others narrow and twisting among trees and bushes. It's very popular with walkers.

Restrictions: Dogs welcome under control

Car Parking: Free parking

Opening Times: Open all year

Telephone: 01562 710025

Website: www.worcestershire.gov.uk

Knapp and Papermill Nature Reserve

Address: Bridges Stone. Alfrick. Worcester. WR6 5HR

Activities: Visit this wonderfully diverse reserve to experience a valley of birdsong through orchards, woodlands and wildflower meadows, lying alongside the undulating Leigh Brook.

Restrictions: Dogs welcome under control. On a lead near wild life.

Car Parking: Limited but Free parking

Opening Times: Open all year

Telephone: 01886 832065

Website: www.worcswildlifetrust.co.uk

Kyre Park Gardens

Address: Kyre, Tenbury Wells, Worcestershire WR15 8RP

Activities: Kyre Park is a 29 acre garden and shrubbery which was planned and laid out from 1754. It has five lakes, waterfalls, a Grade II listed tithe barn, a ruin, and Norman dovecote.

Restrictions: Dogs welcome under control

Car Parking: Free parking

Opening Times: Open all year

Telephone: 01885 410669

Website: www.ukattraction.com

Ravenshill Woodland Reserve

Address: Lulsley, Knightwick, Worcester, WR6 5QP

Activities: Privately owned woodlands covers 50 acres of semi natural ancient woodland within the Malvern Hills Area of Outstanding Beauty, adjacent to the Worcestershire Way.

Restrictions: Dogs welcome under control

Car Parking: Parking available

Opening Times: Open all year

Telephone: 01886 821661

Website: www.ravenshillwood.org.uk

Severn Leisure Cruises

Address: Waterside, Upton upon Severn, WR8 0HG

Activities: Cruising through the picturesque countryside of the Heart of England, we offer a afternoon tea cruise, a peaceful Worcester cruise, and a Tewkesbury 'Market Day

Restrictions: Dogs are welcome on board

Car Parking: Pay & Display

Opening Times: Open April - Easter

Telephone: 01684 593112

Website: www.severnleisurecruises.co.uk

Severn Valley Railway

Address: The Railway Station, Bewdley, DY12 1BG

Activities: The railway is a full-size standard-gauge railway line running regular steam-hauled passenger trains for visitors and enthusiasts alike between Kidderminster - Bridgnorth.

Restrictions: Dogs are welcome on a lead. Not allowed in the restaurant car.

Car Parking: Pay & Display

Opening Times: Open May - Sept. Open week ends winter months

Telephone: 01299 403816

Website: www.svr.co.uk

Worcester Woods Country Park

Address: Wildwood Drive, Worcester, WR5 2LG

Activities: With a hundred acres (about ten football pitches) of ancient Oak woodland on your doorstep, stroll through the Bluebells or to listen to the woodland birds.

Restrictions: Dogs welcome under control

Car Parking: Free parking

Opening Times: Open all year

Telephone: 01905 766493

Website: worcestershire.whub.org.uk

www.dogfriendly.co.uk

Notes

www.dogfriendly.co.uk

Notes